THE CLEFT ROCK

A Novel

THE CLEFT ROCK

by

Alice Tisdale Hobart

THE BOBBS-MERRILL COMPANY

INDIANAPOLIS   *Publishers*   NEW YORK

To
THE FRIENDS AND
MEMBERS OF MY FAMILY
WHO HAVE
GIVEN ME OF THEIR TIME AND KNOWLEDGE
SO THAT THIS BOOK
MIGHT BE WRITTEN.

PROLOGUE

"The Valley," the people of California call the great Central Valley lying deep-folded between the high and sharply canyoned Sierras on the east and the smoothly molded coastal ranges on the west. At The Valley's foot a thinning mountain spur separates it from the Mojave Desert. At its head stands Mount Shasta, forever white with snow.

The Valley—a place of distance bounded and yet boundless, with smaller secret valleys tucked away in its immensity and wide lonely plains, level as a floor—millions of acres extending from valley side to valley side. Winter winds send clouds freighted with rain scudding across it; summer winds blow across an empty sun-hot sky. The Valley once given over to wild grasses and grains, mesquite and brilliant desert flowers.

Five times great migrations of spent and weary men and women have reached The Valley's edge, then wound down through the twisting mountain defiles, to settle on the valley floor. The Valley in the spring, now filled from rim to rim with the mingled scent of all the blossoming fruit trees of the world, in the autumn a glowing bowl filled with the purples and golds of the harvest.

One thing only is denied to it in abundance—water, the source of growth and symbol of life.

TABLE OF CONTENTS

Then came the children
of Israel into the desert.
~§ And the Lord spake
unto Moses, saying, take
the rod and speak ye unto
the rock and thou shalt
bring forth to them water
out of the rock.

~§ Numbers, Chapter 20

Part One

THE FAMILY

1

EDWARD GRANT DODD, sitting at his desk in the Manchurian town of Lahususu, close to the Siberian border, ruefully acknowledged to himself how deep were the roots that bound him to his California home. Here he was like a transplanted tree which finds no nurture in alien soil. He felt himself tied into a tight ball of misery, homesick not for the Oakland hills where his parents had lived for the past ten years, but for the great Central Valley of California where his childhood had been spent. Waking and sleeping he kept reaching out for The Valley. The pores of his skin cried out for the hot valley sun. He wanted to lie down on the valley earth, fill his nostrils with the scent of its flowers and fruit.

Today, with snow whirling in gusts of white outside his office window, he groped in his mind for what he had expected to accomplish by signing up for three years with the Chinese customs. Had he thought that to be one of the Americans safeguarding his country's foreign loan to China would compensate for not getting into the war? In 1917 he had enlisted in the Army, hoping to be sent overseas.

He believed his father had used his influence to keep him at a desk in San Francisco throughout the war. Had he simply wished to give notice to his father that henceforth he intended to direct his own life? But had he by coming to China proved to himself—let alone to his father who had violently opposed his coming—that he was capable of managing his own life? In this hour of loneliness he felt an agonizing need to know he could trust his own judgment.

While he was in Harbin he had seemed on the right track. He had worked hard and studied Chinese and Russian in the evenings, believing he would be put in charge of a station of his own, but when that station had turned out to be this frontier town he had grown uncertain whether he had got anywhere by defying his father. He now faced the inescapable knowledge that, for months to come, he was shut into the frontier town of Lahususu with no other white man to talk to until the opening of the Sungari River in the spring, and nothing to do, now that the port closed for the winter, except to see that no furs from farther north were slipped through without duty. What service to his country was there in such routine work? And there was this aching longing for The Valley.

He turned his head to look out of the small square of glass set in the center of the paper-paned window. The Sungari River was a stiff line of ice, bare of the steamers which had given it life when he had arrived two weeks before. Junks lay upturned on the shore. There were no trees to break the repetition of the gray-tiled roofs of one-storied dwellings huddled together along the riverbank, or to relieve the monotonous stretch of prairie beyond, where out of the thin covering of snow kaoliang stubble thrust its dark hummocks. An occasional cart passed, its driver in fur hood and straw-stuffed moccasins plodding at its side. Lean, mangy dogs slunk by; beggar children hurried along, crouching from the storm.

And then the bleak town and the low-ceilinged room where he sat faded. He stood in The Valley. It was the end of the dry season. Filmy clouds covered the sky, rain soft as mist was falling, and from the dry clods under his feet rose the pungent smell of earth, held for months in the sun-locked valley soil. Then suddenly he was not in that place but here. From the adjoining room came the click of an abacus, as the Chinese accountant made up the day's report. Around him were the rustling movements of men clad in long gowns and soft-soled shoes. He was conscious now of the earthy smell of the close-packed dirt floor under his feet. The sense of security the vision of The Valley had brought him was gone, and he could not recapture it.

Glancing again out the window he saw that the snow whirling in ever-increasing fury dimmed his view of the boxlike house he called home, which until the snow began to fall he could see clearly set out by itself on the plain. Seen ghostlike through the storm, it looked small and insecure to Edward.

Hurriedly he took refuge in the thought of Katya. Each evening, when he returned from the office, she greeted him at the door, clad in a bright dress, her blond hair coiled on top of her head, long gold earrings which brought out the pallor of her skin framing her face, a provocative smile on her lips. His senses stirred. She was older than he—he was certain of that, even if he wasn't certain of a lot of other things about her. Twenty-five he thought, a very intriguing twenty-five. Her thin face with the etched lines fanning out from the corners of her eyes, the suggestion of melancholy about her mouth even when she smiled, implied a knowledge of the world beyond anything he felt he had acquired—a sophistication European women, he believed, were supposed to possess. Tingling anticipation began to replace the homesickness of a few moments before.

Out there on the plain Katya had welcomed the snow when it began falling. It hid her away, sheltered her behind its blinding whiteness. But as the storm grew in intensity, beating upon the ill-built and exposed house, rattling its windows, sending freezing gusts of air under the doors and across the floor, at times setting the whole structure trembling under the terrific spasmodic blasts, it threatened her. The violence from which she had so recently escaped was again all around her, penetrating this refuge the American had given her. She was in Russia! She was in the Ukraine! She was in her father's house and her father's laborers in a black column were winding down the road! The ominous murmur of their voices reached her over the wind. Her hands clutched at the rattling window. A pulsing vein in her throat beat out her remembered agony as she fled before them.

By three o'clock Edward was unable to distinguish the figures on the invoices lying before him on his desk. Impatiently he pushed them away. Why should he stay here fussing over customs red tape and struggle home later, fighting a blizzard growing momentarily more blinding? Katya would drive away the loneliness closing in over him. In stilted, careful Chinese he instructed his assistant to close the office for the day, then put on his fur coat, turned up the collar, picked up his high-peaked Russian fur hat and went out.

The wind slammed the door behind him.

Pressing his youthfully slender body against the blizzard, he bent his head to see the path leading across the fields. Once he strayed from it and stumbled over a kaoliang stump. Reaching down to disentangle his trouser leg from the broken stalk, he saw he had wrenched its root from the earth. Its brown, fingerlike tentacles still clutched a frozen clod of red soil.

Faintly at first, then louder, he heard high-pitched, wailing music. Out of the curtain of snow on the path ahead emerged a man in frayed green robes playing a long flute. Then came a huge wooden coffin borne on the shoulders of beggars, their rags flapping below their funeral coats. Behind walked the mourners in sackcloth, like ghosts stepping out of the winding sheet of snow, quickly engulfed in the sepulcher of white ahead. Faint fragments of the dirge receding in the distance reached Edward. His loneliness touched on despair. He must reach Katya.

But he could not hurry. Gusts of wind tore his coat open, billowed it out like a sail. With effort he moved forward, reached his house, clutched at the window frame to steady himself against the wind whipping around him. There before him he saw Katya staring out at him, her mouth contorted with fear, her eyes filled with terror. He was angered! She was the only protection he had from this wild and lonely land.

Katya, brought suddenly back to the present, saw him staring up at her. I am not ready for him! Hurry, hurry, her heart said. The earrings, the rouge, the lipstick!

Fighting the storm, at last he reached the door, flung it open. To his astonishment there before him stood not the unfamiliar, frightened girl he had seen framed in the window, but the Katya he knew, her eyes sparkling with animation.

"A little early. You have returned to your Katya," she cried. Hurrying forward, she put her warm hands on his cold cheeks, offering her lips for his kiss.

A Chinese man of fifty, dressed in a long blue gown, entered the room, placed a tray with glasses and syphon on the table. "Master wanchee tea?" he asked.

"No, perhaps later," Edward answered. "Here, take my coat and hat and dry them."

"Now it will be like the night we met in the café. We forget the snow . . . the world," cried Katya, pouring out drinks for herself and Edward.

But it was not as it had been in the café, nor on previous evenings here in Lahususu. There was no merriment in Katya in spite of her effort to whip it to life. Finally her smile died away, leaving her face pale and tense. "The storm!" she cried. "I cannot make gay with storm howling."

Edward felt a sudden, confusing desire to protect her mingled with resentment that she should need protection and a faint sense of shame that he wanted protection himself. He poured himself a second drink, a third.

He was drinking more than Katya had ever seen him drink before. "The night, the snow. It makes you sad, yes? Maybe you think of your home, your mother?" Perhaps she need not be gay, just tender.

For one moment he had a vision of The Valley, himself a small boy. It was a day in early summer. All the family were away except his mother and himself. They were having luncheon together on a side porch overlooking the orchard. How pretty his mother was, and all his for this long day! But he didn't want to talk about his mother to Katya. Then he had a disturbing idea that she was implying he needed his mother.

"For God's sake," he cried, "don't treat me as if I were still in short pants!"

"Short pants. What is short pants?" she asked, thoroughly alarmed now, realizing that she was unable to cast a spell over him this evening. Upon her ability to do so her chance for food and shelter depended.

The Chinese houseboy brought in the dinner. It was the usual monotonous diet with which he provided them: potatoes, tough beef bought in the local market, bread raised with native sour dough.

"You might exert yourself a little, see we get some decent food." Edward threw down his napkin, pushed his chair away from the table.

"I am as much your servant as your houseboy. He would consider orders from me improper," she answered in a low voice. With sudden indignation she went on: "This is good food. It is wicked to waste it. If you ever creep on your knees, beg for scrapings fit only for hog, then——" Suddenly she stopped. Her anger gave place to consternation. She was destroying her chance to live.

Edward studied her. Who was this Russian woman who had appeared so experienced until this evening? He knew only that she was a White Russian, a refugee who stirred his senses, but on whom in his heart he looked down. He had met her in a café in Harbin, and she had consented to come with him for the winter. It was a business arrangement with no other obligation than money on his part. But again he felt that desire to protect her, not to be denied this time. "Katya, you don't need to put on an act. Better tell me what's wrong," he said.

She looked up at him, mingled surprise and consternation in her eyes. "Nothing wrong," she answered hastily. She wanted to tell him that she wasn't the experienced café girl she had led him to believe, that in reality the night he had met her was her first evening in the café, that she had taken the place because otherwise she would starve. She had come with him because living with him seemed less of a risk than staying at the café. But dared she trust that new note of gentleness in his voice? She was not certain of his kindness or of the kindness of his people. Americans were strange to her. Did they always just want to be made happy? His sudden gentleness might mean less than nothing; she did not know.

His was a charming face, aquiline nose, thin but softly curved lips, large, black eyes. What kind of man lived behind them? All she was certain of was that until this evening she had had power over him and now she had not.

Edward went over, sat down beside her. Resting one elbow on the table, he tried to look into her face, but she had lowered her head. He put his hand over hers. He could feel her locked fingers pressed against the table's edge trembling beneath his clasp. He felt he had nothing to lose by showing a little human kindness. "Maybe I could help. I'd like to really." There was sincerity in his tone.

All at once she found herself talking, English and Russian mixed together. She explained that her father had been a large landowner in the Ukraine, where they lived until the Revolution. "Then we went to Moscow. First my father was taken away. Then my mother died. My brother was in the army. I tried to reach him, but I couldn't. I went back to the Ukraine. I thought I'd be safer there. One night my father's laborers . . ." She felt again the throbbing vein in her throat, but she managed to go on: "I had to get away. I had a little money and my mother's jewels——"

She stopped. This was the tale of every Russian fortune hunter along the coast of China in the year 1920, a tale that had spread across the ocean to California, making the real Russian refugee suspect everywhere. After all, weren't things just the same as they were before? To this prosperous American I can only be the girl who came away with him, she thought despairingly.

Edward rose, walked around the room more disturbed than he dared admit, yet not quite believing her story, not wanting to believe it. If it were so, he would have to face the fact that in bringing her here he had not, as he had thought, brought with him a woman older than he and experienced in what he asked of her. "Nineteen years old," she said. Surely she was more than nineteen!

2

AFTER that night, hard as Katya worked to re-establish it, her role as café girl lacked validity. Beneath her insouciance Edward kept seeing the refugee. The rouge on her cheeks seemed only to emphasize the hollows beneath her high cheekbones, reminding him of what she had suffered—that is, if her story were true. Always there was that niggling doubt. The droop to her mouth, which once indicated to him an interesting melancholy, these days gave the impression of genuine distress. Or did it?

He was angry that she no longer made him forget the darkness closing in around them earlier and earlier as the daylight in this far north was cut down to a few hours. With a book for a guard he watched her drifting about the room in her red dress, the scent of her perfume driving him to viciously unkind remarks. If he could only take her! For the moment at least the close embrace would bar out the night and his aloneness. But now that there was the possibility that his bargain had been made with a desperate girl, he could not press his claims, although he cursed himself for a romantic fool because he could not. He had a suspicion that he was not the man of the world he had pictured himself—at twenty-one a blow to his pride.

Less and less Katya was able to hide her fear over the predicament in which she had placed herself. The desperateness of her plight if Edward should turn her out paralyzed her against every effort to be gay. The sardonic eyes of the houseboy bored away at her last defenses.

She did not rise now until time to dress for Edward's return from the office. One day, although she huddled under a pile of blankets, she grew colder and colder. When she put out her hand the air in the room felt like ice. She called for the houseboy, but there was no answer. She dressed hurriedly and went in search of him. He and his belongings were gone, and the fire was out in the stove.

It was a Russian stove erected in the middle of the house like a great pillar warming the four rooms that surrounded it. She had never built a fire in such a stove, although she knew something of its intricate dampers. The house grew colder. She put on her heaviest clothes and went to work. Time after time the kindling flickered and went out. The sun was going down. Over her own garments she put on a coat of Edward's and mittens. Again she knelt, laying the sticks carefully. They were too big. She had used up all the kindling in her previous attempts. She rearranged the dampers, fanned vigorously. Inside the stove she heard the faintest crackling. Then it was gone. "O Mother of God, help me to make it burn!" she prayed. An icy draft of air made her turn. Edward stood in the open doorway.

"What are you doing?" he exclaimed.

"The boy go; the fire go, too." She turned to the stove again.

"Here, let me do it. But get me something to cut this wood with," he commanded.

Frantically they worked, the cold gaining on them with the sinking sun. It was forty below zero outside. What it was in this room Edward tried not to think. And then finally there was an unmistakable roar in the chimney. They huddled close to the stove for its first warmth. Suddenly Edward laughed. "You look so funny. You've got a smudge on your nose and a blob on your cheek."

He stopped. Without the powder and the rouge and the earrings he saw how young she really was. She seemed more like a little girl with the pinched look of the underfed than a woman. "Why, you're just a kid!" he exclaimed.

"Not kid," she answered indignantly, defending her grown-upness as she used to with her brother Petya.

Then both of them rocked back on their heels, laughing hard the way children laugh. But only for a moment.

Edward pulled her to her feet. "I won't hold you to your promise, Katya. You are free." He must say it now before he changed his mind.

Did he mean he was turning her out? "Please don't send me away," she cried in her despair.

He gathered her into his arms, greatcoat, mittens and all. His voice broke. "I can't live here without you. It was only——"

"I have need, too," she answered simply.

Now that there was no necessity for Katya to be the experienced café girl, entertainer and bright seducer, she wore her hair as she had worn it in the Ukraine, its yellow strands drawn back over her ears and gathered into a loose knot at the nape of her neck. Over her shoulders she tied a Russian head shawl. With quiet dignity she greeted Edward each evening on his return from the office, watching him closely to gauge how much during the day he had succumbed to the homesickness which assailed him so often. Gradually she came to understand that she was Edward's shelter as well as his lover. The knowledge gave her stature in her own eyes, the will to fight back the terrible memories of her last days in Russia, the pain over the loss of her parents and her anxiety over her brother Petya. Had they killed him, or had he escaped? To keep her mind from such terrifying thoughts during the day she studied Edward's language. To be a better and better companion to him became a passion with her.

Each evening, with the darkness and fierce northern winter shut away beyond closely drawn curtains, they would sit side by side on an old couch drawn before the fire. Edward would ask endless questions about her home in Russia. For some reason he could not understand, her tales relieved him of his own homesick longings. Sometimes Katya would forget that her home had been destroyed, so vivid was the memory of the days before the Revolution: the fertile Ukraine land, the horses her father bred for the cavalry, the white-footed mare he had given her for her own, the peasants arriving for the Christmas celebration given each year by her mother and father, the afternoon of her seventeenth birthday, the last festival celebrated before the Revolution—cousins and aunts driving up to the house in their droshkies, her mother receiving them, Katya standing by her side with her hair up for the first time.

"You seem to have been an awfully nice family," Edward said, forgetting he had ever doubted the truth of her tales.

"You should have seen my grandmother!" Katya exclaimed. "She was very old-fashioned, and she was very stern with Father." She laughed, remembering her tall, dignified father standing humbly before his tiny, imperious mother waiting for her instructions about the crops and the horses.

"She sounds something like my grandmother," said Edward.

"Tell me about her," Katya demanded. "It's time you told me about your family."

"She's not little like your grandmother. She's tall. She is very old—nearly ninety. She rules us all except my mother. Until lately she managed Grandfather's estate."

"So you had big estates!"

"Have," corrected Edward.

Katya shivered. "It was like that with us before the Revolution," she cried, forgetting she was Edward's shelter. "But now I can't stop thinking about what it was like after the Revolution. All those people who had served us, so angry . . . so hating us, I guess. The night Dunia and I hid from them, not even my old nurse helped us to get away. Dunia and I came to China. Then I lost Dunia. A Chinese war lord took her for his concubine." Her voice sank to a whisper. Her face looked pinched and drawn, and there was no youth in it any more.

"Don't let's think about it," Edward pleaded. "I'm going to show you some pictures of my family." She could hear him opening his trunk, hunting about in it. "Look," he said, coming back with a handful of pictures and laying one in her lap. "This is my mother." It was a snapshot of a young woman sitting under an old branch-twisted tree.

"How sweet, the mama!" Katya exclaimed. "Little like a doll." She smiled, pushing the tragedy of her own family to the back of her mind.

Edward studied the picture. Nice to share his admiration of his mother with Katya. He forgot how long ago the photograph had been taken. "She is pretty, isn't she? When I took this, the tree had feathery red blossoms, and the seeds of last year hung in clusters from the branches. They were like a lot of small wooden bowls turned upside down. When I was a little boy, I liked to lie on my back on a bench under this tree, twirling the pods on my fingers. Sometimes my mother would sit beside me." Why had he told her this?

"Here," he said, changing the subject, "is a picture of my grandmother's home." And then for the first time he told her of The Valley where he lived as a child; how, when the first settlers came, they found nothing growing in it but cactus and wild oats, how they began making level fields and saturated them with water brought from the rivers and mountain streams. On his grandmother's land the irrigation ditches now ran the length of the orange grove, and when the sluice gates were opened and the water was let in you could scarcely tell soil from water, each made black with the substance of the other. In the spring the air was filled with the scent of thousands of orange blossoms, and later the oranges hung everywhere among the leaves.

For days afterward Katya, looking out over the frozen plain— unbroken except where a boy, black against the whiteness, painstakingly swept up dark excrement dropped by passing mule or dog—saw growing up out of the snow lemon and orange trees, the yellow fruit among thick green leaves. She came to put aside Russia as something too painful to remember. In its place The Valley, the beautiful land of America, the dream of people like herself who needed refuge.

The winter crept slowly forward. The ice in the river was twelve feet deep. The white covering of the earth grew old, stained brown with the red dirt of the plain, then white again with a new fall of snow. Icicles six feet long hung from the eaves of their house. The wind blew about it, making it tremble under the terrific onslaught. The falling snow, the white plain and the gray impassive sky began to seem eternal to Edward. "Nothing matters except our love," he whispered to Katya in the dark isolation of the night. He felt as if he were the first man in the world, and out of that lonely land had come to him the first woman.

Katya loved him utterly. Yet the hard conditions under which she had existed since the Revolution had made her too much of a realist to accept Edward's ardent statement that nothing mattered but their love. There was a hostile world beyond the barrier of the frozen river. But at night, lying in her lover's arms in the great silence that followed a drop in the wind, the only sound sharp pistolshot noises of house beams contracting in the intense cold, she built a permanent abode out of the illusion of an unending winter.

3

IN THE far north spring came so slowly it was all but imperceptible at first—a fraction more daylight morning and night, a driving cold rain changing the snow into ice, soft places in the road that led over the frozen river making it unsafe, finally the path from the office to the house muddy at noon, and the sun shining warm and strong. One day water dripped from the ends of the stalactites of ice hanging from the eaves.

It isn't spring, Katya told herself, just a little thaw. So far north winter lasts much longer. Edward has said nothing about receiving any notice of shipping being resumed. The river won't open for weeks yet, she was sure.

She called the coolie to stoke the stove.

"Missie, too hot, more better little fire." As he spoke, from over their heads came a heavy thud as if someone were moving a mammoth trunk. Beyond the window Katya saw a mass of snow fall from the roof. "Snow, he come down!" exclaimed the coolie. Suddenly a stalactite just outside the window snapped and fell with a brittle noise.

That afternoon very early Edward rushed in crying, "I've news for you! There's a steamer due in a few days. I wired for the captain to pick up something fresh for us to eat. Bananas or oranges. You're always talking about oranges."

"It's too early for steamers!" cried Katya. Faced with the hard reality of her position, she began to cry, not much, just a few difficult tears.

"I thought you'd be pleased." Edward was nettled that she did not appreciate his thoughtfulness, puzzled too for a moment over her distress. But as its meaning penetrated his mind he was angry. "You don't trust me very much, do you?" he burst out. But he did not say she could trust him.

The appalling suspicion had come over him that maybe she couldn't trust him. The crystal ball he had lived in so long was melting away with the snow. He loved Katya, but did he want to marry her and some day take her home with him? He had an uneasy feeling that it would be a betrayal of his mother to marry Katya, a betrayal of Katya if he did not. Her fate, if he abandoned her, was something too cruel for him to contemplate. But after all, didn't they have to face reality, hard as it was?

"I've got to go back to the office," he said, picking up his cap which he had dropped on the table when he came in. "I just ran over to tell you about the steamer." Hurriedly he went out, walked along the path to the village and down to the river's edge, watched the floes moving down the river. Like Katya he wished now for the solid mass of ice and the isolation which so many times he had ardently desired to have ended. Intertwined with his very heartstrings was this woman who had shared the long night with him, for so the winter seemed to him as he looked back upon it. The tenderness which for many months past had been an integral part of his love for her reasserted itself. And yet as communication with the world was about to be re-established the demands of his family seemed in some mysterious way more important than his obligation to the woman he loved. He knew his parents wanted him to marry the daughter of his father's business partner.

He went back to the office, cleared his desk of the papers placed there by the clerk in his absence. When he had finished, he had a good sense of work done. For the first time he realized that he had gained in ability during the winter. He felt pride in the way he had carried on in this lonely outpost where most men went to pieces. With it came a sudden sense of gratitude to Katya. He couldn't have done it without her. Hurriedly he put the thought from him. He didn't want to feel he owed her anything.

The hour for closing had passed. He was alone except for the coolie moving about in the outer room. He began looking over the records of the winter—filing and sorting. Everything must be in order if the customs authorities sent an inspector up on the incoming steamer. He came to the first letters he had written to the central office. Vividly they brought back how he had felt when he wrote them—the day of the early winter storm, his panicky feeling that he had done for himself by coming to China. It began to be clear to him why he had come. It had to do with his manhood. It was the need however vague and half-formed to gain self-reliance somehow denied him under his father's strong will and ability, by his influence, to shape things for his sons.

I am more of a person than I was when I left home, he thought. It was for that reason I came away. Yet I was about to surrender my will again, go against every instinct of decency within me to do what my father would want me to do. And I am three thousand miles away from him! Of course I'll marry Katya. It's unthinkable that I should do anything else.

But he still felt an uneasiness associated with his mother. I wonder why? he asked himself. I've always been able to make things right with her.

With this assurance he put her out of his mind. He was a man with a man's responsibilities. Quietly he walked back to his house at peace with himself.

When Edward went out, Katya sank into the nearest chair. The end of her security and happiness had come too suddenly, catapulting her into a fright which took all power of motion from her, her mind set in a catalepsy of fear as rigid as that which possessed her body. She had no knowledge how long she sat there, no knowledge of the advancing day. Edward had gone and would never return!

When the door opened and he came in, she had no sense of reality in his presence. She passed her hand over her brow, seeing him and yet not able to believe he was there. But when he came over to her, put his hand under her chin and lifted her head so he could look into her eyes, saying, "It is true, Katya; nothing matters but our love," slowly she accepted his presence. She saw at last the man behind his eyes and believed.

That night Katya carried blankets to the living room, made herself a bed on the couch. If she were to marry Edward it was a spiritual necessity again to be the beloved daughter of landowner Suvorov, the adored sister of Petya, the favorite grandchild of the dear little grandmother—once more the young girl Katya, galloping over the steppes on the back of her white-footed mare.

She awoke. Her pillow had slid onto the floor. The blankets and sheets, too wide for the couch, had followed the pillow. The sharp, staccato barking of dogs in the village struck into the hollowed quiet of the room, bringing her back to the present. She was not that young girl who had lived in the Ukraine. Many things had happened since which had changed her completely. What had she to offer Edward— she a refugee without money, without family? For the moment she distrusted even the singleness of her love for him.

During the long months here in this white desert when her body had cried out for fresh foods, Edward's stories of the fruit-laden valley where he had been born had been stamped indelibly on her mind. In bare, unadorned words marrying Edward meant a passport not only to safety but to plenty. For he would take her to California sometime. He loved it too much to stay away long. To live in America was the dream of every Russian refugee. Assured now of his love and protection, she began to doubt her right to accept them. Edward, Edward, believe me, it is not just for the things you can give me I am marrying you. Her heart cried out in extravagant gratitude, I adore you.

To Edward's surprise and delight, after the inspector had visited him, he was transferred to a more important post, partly, he was told, because it was a policy of the administration not to keep a man long in such an isolated place and partly in recognition of the efficient way he had performed his duties. The unsolicited praise and reward strengthened Edward's growing belief both in his own judgment and in his ability to carry through what he attempted.

When they reached Harbin on their way to their new station, he and Katya were quietly married. As much was taken for granted in Manchurian cities bordering on Russia during the years following the Revolution, Edward's statement that they had been secretly married before they went to Lahususu was accepted at its face value. The White Russians were happy that one more of their number was cared for; the Americans and British lifted their eyebrows but slightly and gossiped only a little about this latest international marriage.

As the train left Harbin, moving south across the level stretches of Manchuria, Edward's happiness grew. He took deep satisfaction in thinking of the letter he had written his family, telling them not only of his change of address due to his promotion but of his marriage. Katya's faith in him was a profoundly moving experience. No one before, it seemed to him, had trusted him completely.

The dignity and security of marriage had begun to do its work with Katya. She had moments of pure joy produced by nothing more than a fluffy cloud she glimpsed outside the train window, or the sun shining down on the pale-green kaoliang spears just piercing the red-brown soil. Sitting close to Edward with his arm encircling her, she dreamed of their future. The southern city where they were being sent was a nice place to live, so she had been told. The houses of the customs people were set in a sheltered garden. And after a while they would have their first home leave, and it would be spent with Edward's people in California. Perhaps they would never return to China.

The train drew to a stop at Changchun, the great railway center in the middle of Manchuria. Katya and Edward leaned from the open window of their compartment, watching the mass of humanity moving along the platform.

"Meester Dodd, Meester Dodd." The words rose shrill and clear over the chatter of the crowd. "Teleegram, teleegram."

Edward motioned the messenger to him, dropped a coin into his hand, took the white envelope, hastily slit it open with his forefinger. His head and shoulders disappeared from the window. He wondered if there had been a change of plans and he was being called back to Harbin. He couldn't yet believe in his luck.

"What is it?" cried Katya.

Edward stared at the open telegram in his hands. Gently Katya took it from him. The word "Mother" at the end caught her eye. Then it was a cable. The office had forwarded it from Harbin. "Your father is ill. Please come. Mother," it read.

The bell clanged, the train pulled slowly out of the station. "It changes everything," said Edward as they sat down opposite each other. "I'll have to give up what I've started here." With the toe of his shoe he pushed a wad of paper on the floor back and forth.

"You don't want to?" Katya asked, disturbed at his distress.

"I am all at sea about it. If my father's really seriously sick . . ." Edward's words trailed away.

"But your mother wouldn't ask you to come if he weren't," Katya exclaimed in surprise.

"Of course Father's sick," he answered. He was thinking, Has my marriage anything to do with it? He began calculating. Yes, she has just had time to get the letter I wrote to her the day after the wedding. What does sending for me mean?

He straightened his shoulders. "Well, anyway we'll be going back home, and that is something. I was upset for the moment naturally. It was so sudden. But are *you* glad to go?"

"Oh, yes!" she exclaimed.

He looked across at her. She grows lovelier every day, he thought. The dark hollows had gone from under her eyes. Her long, narrow face now that her cheeks had filled out was perfectly proportioned. Her eyes with their dark lashes and her blond hair made a striking combination of color. Her body had a long-boned grace that only tall women have. And more, she had breeding. Since he had known Katya, he had come to the conclusion that there was an over-all culture, common to all peoples, that transcended racial barriers. His mother would love her once she saw her. She couldn't help it. No one could. Katya's capacity for enjoyment captivated people. He did not understand how anyone who had suffered so much could be so lighthearted in her happiness. It indicated a resilience of spirit that would help her through the difficult time of adjustment at home in case the family did not entirely accept her at first. Katya met every test.

4

THE trans-Pacific steamer on which Edward had booked their passage was nearing San Francisco. Katya walked quickly down the empty deck. She had come out early before anyone else was abroad because there had been a rumor the night before that they might sight land very early. She wanted to be alone when she caught her first glimpse of America. Even Edward did not entirely understand what his country meant to her.

There was another reason why she had come out early. She wanted to be alone to think. She was beginning to realize that the return to his home had complications for Edward. Was it bound up with the quarrel he had had with his father before he left home, or was it because she was a Russian? Ever since he had received his mother's cable he had been so anxious to have her look and talk like an American. He had drilled her constantly on her English, correcting the slightest mistake. Should she speak to him about it? Would it help? Shouldn't everything be understood between them before they landed?

She stopped at the forward part of the deck looking down on an uncovered space filled with steerage passengers, among them some of her own countrymen. Except for Edward, she would have come as they were coming, without security or dignity, if she had ever succeeded in reaching America at all. "Dear God," she murmured, "make me an American for Edward's sake!"

She felt a light touch on her shoulder. It was Edward. "Let's get some breakfast," he said.

"Now? Isn't that dark line land?"

"America will keep," he answered, almost, she thought, as if he wished it weren't so near.

Indeed Edward wished the voyage were not over. In many ways he dreaded his home-coming. He feared his father would insist he go into his office, but that was not what he intended to do. In the days since he had received his mother's telegram, he had thought a great deal about his future. In his bunk in the steamer, many nights he lay awake trying to rid himself of the feeling that he was walking into some kind of trap. Once in his adolescence, twice since he was grown, he had mapped out what he wanted to do with his life. Each time he had been thwarted by some adroit move on the part of his father. That was the aspect of his situation that baffled him. Always, somehow, his parents circumvented him, made him do what they wanted. He loved his parents. He didn't do things contrary to their wishes just to defy them. What he had wanted to do in the past, as he looked back on it, seemed sensible enough, and what he now wanted to do.

He wanted to become a lawyer, live in The Valley, specializing in Water Law. His father wouldn't like the idea, he felt certain. As he was sick, it would be difficult to fight it out with him. Every time he reached this point in his thinking, Edward would feel himself up against a barrier. He would turn back to the beginning and think his way through again, but in the end it always meant arriving at the same conclusion—his father would win. Sometimes he would get up and crowd himself into the lower bunk with Katya to feel the warmth and comfort of her presence. Now, as he saw land on the dim horizon, he wished for a brief moment he were steaming out instead of into the harbor.

It was noon, and still they had not passed through the Golden Gate. Another hour dragged itself out. Suddenly Edward cried, "Look, Katya! That's the Gate off there. I'm sure it is." Katya could see two faint lines that looked like land, a space between them. The lines grew clearer. The rail was suddenly crowded with passengers, all with their eyes turned toward America.

After the ship had steamed between the two projecting land masses, Katya went below, put on the suit and hat Edward had selected for her in Shanghai. She'd waited until the last moment in order that she should bear no mark of travel. A final glance in the mirror assured her. Very American, she said to herself with only a small doubt. Then she joined Edward at the ship's rail. "Am I right?" she asked him.

"Yes," he said after a moment's scrutiny.

"Why are you so anxious about my looks?" she asked in spite of her resolve not to probe at his uneasiness.

"Because," he answered, "you are meeting my family for the first time, and a man always wants to show off his bride."

So that's all there was to it, she thought. I've been foolish.

"That's Oakland over there, where we live," he cried.

Katya stared at the hills set with white houses. This was America! This was to be her home!

The ship eased into the dock. "Look," cried Edward: "that girl in blue, that's my sister Margot! There's Mother! See—over there!" He pulled Katya's arm through his, pushed his way to the rail. "There's Tom. There's Bettie! You know—my little sister. She's grown. I almost didn't know her."

How finished-looking they all are, thought Katya, even the little sister in her white gloves with her handbag held at the same angle the mother held hers. There was decorum, too, in the way they waved, no wild tossing of arms and handkerchiefs.

As they stepped off the gangplank, Edward's family closed around him. Standing a little apart, Katya had an odd feeling that Edward was changed, stamped by some unique family quality she had not noticed in him before. Suddenly she understood. It was some mark people lose when they are entirely separated from their backgrounds, as Edward had been out in China. As she had been. And now Edward was not. But she still was. She stood beyond the boundaries of the family.

Then Edward reached out, took her hand and drew her into the group. "Here she is, Mother. This is Katya."

"You can't know how impatiently I've waited for this moment." Mrs. Dodd smilingly held out her hands, taking Katya's.

Katya felt confused, not certain whether the meaning behind her mother-in-law's words was wholly friendly, but courteously she bent and kissed Mrs. Dodd on each cheek.

"How very quaint!" Mrs. Dodd murmured.

Katya realized that her salutation was out of the ordinary and not wholly acceptable. "It is our custom," she said quietly. Pride rooted in generations of Russian tradition had come to her support.

Mother couldn't have answered better herself, thought Edward with pride.

Bettie, the ten-year-old sister, threw her arms around Katya crying, "Please kiss me twice. . . . You're nice. I like you," she whispered as she received the kisses.

In an aside to Tom, Margot murmured, "We're acting like a lot of foreigners."

"You don't mind if we call you Katherine, do you?" Mrs. Dodd asked brightly.

"Please do if you prefer it to my real name," answered Katya.

Now Tom shook hands with her saying, "I've got to get along to the office, but I'll see you later." He lifted his hat and disappeared in the crowd.

Later after they were cleared by the customs and were leaving the dock, Edward fell behind with his mother. "You like Katya, don't you, Mother?" he asked eagerly.

"You must give me time, Edward," Mrs. Dodd answered after a moment's hesitation. "For you to marry a Russian girl is still hard for me to accept. Surely you can understand that. I have not told your father that she is Russian. I see now that I have made a mistake. I should have prepared him. I had not realized how foreign she would seem. You know your father, with his dislike of anything un-American."

"Why did you send for me then?" Edward demanded. "I wrote you Katya was Russian. We couldn't do you any harm over there. If you think we will disgrace the family here, we can go away again. I can go back any time. I did well. They liked my work."

"Don't quarrel with me, Edward," Mrs. Dodd pleaded. "I did it for your father's sake. I thought it would help him to have you home, and I needed you."

"But you just said——" Edward stopped. She had lifted her eyes to him, and they were full of unshed tears.

"I'll arrange things somehow." She patted his arm reassuringly.

"How *is* Father?" Edward asked.

"Better. He is sitting up, but he isn't able to come downstairs yet. This sickness on top of the necessity for an operation on his eyes . . . it means we must harbor all his strength."

"You never told me about his eyes. I'm terribly sorry." Edward had the uneasy feeling his mother was putting on him the responsibility for his father's recovery.

To Katya everything had a dreamlike quality: the luxurious motor-car with its exquisite appointments, the cornucopia vases at the sides, a red rose in each, perfect against the gray upholstery, the tube Mrs. Dodd talked into directing the liveried chauffeur beyond the glass partition, the chatter of Edward's mother and sisters, the odd quality of their voices asking him innumerable questions about their trip and the Eastern cities he had seen.

Entranced, she watched the car take its place on the ferry, felt the slow movement carrying them across the Bay. Wisps of drifting fog lent unreality to the sky and water and approaching hills. Then the car was again in motion. Higher and higher up the hills they went with the sun striking against the windows of the houses, making them glow with fiery light. At last, far up among great trees, the car turned into a winding drive and stopped at the door of Edward's home.

"Take off your hat, Katherine," Mrs. Dodd directed as they entered the house. "I know you're tired after your long trip. I think you ought to rest. We're dining at eight tonight."

As the front door shut behind them a bell rang sharply. Mrs. Dodd hurried away. For a moment after she had left no one seemed to know what to do.

"Don't you want to see our view of the Bay?" Bettie asked, breaking the silence, anxious to help Edward out. Something was wrong about his home-coming. He'd done something to displease their mother. But what could it be? She led Katya over to the window which extended from floor to ceiling at the end of the long hall where they stood.

Below lay a mosaic of roofs, red, blue and gray, and far out beyond a flat shore stretched a sea of fog shrouding the Bay. The sun was setting behind the hills to the right in a red ball untouched by the low-flying fog. Each separate color and lighting seemed to be indelibly pressed into Katya's consciousness. This strange country. Overpowering, in these first moments.

"Wait until you see The Valley," said Edward.

"The Valley," mocked Margot. "Surely you've got over your silly love for it."

"Edward." It was Mrs. Dodd's voice calling from the stair landing.

Edward left the group at the window, running up the stairs to join his mother.

"Your father wants to see you both, but he isn't strong enough for the excitement of seeing a stranger today. I've persuaded him to wait until tomorrow to see his new daughter-in-law. If he overdoes now before the operation——" She sighed. "I must prepare you," she went on. "You'll find your father changed. When you see him, you'll understand why I am so careful of him."

She led the way into his father's bedroom. In a chair by the window, a rug over his knees although the day was warm, sat a thin, bowed man, his blue eyes clouded, his gaze groping.

In spite of what his mother had said, Edward was not prepared for the change in his father. When he had gone away, his father had been a tall, heavy-set, vigorous man with crisp iron-gray hair, shaggy eyebrows from beneath which his bright blue eyes surveyed the world—his world, Edward had thought bitterly, in that final quarrel between them.

"Your mother is a great negotiator," Jeremy Dodd said in a tone Edward knew very well. "She should have gone in for politics. She would have made a better member of the state legislature than I ever made." Edward was never certain whether his father was being complimentary or sarcastic in his reference to his mother when he spoke in that tone. Before he could decide if he ought to go to her defense, his father added in a gentler tone, "She thinks we did not understand each other just before you went away. I guess maybe she's right. She usually is." He groped for his wife's hand.

Overcome by this unprecedented softness in his father, Edward's defenses went down. He was forgiven, accepted, reinstated in the family.

"It's good to be home, sir." Edward reached out for his father's free hand, unable to say more.

"And now as to this wife of yours. I want to see her." Jeremy Dodd's voice had its old commanding note.

"Please wait until tomorrow, Jeremy. You've had enough excitement for today," Mrs. Dodd begged.

Suddenly realizing his own weakness and that he was tired, he answered with unexpected docility, "Very well, my dear."

Awakening an hour later after a heavy but troubled sleep, he had a definite sense that something was wrong, something carried over from his talk with his wife and son. Gradually his uneasiness focused on Edward's marriage. In some way the girl was a threat to the family. That was why his wife had postponed their meeting. He reached for his bell and rang it with an urgency which brought Mrs. Dodd hurrying to him.

"Is anything wrong, Jeremy?" she asked anxiously.

"Why didn't you bring Ed's wife to see me, Beatrice? What's wrong with her?" he demanded.

Beatrice Dodd felt herself backed into a corner. How could she present the girl in a way that would protect Edward from his father's displeasure? "She seems to be a nice girl, Jeremy. She's almost beautiful in an odd way and I think definitely aristocratic-looking."

"What's wrong with her then?"

"Well, there is a little foreign look to her, but I'm sure after she's been here awhile it will wear off."

"You mean she's a foreigner!" Family pride in Jeremy went deeper than his wife's concern over appearances. With a family like the Dodds, appearances took care of themselves as far as Jeremy Dodd was concerned. The basic structure of the family was what he valued. A fine strain leading back to America's beginnings. French Huguenot on his mother's side, English on his father's. He had a curiously mystical idea that the family's American blood would be contaminated if any new strains were introduced after that one blending.

"Oh, Jeremy," cried his wife, "despite this marriage which seems perhaps a little unfortunate, Edward has matured! Didn't you feel that he is more of a man?"

"Just leave Ed out of it for the time. I want to know about this woman."

Realizing that she would gain nothing by postponing telling him the facts she answered, "I should guess she is a White Russian."

"A princess, I suppose." He laughed a cynical laugh. "There are a lot of grandees in San Francisco, if we are to believe what they say of themselves. There's been a steady flow of them into the city ever since the beginning of the Russian Revolution. Shabby-looking lot, calling themselves royalty." Shabbiness of any kind affronted Jeremy Dodd. America was built on thrift, and for anyone who could not keep himself and his home in repair he felt scorn. "So this is the kind of person my son has brought into our family. And you try to tell me Edward has grown up!"

"You're rested now. Probably you'd better see her," Mrs. Dodd replied, avoiding an answer to his remark about Edward. "But you know what the doctor told you about keeping quiet."

He pushed the pillows up behind his head. "No, I'll not see her. But not because I haven't enough strength. You'd better arrange for a place for them to stay over in San Francisco."

"Oh, Jeremy, don't turn them out!" Beatrice begged. "Edward left home once; he might again." She did not tell her husband that this was what Edward had said he would do if his wife were not made welcome. "They could go down to see your mother for a few weeks. You know how impatient she is to see Edward. We can work out what's best all around while they're gone."

"You have had your way with Edward all his life," Jeremy Dodd retorted, "and this is the result. Now I'm going to have mine."

Mrs. Dodd was frightened. She hadn't expected Jeremy to be as upset as this. "I'll call your mother right now." Hurriedly she left the room before he refused his consent.

Until now she had thought only of getting Edward home so that she could direct his life. That she meant in time to alienate him from his foreign wife she had not acknowledged even to herself. Neither had she faced the possibility, now evident, that Jeremy's rejection of the girl, something she had counted on to further her plans, might mean the rejection of Edward too.

When he was alone once more, Jeremy's flare-up of anger against his favorite son turned into a calculating determination to get this foreign woman out of his family, no matter how much suffering it entailed. Edward was his last chance to achieve the ambitious plan for one of his sons which he had once held for all of them.

In their childhood he had endowed the three with the attributes he admired—shrewd business sense and political acumen. Jeremy Dodd had lived in an exciting world of business ventures and political maneuvers. He was very young when he had been elected by his district to the state legislature, first to the Assembly, then to the Senate. As he was running in the county where there was a preponderance of large landowners, his father one of the largest, his election was foreordained. Later he had accepted the general managership of one of the state's electric companies, in time becoming its principal stockholder and president.

As his sons grew up he had hoped each would become another Jeremy Dodd. His eldest, John, only child of a former marriage, had turned out a failure. A teacher on a small salary in a boy's reformatory, he had neither made money nor maintained the family's social position. Tom, his and Beatrice's first-born, would always be a solid citizen. Jeremy need never worry that he would do anything eccentric as John had done, but neither would he do anything smart in business or politics.

So finally Jeremy had channeled all his ambitions into Edward, his and Beatrice's second son. In his adolescence Edward had displayed traits which had led his father to believe he could be groomed to take an important place in California. He was imaginative. He was a leader. Many a time Jeremy had taken solid satisfaction in observing that Edward, even when he was small, was the one others liked to serve. He was smart, too. But as Edward had grown older, his father had been forced to the conclusion that he lacked stability and good judgment. There was a social streak in him he distrusted.

It had shown itself first in high school. Jeremy had laid it, then, to the influence of the boy's half brother John. As long as they lived in The Valley the two had been inseparable. John had taken up with the ideas of Theodore Roosevelt and Pinchot, head of the National Forest Service, and had passed them on to Edward—crazy ideas about the evils of large landholdings, and water and power monopoly, and God knew what not. He'd succeeded later in knocking such utopian ideas out of Edward, but when the war came along, the boy had not wanted a safe berth in the States. Then as soon as he was out of the Army he'd gone off to China. And now there was this marriage! Because of his original satisfaction in Edward, Jeremy's disappointment in him was the more bitter. Coming on top of Jeremy's sickness and apprehension over the coming operation, it was unbearable. No matter what it cost this time, Edward would have to fall in line. For a moment his love for his favorite son bordered on hate.

There was a tap on his door. It was Margot. Since her father's sickness, whenever she was at home, she offered to read to him at this hour. In reality there was little reading. More often they talked. Jeremy Dodd during his illness had discovered his elder daughter. She understood him. He didn't have to change her to get what he wanted out of her, just guide her. If she'd only been a boy he could have achieved his ambition for one of his children. As it was, he found her a great help in an advisory capacity. She often contributed ideas of her own. He was glad she had come in this afternoon.

"Why couldn't Ed have married somebody of distinction instead of a foreigner?" she burst out as soon as she had taken her seat close to his bed. "He's always doing something queer. It makes people think *we're* queer." With a paper knife she had picked up Margot slashed vehemently at a memorandum pad lying on a table beside her.

"I don't like it any better than you do," he answered, "but you don't need to be upset. Edward's going to take the girl down to see your grandmother tomorrow. By the time they're back, your mother will have an apartment rented for them in San Francisco."

"I knew you'd understand, Father." Margot leaned over him, kissed him lightly on the forehead.

When she had gone, a fresh wave of anger against Edward swept through Jeremy. He had always had an especially warmly protective feeling for his daughter Margot. He guessed her undue concern over Edward's marriage was because she felt it jeopardized her chances of marrying young Tilbury, the socialite who had been very attentive to her lately. Jeremy picked up the telephone, called his lawyer. "Can you come to see me tomorrow afternoon, Hawkins?" he asked. "And bring Boynton the detective with you if you can. I'll call you in the morning and see if you've got hold of him."

He put the receiver down and leaned back against his pillows. A plan was taking shape in his mind. Certainly there was bound to be something in the girl's past if he could get hold of it that would turn Edward against her. He had learned from experience not to oppose his son directly. He could feel his pulse beating heavily in his wrist. A warning! I've got to get myself quieted down or Beatrice will keep me from seeing Hawkins tomorrow. Trip hammers were beating in his temples. But he didn't call Beatrice.

5

THE uneasiness over her welcome that Katya had felt on her arrival dissipated during the ride across the Bay, gained on her during dinner, although Margot, the most aloof of the family, had gone out for the evening.

Already Katya had divined that Edward was not only his mother's favorite son but her favorite child. She seemed determined to use the present emergency as an excuse to monopolize him. She talked a great deal of her husband's sickness and the strain on her. "But now you are here," she kept saying to Edward, "I have a son I can call on. Not," she quickly added, "that I can't lean on Tom, but he has his own family."

"Edward's got Katya to look after," Bettie interposed.

"I wasn't meaning Edward didn't have responsibilities," Mrs. Dodd hastened to say, "but I'm sure Katya will be generous during these trying days."

There was an appealing look in her eyes which Katya did not trust. A husband should be a son first, she tried to tell herself.

With Edward sitting beside her on the couch after dinner, her hand held in his, Mrs. Dodd's fears lessened over what her husband might demand of Edward and Edward refuse to do. She could trust Edward to do whatever was necessary to make her happy.

When she bade Katya good night, she said, "I've arranged a surprise for you. You and Edward are to take Father's small car and go down to see Grandmother tomorrow. Make her a little visit. She's getting pretty old. We have to humor her, and she's determined to have her share of you."

When their bedroom door was closed, Edward laughed at Katya's puzzled expression. Whatever misgiving he had over the somewhat inconsistent course of events—his mother's bringing him across the ocean to help her and then sending him off on an unnecessarily hasty visit to his grandmother—he kept to himself.

Katya was only a little disturbed the next morning that her father-in-law did not see her before she and Edward left. Mrs. Dodd told them at breakfast that the doctor had said Mr. Dodd must see no one today. Excitement over Edward's home-coming had sent the sick man's temperature up.

The first few miles both of them were sobered over Mr. Dodd's set-back, but then, not being able to do anything about it, they began to enjoy themselves. Katya had never seen anything like these mountains—shining mound after shining mound. The road dipped and rose, dipped and rose, towns strung out along it. Walnut Creek—the creek was dry, but the walnut trees were there, great orchards of them beside the road, their green foliage massed at the foot of the golden hills.

"Is this The Valley?" asked Katya. This close-folded valley fitted her dream.

"No," Edward answered, "it's wide, not like these narrow cuts between the coastal ranges."

The parched, boldly molded coastal hills glistening under the fierce summer sun, through which they were now driving, the wild oats which covered them seeming almost to give off heat waves of their own, brought Edward a familiar feeling of excitement. After they had moved into Oakland, he had felt like this every summer when he went back to his grandmother's home for his vacation.

Danville, Dublin passed. Soon the road began to ascend toward the top of Altamont Pass. The tawny hills grew bolder, higher. The wind whipped about the car, giving Edward all he could do to hold it to the road. "There," he exclaimed, "through that gap in the hills you can see it!" But before Katya's eyes could follow his pointing finger, the tawny, rounded mountains had closed in across the opening. And then all at once there were no mountains ahead. They were at the top of the pass. Katya stared down upon a vast checkerboard of green and brown, the valley floor.

As the land leveled, the road straightened itself out, a hard mac-adamized thoroughfare leading straight on through the flat land that stretched behind them and in front of them to the hill-guarded horizon. After a little the coast range became but a faint, misty line finally entirely lost to their vision.

Katya knew the limitless, formless plains of Russia, but never had she seen so wide and limitless a valley nor one so trained to efficiency. Fruit trees and vines stood close together, pruned to dwarf size for bearing. No extra, unnecessary shoot was left for beauty's sake. The ground beneath was plowed and cultivated leaving neither grass nor weeds to draw off moisture. Edward told her water was the most valued possession in The Valley. You owned the right to draw it out of the rivers into canals and irrigation ditches running through your fields. Your pumps drew it up from deep underground basins. The sun shone daily for six months without interruption.

Trees and vines glistened in the sun's brilliant light. Wind swept across a vineyard, exposing the pale-green undersurface of grape leaves. A composite of movement and light spread across barley and wheat fields. Orchards flashed by with trees so weighted with fruit that their branches were propped up to keep them from breaking. Katya's amazement grew.

"We have to live up to Paul Bunyan," said Edward, his black eyes filled with merriment.

"Who is Paul Bunyan? Maybe an uncle?"

"Kind of. He'd just take two strides to get to where we're taking all day. When he makes flapjacks, he used a griddle so large he has to skate over it to grease it."

"You're laughing at me!"

"Well, maybe," said Edward, adding, "But America *is* a giant's country."

The people giants controlling their country, thought Katya. On Russia's giant plain, bounded only by immensity, man was dwarfed, surrendered to snow, mud and sometimes drought.

Suddenly they came upon a deserted house. In the orchard around it the trees were dead, their bare branches sticking up like twisted arms. "Why do they die?" she asked.

"Lack of water, I suppose," Edward answered. "But we're in a wet cycle, snow in the mountains, plenty of winter rains, underground water level high. They must have lost their irrigation rights."

So there were people in America too who did not control their destiny. Katya felt a slight dimming of belief in the magic of America. She began to notice uncultivated stretches given over to mesquite and tumbleweed. "Why did you keep telling me The Valley was never barren?" she asked finally.

"I guess I forgot about places like this." Yes, he hadn't told her about the shadow which always had hung over The Valley, the scarcity of water and the sometimes violent ugly struggle to get it.

"If you'd heard my grandfather talk," Edward said in defense of his silence, "you'd know what it means to take barren land like this, give it water, make it yield. When it begins to produce, you buy more land. It's a kind of fire in the veins that's never satisfied," he said with sudden vision.

Late in the afternoon they reached Fresno, passed through it, turned east from the main road. For the first time Katya saw groves of orange trees. They were just as she had dreamed them to be last winter. Only now they did not rise out of the cold and bleak Manchurian plain but out of earth plowed and harrowed to incredible smoothness. The glossy leaves grew in compact masses, making each tree a green shining mound. Row upon row, orchard after orchard, the houses all but buried among the trees. And along the roadside, just as Edward had said, were gray-green olive trees. The shadows cast by olive and orange grew long across the road, but in the orchards they were lost in the plowed soil. As darkness settled down the car turned into a private road. The headlights picked out a sign by the wayside reading DODD ORCHARDS.

"Is this the ranch?" asked Katya.

"Oh, no, we don't live at the ranch. I thought you understood that. It's over on the west side of The Valley. Grandfather built his home in a district of moderate-sized farms, near the nicest town you can imagine. It's like a jewel set in the center of the garden of the Lord." He stopped, embarrassed over the way he was letting himself go. "A lot of fruit farmers with medium-sized ranches around here, small potatoes as compared with the big owners, but they've made a good town," he added in a matter-of-fact tone, feeling he'd come pretty near talking like a crazy poet.

That's what The Valley does to me, he thought, grinning under cover of darkness. Then as he turned into his grandmother's drive, he felt himself choking up with emotion. In a moment he brought the car to a stop before a large imposing house overtopping the low-growing orange trees which surrounded it.

"Well, we're here, Katya." His voice was filled with suppressed excitement. Katya was excited, too.

A thin, white-clad, old man appeared in the doorway above them.

"Hello, Fu!" Edward cried.

The ancient Chinaman came slowly down the steps. "Meester Ed, very good you come. Missie, she all same before, not like to wait. This belong your missie?" He bowed to Katya.

Edward took her hand. Together they went up the steps, through the long hall to the back of the house and into a great, high-ceilinged room with flowered wallpaper. The long windows were black oblongs standing out against the brightly lighted wall, for they were uncurtained. Evidently they had been taken down for the summer, for the tiebacks were knotted into brass rings at the side. Dark, elaborately carved tables and heavy upholstered chairs crowded the room. In the center sitting in a wheel chair was a tall old woman. She was not fat, but the thickening of age had given waist, breast and shoulders an equal breadth, robbing her of every feminine curve. But her face, lined and withered as it was, bore the marks of a strong and forceful character

and a penetrating mind still functioning behind the eyes, blurred
though they were.

Edward dropped Katya's hand, hurried across the room and put his
arms around his grandmother, giving her a loud smack on the cheek.
With trembling hands she held him off, surveying him.

"So you married without asking your mother? I'm proud of you."
Grandmother Dodd had never cared for her son Jeremy's second wife.
Perhaps because she was so fond of Jeremy's first wife, she had never
been able to accept the second one. Or perhaps it was because her
son had married again within the year after his wife's death—a highly
indecorous performance from the standpoint of a woman born and
bred in the strict tradition of mourning held by her Calvinist forebears. Angry and not a little ashamed of the need to exonerate her
son, she had blamed the new wife, who in her eyes lacked the character she thought fitting to be Mrs. Jeremy Dodd. Winding Jeremy
around her finger, teaching him to be evasive and expedient rather
than the forthright fighter his mother had brought him up to be.
These were not characteristics the elder Mrs. Dodd tolerated easily.
Nevertheless, Edward was her favorite grandchild, and the close bond
between him and his mother had never ceased to annoy her. But now
Edward had defied his mother. Grandmother Dodd was ready to
champion Katya whether she liked her or not. "Come here, my dear.
You are welcome to this house," she said, releasing Edward.

Katya took the heavily veined hand held out to her.

"Kiss me, child," commanded the old lady. Katya stooped, giving
Grandmother Dodd the traditional two kisses, certain somehow of
their acceptance this time. "We'll get on," Grandmother Dodd said.
She liked the Old World deference expressed in the girl's greeting.
Turning to Edward, she asked, "You haven't had dinner, have you?"

She rang a bell on the stand beside her. Immediately a table was
wheeled in by Fu and placed before the old lady. With satisfaction
she lifted the covers from an array of silver dishes, freeing the hot,
appetizing odors that rose from the steaming contents.

With the deep concentration old age often gives to food, she
served herself and then her grandchildren. Edward was right, Katya
thought: there was no need to get dinner before they arrived. There
was crusty bread, something like bread she was used to in her childhood. There were spaghetti with a spiced sauce of green peppers and
tomatoes, steamed dumplings filled with meat and a fish browned and
smothered in soy sauce, a dish Edward and Katya had eaten in China,
evidently prepared by Fu, for Grandmother Dodd congratulated the
old man on its goodness.

A nurse in a starched white dress came quietly in from another door and stood behind Grandmother Dodd's chair. After a little she reached out removing one by one the dishes containing the food—the bread, the spaghetti, the dumplings, and finally what was left of the fish. At that the old lady smartly tapped the outstretched hand.

"Now, now," the nurse spoke for the first time, "we can't have you sick." The energy and fire Grandmother Dodd had shown since her grandchildren's arrival left her. She looked like some angry old eagle moping on its perch. The nurse resolutely wheeled her charge away, and Katya and Edward were left alone.

"She's very old," Edward whispered.

"The nurse did not need to speak to her as if she were a child," Katya whispered back indignantly. "Your grandmother is the head of your family."

6

As THE days slipped by, Katya and Edward found themselves meeting over and over on common ground, a leisurely, comfortable life such as both of them had been accustomed to in their childhood. But sometimes it troubled Katya that Edward gave himself to it so wholeheartedly. Did he feel no need to start about earning their living? Or in this rich family was he not supposed to do that? But if so wouldn't he become an officer in the Army or help with the land? Then her uneasiness would pass. There was so much to do, so much to think about.

"This olive orchard Grandfather bought when I was born," Edward told her one morning as they rode horseback along a road some distance from his grandmother's orange orchard. "He always bought a piece of land whenever he had a new grandchild. He didn't will it to us, but he said it was a good way to tie us to The Valley."

"But none of you has stayed in The Valley," Katya answered, "unless maybe you might," she ended, hoping he would tell her what he was planning for them.

But he ignored her remark, saying land was a passion with Grandfather. "He kept buying more and more, right up to the time of his death. Whenever there was a foreclosure of some unfortunate guy he'd be on hand to buy his property. One of them is Grandmother's manager now. He's good at it. Granny trusts him; so does Dad. Good thing, too, for Granny's too old and Dad's too busy and sick now to look after it."

"I'd like to see the ranch, Edward. Could I?" Katya asked, thinking again, Why didn't Edward help his grandmother here in the country. In old Russia a grandson would do that, if the father was occupied with other matters.

"I'll take you there one of these days, but we can't go horseback. We'll have to drive," Edward answered. Somehow Katya felt he was putting her off.

The irrigation ditch that skirted the olive grove was running full with water. Katya stopped her horse to watch it spreading into the shallow trenches between the rows of gnarled gray trunks, the earth sucking it up as if it would never be satisfied.

Edward put his horse into a canter. Katya set hers cantering after. The sun fell warm on their backs. "May we ride our horses around the town?" she asked when she caught up with him. The town was a never-ending source of delight and wonder to her with its white houses, its green lawns, straight, macadamized streets. Russian villages in the country had only one or two good houses. The rest were poor and cheap. And the winding roads were muddy or dusty. "Look, Edward, I'd like to live in that house," she had said so often he teased her about it.

Today she said, "I guess it wouldn't make any difference which we lived in, they're all so nice."

"I used to think of that cottage last winter." Edward pointed out one of the smallest houses in the town, low, one-storied, with the branches of a pepper tree almost hiding it. "Sometimes when I'd be coming along the path through the kaoliang field I'd think I really saw it."

"I wish we could live in it," said Katya wistfully.

"Perhaps I pointed it out to see if you liked it. Ever since I received Mother's telegram at Changchun I've been thinking about a house like that for us. I haven't said anything before. Perhaps it's too early yet. I'm afraid Dad will want me to go into his office—he did before I went away. What I want to do is study law and then come down here to practice. There is always a lot of litigation over water rights."

So Edward *was* thinking about their future. Suddenly security became a reality that reached down to that stratum of her being which was maternal and which said, It is safe now for a child. She felt around her the walls of the home Edward would prepare for her, and she was heavy with child, his child. She was a little tipped back to carry it. But it was for only a moment. There was no house to call their own and she sat lightly on her horse, and the future was still uncertain. Edward had spoken of what he wanted to do, not of what he would do. Things she did not understand stood in the way of fulfillment.

Somehow Katya believed Grandmother Dodd was the only one that could bring about that fulfillment. From the first the two liked each other, or perhaps more correctly, they needed each other. Katya felt secure when she was in the presence of this ancient woman who by her very age created for the Russian girl the sense of permanency snatched so violently from her by the destruction of her own family. Grandmother Dodd, seeking a dignity slipping from her as she became more and more helpless, more and more dictated to by the nurse who in her boredom tyrannized over her charge in many small ways, found that dignity again in the deference Katya showed her.

That evening Katya was delighted when Grandmother Dodd, learning that Edward was going off the next day on a shooting expedition and that Katya was not going, said to her nurse, "My granddaughter-in-law can look after me. You may have my car and go where you please."

"You won't give Mrs. Dodd anything she shouldn't eat, will you? And you'll make her rest?" Miss Tibbets asked, turning to Katya.

"Give her your orders. I'm sure she's trustworthy," Grandmother Dodd's voice held a slightly ironical note. It was she who intended to give the orders. She meant to use the opportunity to impart to the new member of the family something of the wisdom gained in her ninety years.

Until thirty she had been an important member of a Maryland family who took pride in the fact that they dated their history in America back to 1665 when their Huguenot ancestors were exiled from France. Although the rebellious nature of the family had softened in succeeding generations, much of the original independence of thought actuated her father, a Presbyterian minister not entirely dependent upon his church for support.

In her thirty-first year Grandmother had married Wilson Dodd, New England blueblood of Puritan background, steeped in the laissez-faire philosophy of Locke. On the vast and uninhabited stretches of Central Valley to which he took his bride, there was nothing to stop him from carrying free enterprise to its furthermost limit except other men whose land and water claims impinged upon his. It was a tooth-and-claw struggle but Wilson Dodd had emerged a wealthy man convinced that the spoils went to the competent.

The hard years spent on a ranch far from neighbors increased his wife's natural individualism and self-reliance, but his faith in their wealth was tempered in her by her earlier experience in the non-competitive atmosphere of her Maryland home, where wealth was not considered—as her husband believed—the ultimate good. Life had taught her, too, that often money could not give you the things you desired most. Although she had spent lavishly in a last desperate attempt to bring back health to her son Jeremy's first wife, she had failed. She could not be reconciled to the death of the gentle girl who at times annoyed her excessively but whom she loved utterly and completely, pouring out on her the affection she would have given the daughter she never had had and had never ceased to long for. Jeremy's second wife had offered her no affection, nor would Grandmother Dodd have accepted it had she offered it.

But now Edward's Russian wife miraculously, it seemed to the old lady, was turning out to be the kind of human being on whom again she could lavish her affections. As the days had passed, the old woman's natural perspicacity made her aware of the fact that the girl, accustomed though she evidently was to gracious living, had had some sort of troubled past that ill prepared her for the struggle ahead to establish herself with the Dodds. Her excessive gratitude to her husband for small courtesies she should have taken for granted, and an undue humility betrayed her. If whatever misfortune she had had were found out, Jeremy Dodd, who held his father's belief that misfortune was of one's own making, would be against her. That Beatrice Dodd was already against the girl the old woman had known from the start. Why would she send the young couple away almost upon their arrival unless it had furthered her plans to have Edward with her more completely later on? Grandmother Dodd intended to strengthen the girl's confidence in herself—yes, and warn her that she'd have to fight if she wanted to hold Edward.

Next morning once the nurse was gone, Grandmother Dodd sent for Fu, ordered the food she wanted, then with the wave of a hand dismissed him. "Take my keys, child," she commanded Katya, placing her hand on a great chest that stood near her chair. "I've things here that as a member of the family you should see." Katya took out laces and jewels, children's toys and dresses, a miscellaneous collection of keepsakes such as most women acquire in a long lifetime.

Picking up one article after another as Katya laid them in her lap, Grandmother Dodd recounted bits of the family's history: something of the hardships of her life as the wife of one of The Valley's early ranchers, the loneliness, the vast, terrifying solitude, the bitter effort to turn a desert into a valley rich in fruit and grain, effort and accomplishment.

The old lady was pleased with the interest the girl showed and in her eagerness to learn all she could about the family, but she was annoyed with her, too. A decent reserve is all right. I know it is a sign of good breeding, she thought, but we've only today to come to know each other.

The sun was throwing slanting rays into the room when at last Grandmother Dodd surrendered one keepsake after another to be laid away again in the chest until only a filigreed gold brooch remained in her lap. She hesitated a moment, then placed it in Katya's hand. "Better take it. I'll not wear it again. Beatrice has always wanted it. I told her I was going to give it to Edward's wife if I liked her."

As the intricately patterned pin lay in the palm of her hand Katya was carried far away from this rich room. She was in Harbin. She held the last of her mother's jewels, two intricately patterned earrings— the ones she had worn the night at the café when she met Edward, and afterward in Lahususu.

Grandmother Dodd caught the distress in the girl's face. "So we've struck bottom at last," she said. "You better tell me about yourself. You've got breeding, girl. . . . I've seen that," she added, softening her first words, "but you've been in trouble."

"There's not much to tell," Katya answered, with difficulty maintaining her composure. "My parents were large landowners. There was the Revolution. They were killed." How many times was she going to try to give proof of the improbable? "I fled to China."

"Then you met Edward," the old lady prompted.

"Yes."

"Where?"

"In a café." For a moment Katya was tempted to tell this wise old woman about the lonely winter, how Edward and she had needed each other. But caution said, What the family doesn't know won't ever be used against you.

"I see," said the old woman. "There's a good deal you don't intend to talk about. The breeding's there. Forget about the café." Suddenly Grandmother Dodd was very tired. She closed her eyes.

Katya was frightened. The day had been too much for so old a woman. She hurried toward the door, intending to call Fu to help her get Granny into bed.

At Katya's first movement the old lady's head came up with a jerk. "Come back. I'm going to give you a little advice even if you haven't asked for it. Don't let the family fool you. You've seen today we were not always rich. And whatever my son may tell you, like all Americans we are a mixture. A little Russian blood won't hurt the strain. My family has French blood. They were refugees. Fled France just as you fled Russia. Mention it to Edward's mother sometime if she's a bit hard on you."

Katya thought, Now is the time to ask her to help us get started . . . but I have no right to interfere with Edward's plans. He might well be angry.

That night long after Edward was asleep Katya lay awake thinking of what Grandmother had said. She could no longer avoid the fact that she was not accepted by the family. She wished she'd confided in Granny, telling her not only how strong and reliable Edward had been last winter and how he had come home only because of his mother's cable, but also how much he wanted to choose his future but didn't know if he could manage to do so. Maybe Granny would have offered to help. I could have asked to be her nurse if she didn't like to give money outright, she thought. But she hadn't spoken; neither had she told Edward what Grandmother had said. She had intended to, but when he had come back late in the evening he had seemed so happy over plans he had made for the coming day that she could not bear to disturb him. They were invited to a barbecue on the west side of The Valley. "If we're not too late, we might go around by our ranch on the way home," he had said.

7

IT WAS nearly dark, on their return the next evening, when Edward gave the car a sharp turn and said, "Look your fill. This is the ranch."

She leaned out, but she could see nothing save a vast stretch of flat land, and near at hand a row of cabins, the doors open, for the night was very hot. The light beat down from bare electric bulbs revealing interiors not unlike, in their poverty, the interiors of Russian huts. "Do poor people live on your ranch?" she asked.

"Laborers," he said sharply.

The road ahead was crowded with all kinds of vehicles, broken-down Fords, even defunct old carriages; bedding piled on the roofs, babies and bundles inside.

A man leaned out of a car beside them. "Stranger, this the road to Doddstown?"

"Just ahead and to the right," Edward answered shortly.

"You didn't tell me there was a town named after the family," Katya exclaimed.

"Doddstown is only an epithet," Edward answered in an annoyed voice.

"What's an epithet?"

"Oh, kind of a byword, if you know what that is. The workers call it that. I guess they mean all things in it come by way of the Dodds."

They passed down the main street. The one grocery store was crowded with women. Into concealed speak-easies that looked like stores men were crowding. It was an ugly town, Edward knew. No sewage, no public garbage disposal, no playgrounds for children, no bank, no movie theater. But to Katya, unaccustomed to a country town lighted by electricity, the bright street crowded with the mushroom population of laborers was nothing short of wonderful.

"These are our summer residents." Edward's ironic tone did not escape Katya, enthralled as she was with the bustle and life around her. All the rest of the way home he did not speak, but he drove with reckless speed. Something has made him unhappy, thought Katya, something about the ranch. She feared she'd asked too many questions. She was so eager to learn, but she realized this time in asking about the name of the town she had inadvertently bared a hurt in Edward.

Early the next morning Fu knocked at their bedroom door. "The honorable father call you, more better come."

"Evidently Father's better. He has some plan for me. That's the way it always is. Once he's made up his mind to anything, he drives through on it," Edward told Katya.

As he went down the stairs to take the call, it occurred to him his father had arranged the visit to Grandmother Dodd to gain time until he was ready to take the initiative. My chance was in telling him first what I wanted to do, showing I knew my own mind. He'd have had to fight me then. Now I've got to fight him. Edward braced himself to resist his father if he proposed that he go into his office.

To Edward's surprise when he picked up the receiver, it was his mother's voice that came over the wire. "Edward dear, I feel I must tell you the good news. Sick as your father is, he has arranged for you to go into his office."

"But, Mother, could Father and I talk it over? I've a plan of my own I wanted to put up to him."

The note of happiness in her voice changed to distress. "Surely you are not going to oppose your father while he's sick, run the chance of his having another setback. And he's taken an apartment for you and Katya in San Francisco, so you can have a little place all your own. I think it very generous of him."

Edward felt backed into a corner. Of course it would upset his father. It always did when he differed from him. "I'll try to do what Father wants but at least I think I should talk it over with him," he answered. Quietly he put down the receiver. She wouldn't know but what they'd been cut off. Just now he couldn't say any more.

Slowly he went back up the stairs, carefully opened the door to their room, closed it behind him with even more elaborate care. Katya saw by his expression that something was very wrong. She waited for him to speak.

"So much for my plans!" He snapped his fingers. "I'm supposed to go into Father's office."

"You didn't just say you would without telling him what you'd like to do?" Katya exclaimed.

"*Like!*" Bitterly he repeated the word. "What could I do? I asked Mother to let me talk it over with Father. She put it up to me that he's a sick man. Anyway," he added, "we're to have an apartment of our own in San Francisco."

It was Katya's turn to feel baffled. What she'd feared most—some estrangement growing up between Edward and herself hinted at by Granny yesterday—she needn't fear so much if they had their own home. She hadn't expected Mr. Dodd would be so generous. But a blow had been dealt Edward which she only half grasped. If it was so distasteful for him to go into his father's office, why wasn't his mother willing for him to explain to his father what he wanted to do?

"Don't consent, Edward, if you're going to be unhappy," she begged. "Surely your father would talk it over with you."

"Mother doesn't want me to with Father sick. Suppose it should make him worse. I'll have to think it over," Edward ended. "And now we'd better dress and go and break the news to Granny that our vacation is finished."

When they told her they were leaving, the look in the old woman's eyes hurt Katya. Now, she thought, is Edward's chance to tell her he'd like to live in The Valley. But all Edward said was, "We'll not leave today, and we'll come down often to see you."

"Just like all my grandchildren," answered Grandmother Dodd. "The Valley means nothing to you."

"That's not true," Edward answered angrily. "You know I like it here."

"But your mother has other plans for you."

"You mean Father."

Granny didn't answer. They seemed to have come to an impasse.

That afternoon the thermometer stood at one hundred and ten. The doors and the windows were closed against the dry, hot air. Like all the rest of the members of the household, Katya and Edward had gone to their rooms to rest. Edward lay crosswise on the bed asleep. But Katya was wide awake. She felt trapped in the close-shut room. She took off her slippers so as to make no noise and wandered from window to window. That closed place brought back in all its detail the last terrible night in her father's house, the doors barred against the angry peasants. Would it always be like this, fear slipping in under her guard? If she could open just one window! But it might wake Edward.

The room they occupied had been the playroom for the Dodd grandchildren when they were little. A bookcase extended along one side, full of children's books. She picked up one and then another, trying to fix her mind on them. Finally her attention was caught and held by a battered book with Edward's name on the flyleaf. It was a history of the United States. She had never seen an American history before! America discovered—1492. New England settled—1620. Edward's country was indeed a new world. How old Russia seemed in contrast! She remembered the first page in a Russian history her father had given her as a child, and the date—950 A.D. The long line of czars, imperious emperor after imperious emperor. The terrible wastes of Siberia, place of political exiles. A great-grandfather banished, an uncle exiled and now herself.

She read on, unconscious that the turning of the leaves had wakened Edward, that he had rolled over on his side and was watching her. Suddenly he laughed. Katya looked up.

"Why do you read with your lips?" he asked.

"Was I? Was I funny? It's because the English is hard. But, Edward, I'm beginning to understand America." She ran across the room, thrusting the book in front of him. "It's a country where there is opportunity for everyone."

"Don't idealize us, Katya, especially Californians. There's never been equal opportunity in California. We don't really want it to be that way," Edward answered, a cynical note in his voice Katya had never noticed before.

"I don't believe you," she stubbornly insisted. "In Russia, California was—" she searched for the right word—"what you say, pinnacle. Something splendid here made us think of it so. Would the idea have persisted among us for years if it didn't have some foundation in fact?"

"I used to think that way. I don't know. I'd been all twisted up for a long time. I can't explain it to you very well. You wouldn't understand about our government and politics and my family."

"I believe I could learn." If only Edward would let her in behind his defenses!

"I'd grown up hearing about Teddy Roosevelt. There it is. Such names don't mean a thing to you. Well, anyway, he was our President when I was little. Already lots of our public land had passed into private hands and big railroad combines. Why, here in California any number of men got hold of a lot of public land by outwitting the government. For instance, the Swamp Act said you could own as much land as you could row over in a day. A man named Miller put a boat on a wagon, had a driver race the horses, hitching up fresh ones along the way while old Miller himself sat in the boat rowing." Edward laughed. "It must have looked funny. Anyway he got away with it, kept the land. There's your equal opportunity.

"Well a lot of things like that happened. My grandfather used to tell me how men cheated over water rights here in The Valley. It's natural, I guess, when a new country is opened up. But Teddy Roosevelt thought the time had come to stop it. He withdrew a lot of public land from sale because there was a good deal of water power on it and he didn't want the power to fall into the hands of corporations and big owners, and he withdrew forest land. There was an awful lot of trouble over it all later. Grandfather and Father hated Roosevelt. They said he was trying to limit the pioneer spirit."

Edward stopped, seeing Katya's puzzled expression. "I told you you wouldn't understand, but you're in for it now," he went on. "But my brother John said Roosevelt was a true patriot. He was our hero. We wanted him re-elected.

"And then my father took me to Chicago for the Republican Convention in 1912. I was fourteen. I learned a lot. I saw how a steam roller works in a convention. Men like my father were for business— business first. The people behind Roosevelt didn't seem ever to win out. The strong men believed as Father did. I was all for them when I came home. I believed what my father said about people like us being the capable ones and that we shouldn't be hampered by government.

"Then later I guess I lost faith in Father when he kept me out of the war—at least I think he did," Edward amended, anxious to be fair. "I never knew exactly how I was appointed to a desk job. Once I heard my mother begging my father to use his influence. I was ashamed all during the war.

"I got over it in China. . . . You helped," he added after a pause, and then after an even longer one, "And then, well, you know I had to come home. And now they want to rule me again."

"I think if you'd be that lawyer——"

Light suddenly broke across Edward's face. "I went to China to learn how to be myself. I turned out pretty well. Don't you think so? Got me a wife and managed a promotion all in a year," he said with a grin. "I don't know why I've been in such a lather over doing what I want to now. If Father doesn't like the lawyer idea, I could, as you say, get Granny to lend me the money. But I'll give Father a chance first. So that's that," he ended.

He tossed the book Katya still held onto a near-by chair and pulled her down beside him. With his other hand he ruffled her hair, ran his hand over the smooth, velvety surface of her bare arms. "Katya, you have the loveliest skin in all the world—and it's sweet, as if roses bloomed under its surface."

8

To HIS surprise when Edward explained to his father that he wanted to be a lawyer, Jeremy had said, "It's a reasonable ambition, but what I'd like to see you do is take a year in my office first, get your bearings, find out if you like business. At the end of the year you can choose."

Edward had demurred at first. The law course was a long one. He hated to lose a year. He talked it over with Katya. Finally they had agreed he should make the compromise, as his father was sick.

This evening Edward was a half hour late in leaving the office. He'd stayed to finish some work, not because it was necessary, but as a gesture to show the man he was working under that being his father's son did not mean favors asked. It made him feel pretty fine, though, this extra willingness on his part.

Although his father had insisted that he start at the bottom in the organization, already in two months he had had one raise—he believed because of his abilities. He had found himself grasping the details of the electric-power business quickly, due, he felt, to what he had learned while he was on his own in Lahususu. His father had been pleased and shown it.

As he walked along he was thinking of what Tom had told him about the fight developing between the power people and a group of men interested in state development of water and power—an idea that the state take over existing power installations. They had no definite plans beyond an act for a state bond issue. The power people wanted to defeat the policy of public ownership of water and power. Edward found himself siding with the men who would make the state serve the people. It stood to reason the state could pour more money into such a development than private business. He'd like to write to his half brother John—he knew he'd be for it—only it didn't seem loyal while Edward was in his father's office.

The persistent tooting of an automobile horn made him turn. Well, if it wasn't Tom himself drawing up at the curb! Edward climbed into his brother's car, saying, "It's only a few blocks to my diggings, but it's mighty nice of you to give me a lift."

"Father asked me to come to see him tonight about some business," Tom answered. "It just occurred to me, why not come along? The more you sit in on things, the sooner you'll arrive."

"Well, yes, I suppose I could," Edward answered, "if you don't mind waiting while I get Katherine. Everything's strange for her here, and she's alone all day. It won't take but a minute."

Tom looked at his watch. "I hadn't realized it was so late. If you think you can't go without her, perhaps you'd better not attempt it tonight. I'll drop you at the next corner."

Edward watched the car drive off, uneasiness settling over him. If he were late—reason enough for Tom to refuse to wait. And yet it was just another of the many little accidents that kept Katya apart from the family.

A lot of things pointed to the fact that Katya was not to be accepted. Tom's wife had not called or invited Katya even to have lunch with her. Of course it was summer, and she had been away most of the time with the children—at least they had given him to understand that was the case. He and Katya were never asked to have dinner with the family. His mother hadn't been to see them, neither had the girls. His father as yet had not met Katya. Mr. Dodd's health had seemed a justification at first. When Edward had consented to go into the office he had asked his father if he didn't think now was the moment for him to meet Katya. After an awkward silence his father had said with an evident effort at control, "I don't like your marriage. You've probably guessed that. I feel it was hasty and ill considered. Just now while I'm sick I don't want to meet the girl. You'll have to wait until I'm stronger." Edward felt he couldn't insist in face of his father's reference to his health. However, Jeremy seemed well enough for everything except meeting Katya.

The evening fog was drifting in through the Golden Gate. Usually Edward liked its cool dampness, but tonight its chill seemed to creep inside him. All the sense of well-being he had had when he left the office was gone. Baffled and upset, he started the climb to his apartment. But when he reached the top of the stairs and opened the door and saw Katya, all his assurance came back. Why did he always distrust his family's intentions toward him? His mother had asked him to give her time. She had never failed him. Why should he think she would now? In the meantime why not enjoy having Katya all to himself?

But when week after week went by and there was no change in the family's attitude, Edward found himself growing anxious. Katya, too, he could see realized that something was radically wrong. One evening in a moment of anger she accused his people of intentionally ignoring her, and he had hit back, saying she had no right to criticize his family. They had had their first serious quarrel. They had made it up, but it had left a scar deeper than any quarrel should leave between two people who love each other deeply. Edward's loyalty to his family had kept him from complete capitulation, and the apprehension growing in both of them that Katya might never be accepted built a chasm between them. Yet beneath it their love held. Physical attraction from the day they had met had been strong between them. Their union was sound and good and satisfying. And on it they came to rely more and more.

At closing time one afternoon Edward's father called him to say he must see him on important business. Edward telephoned Katya to go ahead and eat dinner. His father had sent for him; he didn't know when he could get back.

Food, to Katya, was a thing to be shared. Only when she had been starving had she ever eaten alone. After Edward's call she dropped down on the floor by the window, rested her chin on her hands. She had to own she was lonely. She had only a bowing acquaintance with anyone in America. What did American people mean with their easy, surface kindness without the warmth that took you into their homes? She looked across the Bay to the lights of Berkeley and Oakland. Lights meant families sitting down to dinner. Lights upstairs meant children getting ready for bed—all the small home duties. Things like that were the same in every country. Surely sometime Edward's family would let her be a part of it.

It grew late. The noises of the city were dying down. Apprehension, never far removed from her mind since the day of her flight from Russia, began to claim her. Maybe Edward didn't want her to be awake when he came home. Things hadn't been right between them of late. Finally she fell asleep, her head resting on the window sill.

As Edward entered his old home, a wave of longing swept over him for the things he had lost. The spacious rooms seemed incomparably desirable. The maid was setting the table for dinner. It would be good to sit down to the ample meals his mother provided, to be well served after the somewhat haphazard way Katya and he had to live. Through the window drifted the clean, medicinal odor of burning eucalyptus leaves, a smell he associated with the plenty and order of his home. He went up the wide, carpeted stairs. The door of his father's room was open; Jeremy was sitting facing the door. By his side was a man Edward did not know.

"Good, Edward! You got here quicker than I expected. I'm glad, for I want to get this business over with. This is Mr. Green, a secret-service man I have used for years when I wanted special information."

Edward sat down, wondering what could have happened to require a secret-service man.

"I've said little about your marriage thus far," his father went on, "feeling I had no right to express my very great doubt of its—shall I say?—feasibility until I knew more."

All the frustration and anger Edward had felt in the last months came to the surface. How could his father judge if he wouldn't even see Katya! But he held himself in control and waited, conditioned now to his mother's constant pleading with him to help her keep his father calm for the operation so soon to be performed on his eyes.

"I have realized from the first—" the older man's tone was extremely businesslike—"that there was every chance you might have been imposed on. To put it plainly, taken in by an adventuress."

"Father, you've no right to say such a thing!"

Jeremy Dodd motioned his son to be silent. "It's taken us some time to unravel the details, but we have the facts now. As this is painful for us both, I have asked Mr. Green to write out for you our findings."

Edward glanced quickly through the papers. "There's nothing here, Father, that I didn't know," he said, handing them back. "Of course, Katherine is a refugee, but I don't see that that is anything against her." He tried to keep out of his voice the indignation he felt over his father's interference.

"Or that she was working in a café with a not too savory reputation?"

"It was all she could find to do."

"Does that make it justifiable?"

Edward could see his father was getting angry. What was he to do? He felt as if he held his father's eyesight in his keeping, to save or destroy, but he couldn't desert his wife.

"Isn't this all pretty useless, Father? I'm married to Katherine. I believe in her. I think you would, too, if you'd see her. Anyway, isn't it only fair to give her a chance to defend herself?"

Inwardly Edward was swearing at the secret-service man sitting smugly by. He had a thin, pointed nose that Edward had the greatest desire to tweak. Sharpened it poking into other people's business, probably, thought Edward. One thing he hadn't found out evidently—about the winter in Lahususu. Or had he? It wasn't in his report.

"There is no defense this woman could offer." Jeremy Dodd's voice was hard and cold, the voice he used with competitors he intended to squeeze out. "I have tried to save you the humiliation you would naturally feel, Edward, over my knowing how you spent last winter, but you are forcing my hand. I don't blame you. You were young, and there was plenty of temptation placed in your way. A woman like that can do almost anything with an inexperienced boy."

"I'm no inexperienced boy! I knew what I was doing," Edward retorted. "It was I who took advantage of a desperate girl. There'd be no use trying to tell you either, I suppose, that last winter was the biggest thing that ever happened to me. I grew up."

"I don't think much of the result."

"What do you know of the result if you won't see her? She's good and she's my wife, and I'm not going to do such a cad's trick as I know you intend to suggest—so don't make the suggestion!"

"That will do!"

The choked rage in his father's voice and his heavily flushed face brought Edward up short.

"I'm sorry, Father," he managed to say.

Somewhat placated, Jeremy Dodd went on: "I'll give you a few days to think it over. If you decide to divorce this woman, it can be arranged quietly. Nothing more will ever be said about it. If not, there is only one course left to me."

"And that is?"

"To consider you no longer a member of the family."

"I don't need time to decide whether I'll desert my wife or not,"

Edward answered. "I won't." His anger began to rise again. "You've no right to ask such a thing of me. And you haven't any right to say I can't see Mother."

"You have my decision." His father's voice was colder and more remote than Edward had ever known it to be.

"And you have mine, but I don't grant you the right to act for Mother."

"You'd better go now before you say things you wish you hadn't. I'll give you until Thursday."

As Edward reached the foot of the stairs, he saw his mother standing at the far end of the hall, her back toward him. "Mother," he cried, hurrying across the room, "surely you wouldn't have me desert Katherine."

Beatrice Dodd resisted Edward's effort to take her into his arms. "How could you do such a thing, Edward?" she said. "Bring that kind of a woman into our home?"

"But, Mother, if you'd only let me explain. Katya is good. If you'd been in her place——"

"In her place!" cried Beatrice Dodd, backing away from her son. "What are you saying? Do you mean to tell me I would have been like *her*? I never expected words like these from you, Edward—you of all my children!"

"I guess there is no use talking, Mother."

As Edward closed the front door behind him, a sense of hopeless finality possessed him. Striding along the driveway, wanting to get away now as quickly as he could, he was startled by Bettie suddenly jumping out of the shrubbery.

"Well, hello!" he exclaimed. "What are you doing here?"

Her white, strained face peered up at him. "I heard what Father said."

"You shouldn't have been eavesdropping."

"I don't care! And I heard what Mother said, too. I love you, and I love Katherine. I'm going with you."

Edward stooped and kissed her. "You can't leave Mother, Little Sister. She'll need you, but I won't forget what you've said, and I'll tell Katya. Now I must be off."

Looking back he could see her short, stout figure planted squarely in the middle of the drive. In spite of himself he had to smile at the heroic role she had assumed. He could not see in the oncoming darkness the look of peril in her eyes, nor did he realize that her world had fallen to bits as had his. The home, her stronghold denied to her brother!

9

SOFTLY Edward put his key into the lock of his own door, hoping Katya would be asleep, although the crack of light under the door made him pretty certain she wasn't. In his hurried glance around the living room on entering, he did not see her, so he went on into the bedroom. When he found the bed untouched, he returned to the living room. This time he saw her huddled on the floor by the window, her face half hidden, but he could see she had been crying. For a moment he was tempted not to disturb her. She might sleep on until morning. He wanted to get things straightened out in his own mind, something he hadn't been able to do so far. At first he had felt only elation and pride that he had not been intimidated by his father's threat, or his mother's withdrawal. If he had to choose between his family and Katya, of course it must be Katya.

But on the ferry riding back to San Francisco the awful thought took possession of him that his father might be right. What after all did he know about Katya? Suppose she really was simply an adventuress working him because she thought him the son of a rich American, as his father had accused her of doing?

Now looking down on her, he felt ashamed of such thoughts. His love for her he knew was the truest, best part of him. All he wanted was to make up to her for what she had suffered and must continue to suffer at the hands of his people. He knelt and kissed her gently on the forehead.

Katya's eyes flew open. She looked surprised, then happy. "Oh, Edward, I've been imagining terrible things!"

"Here," he said, helping her to her feet. "I may as well tell you, darling, before you imagine a lot of things that I've broken with the family. I've quarreled with Father again. This time it's final."

Relief swept over Katya. Without his family Edward would be wholly hers, as he had not been of late. "If you're out of your father's office, this is your chance to study law," she exclaimed, adding impulsively, "I'm strong. I can work. Maybe Grandmother would let me be her nurse. She'd like me to take care of her."

He hadn't thought of being out of a job! There had been so many other things to think about. The price of his right to choose for himself was getting higher and higher. He began pacing the floor.

"You don't understand. Maybe you can't. To have you do such work would make them believe they were right in what they said."

Katya looked at him intently for a moment. "Edward, what did you quarrel with your father about?" she asked finally.

"They don't like my marriage," he said, turning away from her.

"They. Not just your father? All of them?"

"All of them except Bettie." Edward gave a kind of choking laugh, remembering Bettie.

"Not Grandmother. Granny said you were right in marrying without your mother's consent. Don't you remember, the first night when she hugged you so tight?"

"You needn't drag Mother into this," he answered. "Grandmother's not fair to Mother."

Katya understood now. Mrs. Dodd never would accept her, and Edward hated to break with his mother. But with Grandmother's help—— "Granny is the head of your family, Edward. It's good to consult her," she urged.

"You've no right to take sides against Mother. Perhaps Mother's right."

"What do you mean, Edward?" Katya knew she was forcing him to take a stand when he was tired and overwrought, but tired and overwrought herself, she felt that she must once and for all clear away the miasma of doubt and misunderstanding which had hung over them since their arrival in America.

"I don't know what I mean. I'm all mixed up. I've only what you've told me about yourself." Edward was appalled at what he had said and yet relieved now that he had spoken his doubts. He too wanted to clear away the doubts that were spoiling everything. "Surely there's somebody in this country who knew your father or mother," he added.

So at the root of their misunderstanding was Edward's distrust of her! On the verge of panic, feeling her identity again slipping away, rooted since her marriage in Edward's belief in her, Katya turned, entered the bedroom, lay down on the bed, trying to still her heart, her fear.

After a long time she heard the doorknob turn softly. Edward lay down beside her, put his arms around her. "I didn't mean what I said. Forgive me." But of the distrust he had expressed she could not rid herself so easily. How could he have said it without believing it?

Out in the harbor a fog bell intoned its rhythmic desolation which impressed upon her mind the ocean wastes, blanketed in fog. For Katya they were transmuted into the vast Manchurian plain shrouded in whirling torrents of snow. Her love for Edward awoke in all its original vitality. With a sobbing gasp, she relaxed in his arms, her body molding itself to his with the old submission to his desire.

But nothing had released Edward from the night's happenings—his father's condemnation, his mother's recoil from the woman to whom he was about to give himself. It was as if the right to love her had been snatched from him. There was no response in him. His hold on her slackened.

They lay sleepless, no longer touching each other, longing for day to come, dreading its coming, frightened by the catastrophe that had overtaken their love.

One, two days passed. Edward went out each morning saying he was going to look for a job; came back each evening tired and irritable, to face a worried and frightened Katya. Night, which had been their delight, freeing them of the day's misunderstandings and quarrels, they now faced with foreboding which increased as the evening advanced. The structure of mutual trust and loyalty which would have held them together while passion was in abeyance had been rudely shaken.

On the third afternoon Edward came in early, feeling he had exhausted the possibilities of every business contact he had. He faced the bitter fact that it was only through his father's influence he could get the kind of position he felt his abilities warranted. As a last resort he had called his grandmother, but the nurse had insisted her charge was not well enough to talk to him. He had asked to speak to Fu, only to be told that Fu had gone out for the day. Then he realized that either his father or his mother had cut him off from his grandmother. If only he had a car he'd go down to see her, he told himself. But he had no car!

Deep in his heart he grasped at the excuse it gave him not to see her—not to take the stand against his mother it would entail. Tomorrow was the deadline his father had set for his return to the family. But what difference did that make? He'd made his decision. With a horrible sense of disloyalty to his young wife, he realized that all the week he had held in his mind a possible retreat. Calling himself all kinds of a cad, he hurried back to the apartment. He'd take Katya out for dinner; they'd dance until they were too tired to think. Once tomorrow was passed, everything would be all right.

The evening started off well. The crowds and the gaiety and life at the restaurant to which he took her filled him with excitement. But almost immediately he felt annoyed because Katya's mood didn't match his, or at least it seemed to him it didn't.

He ordered an expensive dinner. "Should you?" she whispered, once the waiter was out of hearing.

"Why do you doubt my ability to make enough to take care of us?" he retorted crossly.

"It isn't that——" she began, then stopped. The presence of the waiter with their cocktails relieved her of the need to explain. "To your ability and my faith in it!" she murmured. In lifting her glass she spilled half its contents. Nervous and confused, she begged Edward's forgiveness.

"Don't make so much of it!" he exclaimed. "Things like that happen." Why didn't she pass the little accident off with a shrug or a laugh, show some sophistication? Maybe she didn't have any to show. Maybe . . . the old haunting doubt.

The dinner was good. The beefsteak was just as he liked it and the French fried potatoes. His doubts and irritation began to evaporate under the influence of good food. Probably that was all he needed. He'd been denying himself luncheon in order to save.

Katya danced well. The synchronized movements of their bodies in response to the music brought them a degree of harmony they had not had for many days. But after a little Katya seemed tired. "I'm afraid I can't dance any more this evening," she said finally.

Back in the apartment Edward tried to read, but he could not. The telephone seemed the biggest thing in the room. He had only to pick it up, call the familiar number his father had had for years. He looked at Katya silently watching him. If only he could take her, in the close embrace bar out his sense of treachery to her, his fears of the future, bar out everything except their love! But he didn't dare put himself to the test. In his anger and humiliation he cried out, "Why did you have to bring us home early, tonight of all nights?"

"Of all nights? What is tonight?" she asked. Did he mean . . . oh, certainly he didn't mean that all nights were in the future to be . . .

Edward thrust back his chair, rose to his feet. "I can't stand this eternal discussion," he said jerkily. "I'm going out."

"Please don't," she begged. "You don't tell me, but maybe there's something terrible just about tonight."

"Of course there's something terrible about tonight. Father gave me until tomorrow to decide whether—— Of course I'd always choose you. But don't you think it means anything to break with your family? Or don't you know what that's like?"

"If you really don't believe in me, it's no use," Katya answered quietly. Any self-control she may have lacked at the restaurant she had now. She looked directly at him, but there was no pleading in her eyes, nor in her voice.

As they stood facing each other, panic seized him. A lifetime of days and nights such as he had been passing through! Anything to get away from the pressing misery within him. He flung himself out of the apartment. For hours he walked about, not knowing where he went, not caring, tortured by his love and the knowledge of how helpless his young wife would be without him, tortured too by what it would mean never to see his family again, never again speak to his mother. And living in poverty! He'd already discovered how impossible it was to get any kind of a position without the family backing. "I cannot go on without them," he cried out at last, all at once knowing that his decision had been made.

He took out his notebook, scribbled a last message to Katya. "It's morning," he wrote. "By this time you'll know I'm not coming back. It's better this way. Too much has happened. We'd both be wretched if we went on as we've been doing the last few days. I'll see you never want for anything."

He had no envelope or stamp. Wanting to get the thing over as soon as possible, he went back to their apartment, slipped the note under the door, then raced down the stairs for fear Katya might open the door and call to him.

Blindly at first, then with more direction, he took the streets that led to the Bay. A sick sense of guilt made him long to step into the white, drifting fog and disappear in the water lapping at his feet, hide from sight forever his shame. Then furious anger against his father gripped him. Although it was very early in the morning, he hunted out a drugstore and called the house, demanding of his mother, who answered the telephone, that he be allowed to speak to his father. Unexpectedly she consented. Edward hadn't wanted it to be so easy. He wanted her to oppose him; he wanted to exert his will over hers.

His father, too, showed no irritation. It was as if he had been expecting the call. Edward's voice was harsh and truculent as he stated his final decision, angrily blaming his father for spoiling his life. Surprisingly, Jeremy this time could not be roused to anger.

"I'm quitting at the office," Edward shouted, wanting a quarrel above all else.

"Very well. I'll phone the bank in the morning saying you'll be around. You'll need money while you are getting yourself placed. Now your mother wants to speak to you."

"Let us help you, dear, over this trying moment. Do come to us. Your room is ready for you."

"No, thank you," he answered and hung up the receiver, thinking grimly of how he meant to spend the days to come. His mother needn't think he was going to be coddled by her.

10

I BELIEVE Ed will take shape now, Jeremy told himself. He'll go places after this.

He would let him have his wish. His facile, active mind trained in the intricacies of law would make him valuable to the firm later on. Some men in the state legislature were proposing a state-wide water plan which, if properly safeguarded, most of the power people believed could be of great advantage to them.

As there seemed little prospect at the present time that any such safeguard could be secured, those of the power people who were most farseeing, to Jeremy's way of thinking, hoped to make the members of the legislature believe that the plan was not well enough thought out and too expensive. Undoubtedly the thing would drag on for a number of years before the final decision was made. When that time came Edward would serve them well as their recognized lobbyist. It would bring him before the big interests of the state and put him in line for a political career later on.

When three weeks went by and nothing was heard from Edward, his mother grew frantic. "He's got to get over it," Jeremy kept telling her. "He may, as you say, go to pieces, but not for long, and the time, my dear, would have been shorter if you hadn't insisted that I give him money for a vacation."

But finally Jeremy Dodd, too, grew anxious about his son. He traced him secretly to Los Angeles. He learned he was drinking heavily, had been on one spree after another. Jeremy was at a loss to know what to do until he thought of his eldest son John. John's recent appointment as assistant superintendent of a state industrial school for wayward boys had meant less than nothing to Jeremy until now. In fact, he had felt a kind of dishonor in a son of his holding such a position. Delinquency was something like insanity, something high-grade people did not allow themselves to touch. But now he was glad that there was someone in the family who might handle Edward's waywardness.

After reading his father's letter, John Dodd had a pretty good idea where he might find Edward. But though he searched the places to which the detective had traced Edward, he did not find him. He did get information about him. In one of the swankier speak-easies the bartender told him he thought Edward had been there a few nights before. Had a girl with him. They'd both been drinking heavily. He remembered the young man because he had bragged about the wealth he would one day have. "He talked a good deal," the man said, "about a lot of land coming to him."

Familiar with the patterns that frustration and desperation take, John decided he'd hunt through the nine saloons of Doddstown, disguised as poolrooms. From what his father had written him of the breakup of Edward's marriage, John reasoned Edward might well feel an unbearable sense of guilt. In the effort to rid himself of it, he probably was blaming his parents for wrecking his marriage. Yes, he might well choose to bring about his own downfall in the town the evils of which he had long laid at his father's door. It would be instinctive, not reasoned reaction, thus to heap retribution on his father. At least it was worth going to Doddstown to see.

In the fifth place he visited, John found Edward looking as if he had not been sober for weeks. His shirt was soiled, his cheeks were white above the black stubble of his beard, his mouth hung loosely open. He had with him a girl who couldn't have been much over sixteen. John ordered a beer and asked if he might sit down with them. The girl giggled and moved over. In his fuddled state Edward didn't recognize his brother.

"This your home town?" John asked the girl.

"Yep."

"What are you doing in a place like this? You're a minor."

"I have to have some fun, don't I?"

"You're too pretty for this kind of fun," John answered. "He's too good for it, too," he added, looking at Edward.

"What's it to you?"

"Well, a good deal as it happens. He's my brother."

"Phew! I'm glad he ain't mine. So long!" The girl picked up her bag and left.

Edward felt himself roughly shaken. The bartender was putting him out. Someone helped him into a car.

Edward awoke to the realization that everything he had wanted to get away from had caught up with him. He was in his grandmother's house where he and Katya had been so happy. He saw her now as she had been that last day in this very room, how luminous had been her eyes and how a kind of radiance had clung about her when he had pulled her down beside him. Then that Katya was blotted out by another Katya with a white, strained face, the old defenseless look in her eyes that he had vowed, the night he had walked along the riverbank in Lahususu, should never be there again. He groaned.

"Better take this." A tall man rose from a chair by the window and came toward him, a glass in his hand. Looked like his half brother John, whom he hadn't seen in years. What other ghosts, he wondered, were hanging around? He closed his eyes.

Toward evening when he awoke, there was no one about, but fresh linen had been laid out, and his suit he saw had been cleaned and pressed. After a little he got up, bathed, shaved and dressed, dreading the necessity of going downstairs and facing his grandmother. As he paused for a moment, trying to steady his still shaky nerves, the door opened and John entered.

"Do you mind telling me what this visit to Granny is for?" Edward asked truculently.

"First let Fu bring you some coffee," John answered, pushing the electric bell at the side of the bed. Taking a seat by the window, he motioned Edward to sit down.

"Now," he said when Edward had finished the cup of coffee Fu brought, "to make a long story short I found you in Doddstown drunk and with a minor. I brought you here to sober up."

"To get me in Granny's bad graces?"

"Suppose we don't go into my motives." John spoke quietly, realizing he had a man with jumpy nerves on his hands. "Grandmother isn't going to bring up the fact of your drinking, but I'm afraid she is going to put it to you straight why you let your mother and father interfere with your marriage."

"Mother had nothing to do with it," Edward snapped. "It's Father who interfered, but of course Grandmother will blame Mother. Why did you have to bring Granny into it anyway?"

"I didn't," John answered. "Your mother did. She was frantic, not hearing from you for weeks. She wrote to your grandmother to see if you were here. Father wrote me, asking me to find you, telling me why you had left home. There is still time to reconsider your decision," he added gently. "I can understand what a strain you were under, and I think Katya would. From what Granny tells me, she is kind."

"What does Granny know about her?" Edward demanded. "Trust Father to ferret out anything that showed bad judgment on my part.

He proved that I had got myself into a mess with a cheap woman."

"I advise you not to tell Granny that. You have to remember she makes up her own mind, and she's made it up about your wife. Grandmother is a very wise woman, Edward. Go down and talk to her before you let your marriage go to smash," John pleaded, watching his brother's face.

It was obvious Edward did not believe what he had said. If he were convinced that Katya was an adventuress, he would be relieved to be rid of her. The drunkenness, the present truculence meant something else. If Edward could only bring himself to one small act of faith in his own right to marry whom he wished, John believed the rest would follow.

"Think what it means to her to have you desert her, a strange land, no friends. The suffering, Edward. Surely you can't let her suffer like that!" John entreated, trying to break through to the man he felt existed in Edward beneath this weak, childish creature who blamed everyone except himself for the position he found himself in.

For one moment rising above the dark, irrational forces which had taken control of him, Edward saw clearly that Katya was being crucified by a kind of tribal hate for the outsider.

But what he said was "I married a Russian adventuress who wanted an American passport. I was a fool, but I've had my eyes opened." As he spoke the words a door banged shut in his mind, closing him off from the guilty knowledge that he was the crucifier. He hated Katya. She had nearly wrecked his life. Let her suffer. She deserved it.

He rose, feeling suddenly able to meet his grandmother or anyone else. The panic of these last weeks subsided. To succeed in a pretty nasty world you couldn't be soft. That is what his father had always tried to teach him. He'd learned it at last, but the hard way.

John rose, too. "I guess I'll be off." He was tired and a little discouraged. In his work it was so often like this—the human spirit had received some injury too deep, it seemed, to be healed. If he could have persuaded Edward to see Katya again, he believed she might have offered him the understanding of himself he needed. John thought gratefully of his own wife. It was she who had taught him to trust himself and to find dignity in the kind of work he wanted to do. He would never be reconciled to her death. Then his thoughts turned to Katya. What would this do to her.

"Good-by," said Edward. "Thanks for everything, including the advice."

Edward's eyes fell before his grandmother's gaze; his bravado was gone. "I know what you think, Granny, but it isn't so. It's my own decision. She wasn't the kind of girl——"

"Stop right there," said the old lady. "At least be a man and shoulder the blame for what you've done. Don't try to tell me she hoodwinked you. Heavens, boy, for once be yourself!" she pleaded.

"Don't say any more," he cried. "I hate her. I won't live with her."

"Now go," she said, "and don't come back unless you bring her with you. I loved her. I can't forgive you what you've done to her."

11

THE first days after Edward left her Katya felt nothing. She kept saying to herself, "I've learned how to take hard things so they don't make me suffer." It was night, it was morning. She ate, she slept. It was night again, it was morning.

At the end of the week she received a letter asking her to call at the office of Mr. Dodd's lawyer. With indifference she accepted the money settlement he suggested in place of alimony. With indifference she agreed to the arrangements for the divorce, which he stipulated were to be so conducted that there would be no publicity. But when he proposed she drop the Dodd name, she cried out, "No, no, I can't do that!" Here was a new threat to her security. The name of the man who had offered her love and protection symbolized for her dignity and safety. At the suggestion that she drop the name, the memory of her former terror at the time of her flight from Russia, pushed below the conscious level of her mind of late, sprang to the surface. Her pulse beat violently, pounding out the whimpering cry of the pursued. Then the moment of panic passed. "No," she managed to say, "I can't give up the name." It was her title to America.

The lawyer, instantly alert to some hidden threat to the Dodd family, tried to figure out what the girl expected to gain by keeping their name. He was convinced that her underlying motive in marrying the young Dodd was mercenary. A pretty adventuress, but an adventuress all the same. She wants to retain some hold over the family was his conclusion.

"Why do you wish to keep the American name?" he asked. "Undoubtedly you will identify yourself with the refugee Russian community here in San Francisco. It will be simpler for you there with a Russian name, will it not?" When still she insisted, he played his last if dubious card. "The payment the family is making you," he said, "is contingent on your surrender of their name."

"Contingent" . . . "surrender." The words were unfamiliar to Katya with her limited knowledge of the language. "I do not understand," she murmured.

"Bluntly, I am saying the family will pay you the money only if you give up the name." The lawyer spoke with a chilling preciseness.

This time Katya understood. She was caught, hemmed in between the menace of want and the menace of the dispossessed. Ignorant of American law, she had no idea she could claim support, no idea that she could not be deprived of the name. "I must have the money," she answered in a low voice.

The lawyer, more convinced than ever that she was an adventuress, said, "Sign these papers then!" He placed before her a legally worded document much of which the Russian woman could not grasp.

Katya returned to the apartment. The rent was paid until the end of the month. Until then she need not give up her husband's name. To the manager of the apartment house she still was Mrs. Dodd. Now each day she went out doing the things Mrs. Dodd should do. Mrs. Dodd should wear pretty clothes. She went to the restaurants Edward had taken her to, but only at noon. A woman named Mrs. Dodd would not go out at night unattended.

But there were the long hours of the evening. From habit she found it impossible to sleep before midnight. Evening was the time of merrymaking in Russia. It was the time when she and Edward had been together. The fearful sense of her future when she would no longer be Mrs. Dodd pressed in upon her. Activity was her only relief. She would turn on all the lights in the apartment, set the table for dinner, wash the dishes, set the table for breakfast. One evening, tense with the elaborate performance of her self-inforced duties, she went to the window to peer beyond the barrier of the lighted hilltops across the Bay to The Valley that lay beyond. There would be safety and protection if she could get to Edward's grandmother. But would there? Why if all the rest of the family refused to accept her should she expect the head of the family to help her? Again she was a refugee without protection of name or family. She meant nothing to anyone.

She sank to the floor by the window where Edward had found her the night he had come back from the interview with his father. Midnight came and passed. Slowly knowledge she had been avoiding thrust itself to the forefront of her mind, no longer to be denied. She was bearing Edward's child. Indeed she was not worthless! She was valuable beyond words! The physical function of creation now taking place in her filled her with a profound recognition of her value. She was precious! She staggered to her feet, throwing her arms over her head, clasping her hands, sobbing and laughing in the ecstasy of belief in herself. She was worthy of Edward. In the morning she would go to him. She now would not have to plead for her rights as his wife.

Then she saw her danger. Edward might take the child from her. He must never know! She could be brave now, resourceful, even cunning if necessary, with some superhuman strength centered in her very loins, she the creator, the source of life. She would hunt out her own people, go to live among them. Russians in Harbin and Shanghai had given her the names and addresses of relatives settled here in San Francisco. She had not wanted to see them before, fearing it might jeopardize her position as Edward's wife. Now they meant safety and sanctuary for herself and her child.

She slept lightly that night on guard, rose early, dressed for the street. With the help of a policeman to whom she showed the addresses, she made her way to the district where her people lived. The contrast of this part of the city with that she had left was striking. Although she had little knowledge of American cities, she recognized that she was in a district that once had been fashionable, but no longer was. The houses, although large, looked dingy and neglected. And she was no longer on the hills overlooking the Bay. She could hide away in obscurity here.

She decided to call first on the widow of a member of the old Duma, Madame Mohkov.

Three women made up the Mohkov ménage. Countess Molinka, an old lady of eighty who lived in the past, only dimly aware of the present. Her daughter Madame Mohkov, sixty years old, was too close to reality to allow herself the luxury of escape from the grim necessity of helping her daughter Maria, the third member of the household, to earn their living. Work was necessary, too, to keep her from thinking of her husband, once a prominent Liberal member of the Imperial Duma whose ideals and struggles for a better Russia she had shared.

During the Revolution he and his two brothers had been carried away. When the news was brought to her that he had been shot and his brothers had been beaten to death, she had gone alone to the place where they had been hurriedly buried. Until the bodies were disinterred she refused to believe that her husband had been killed. Half crazed, starving, she waited with Maria in Moscow until her parents, the Count and Countess Molinka, joined her. When at last they arrived, she managed to get them all to Paris. There the count had died. Through the help of friends, the three women reached America. Of her daughter Tania, Madame Mohkov knew only that she had escaped to Harbin but without her husband.

Yes, this was the number Katya sought. She rang the bell.

A woman spoke from the hall above. "Is it Madame Mohkov you wish?"

"I am Katya Suvorov with a message from your daughter." How frightening the name sounded! A vein in Katya's wrist again beat out the rhythm of her frightened heart. Flight, instant flight! Flight from all that was Russian. Then her terror subsided. This was not Russia, but America. She went up the stairs to her waiting countrywoman.

"My daughter wrote me, but it is a long time you have been in coming!" the woman exclaimed, embracing Katya and drawing her into the room beyond. At a table by the window heaped with bright cloth and piles of gay-colored threads sat a tall, old woman. Apparently unwilling to waste time, she simply nodded to Katya.

Madame Mohkov seated herself opposite, picked up a half-finished piece of embroidery. Her needle ran in and out, as in one breath she asked, "How is my Tania? Is she well? What is she doing? I think she does not always write me the truth. Is she hungry? If only she could have come with us!"

"Tania is waiting for her husband to get out of Russia. When he joins her, she said to tell you they will try to come. She is teaching Russian to an American businessman in Harbin. She earns enough," Katya answered, not telling how much Tania had to give to make it enough.

"It is good. Soon you must have dinner with us. You and the American husband. My daughter wrote me of your good fortune. Madame Dodd, is it not?"

Hearing her own language, sitting with Russian women once more had broken down the reserve with which Katya had come. "I throw myself on your mercy," she cried. "I am alone. I want it not to be known except to you that I was Mrs. Dodd. I must find somewhere to stay. I am to have a child."

Madame Mohkov left her table, came over and put her hand on Katya's shoulder. "Tonight come to talk to my Maria. She works all the time to help our people. She will know what to do to help you." She went back to the table, picked up her work.

Katya was ashamed that she had not sought her people when she was happy, only now when she needed them. Yet there was no word of reproof from Madame Mohkov.

That evening when Katya arrived at the Mohkov apartment, the table which had earlier held the embroideries had been moved into the center of the room and set for dinner. Madame Mohkov greeted her, then disappeared behind a curtain. "It is a feast we will have tonight in your honor," she called out from what was evidently the kitchen by the fragrant odors issuing from the curtained-off space. The familiar odors took Katya back to her own country more vividly even than the sound of her native tongue had in the afternoon.

The door into the hall opened, and a young woman entered.

"Maria," Madame Mohkov called from behind the curtain, "this is Katya Suvorov, who brings us word of Tania. She saw her, spoke to her just before she left Harbin."

Katya's eyes fell under the penetrating gaze of this young woman, feeling again ashamed that she had not come before. Little, she saw, could be hidden from Maria Mohkov who greeted her so quietly.

Maria dropped into a chair, took off her hat, started to toss it on the floor, thought better of it and laid it on her lap.

"It is almost seven." Madame Mohkov brought the steaming samovar and set it at one end of the table. Maria rose, smoothing her short, straight hair as she moved toward another curtained-off space. There was a sound of running water and in a moment she emerged and went quickly to a door at the end of the room and threw it open, saying in Russian, "Grandmother, dinner is served."

Katya could hardly believe that the stately lady who walked into the room was the silent old woman whom she had seen sorting colored threads earlier in the day. Now Countess Molinka was clad in a black silk dress of ancient cut, tight basque and a full skirt reaching to the floor. In her hand she carried a tiny lace handkerchief. She came forward, kissed Katya on either cheek, saying, "We are only women here, but we are Russian women, and this is a Russian home to which you are welcome."

For the hour that followed the four lived in Old Russia. As they ate the familiar foods, they peopled the room with those they loved, lost to them except in memory.

When the meal was finished, Countess Molinka rose and without a backward glance went to her room, shutting the door behind her.

Madame Mohkov turned to her daughter. "Katya is in trouble. She needs a place to live. While I prepare for tomorrow, you two can talk things over."

Katya looked at the older woman's face set in lines of resignation.

She determined to be as brave as Mrs. Mohkov. Turning to Maria, quietly this time she told her story, ending, "I want to belong to my own people. I would not be one with you with the American name. Please, will you never mention it?"

"But why not keep your American name?" Maria urged. "It might be easier for you."

"It's for another reason," Katya answered, giving up the subterfuge. "The lawyer said if I wanted the money, I must take my own name. I had to have the money, so I consented."

"The lawyer was trying to frighten you," Maria told her, "to get what he wanted from you. You must learn how to live in America, Katya. It's not easy for any of us. The ways are strange. There are good people and bad. If you wish it, we can go to court and insist that you have the name and an extra allowance for the baby."

"No, not that!" Katya was alarmed. "They might take the baby."

Maria was silent. She was thinking, We might lose. Katya is right, they might want the child. If they are hidden away here among Russian people, her secret could be kept.

She felt doubtful of the wisdom of it for the sake of the child. And yet—— She was tired, and there was an urgent case coming up tomorrow—the deportation of a Russian musician unless somehow his friends could guarantee his support.

"Perhaps your way is better," she said at last. "And now to get you settled." Pushing away her fatigue, she talked over plans.

"There is an empty apartment in this building. It is small, but you can manage. There is a Russian doctor here who had a fine reputation in Moscow. He cannot care for you himself, for he has no license to practice in this country. He is too old to learn the language and take the state examination. But he can tell you of a reputable American physician, and he himself will be a good friend to you. Tomorrow night I will take you to see him. He works during the day. We all work."

12

THE apartment Maria had mentioned, consisting of two small rooms and a bath, was on the floor below the Mohkov apartment. It was at the back of the house, its windows overlooking neglected back yards. Beyond, a row of apartment houses made a high barricade.

"Perhaps too poor a place as you have money," Madame Mohkov said when the next afternoon they went to see the rooms. "We could probably find a better one in another house."

"Oh, no!" cried Katya. "I'd rather have the small place near you." In fact, the tiny apartment answered the special need in her for refuge. She could not have asked for rooms away from the street, darkened by tall buildings, without feeling that she should make better preparation for her baby. But when taking them meant the advantage of help from friends in an emergency, she yielded to her only half-understood desire for this dark retreat.

Several days later Katya moved in. After she and Madame Mohkov had arranged the simple furniture in the one room with its curtained-off kitchen, and Madame Mohkov had returned to her interrupted needlework, alone in her own home Katya felt out of reach of the hostile world that for years now had delivered to her blow upon blow. Her thoughts turned inward in contemplation of the function to which she was dedicated. She experienced hours of bliss, absorbed into some universal joy. With her the eternal desire man has for peace was accentuated now in her pregnancy because of the series of shocks to which she had been subjected. Retreat from the outside world was a necessity. If it had not been for Madame Mohkov, she would have starved herself rather than go in search of food. The trips to the doctor were times of anxiety.

Then suddenly the shelter of the four walls she had drawn in around her no longer was a shelter. She was invaded by fears and forebodings that she would never live to bear the child. In this new dilemma she reached out for some human being to help her. Such terror would come upon her in the night that she longed just to stand by the door of Madame Mohkov's apartment. In the daytime she would ask to be allowed to help with the embroidery that she might sit near the older woman. She was not conscious that most of the time her hands lay idle in her lap while her eyes rested on Madame Mohkov. She studied every detail of the older woman's face—the sagging fold under the chin, the aging look of her flesh, the loose softness of her skin, in order to re-create the image of her own mother.

Uneasy under such concentrated observation, Madame Mohkov would look up from her work only to find the girl's gaze seemingly turned inward on some dream of her own. Then the older woman remembered her own pregnancies, the deep absorption and the moments of depression. Yes, and the need for her mother. Her sense of duty to help Katya because she was another Russian refugee deepened into loving solicitude. The terror of death and decay which had hung over her ever since she had looked on the mangled bodies of her husband and his brothers huddled in a common grave began to leave her.

At first Maria was indignant with Katya for the demands she made upon her overworked mother, and then she was grateful, for she saw that the shadow was indeed lifting from her mother's mind. So they all waited in expectation of the baby's coming.

But as the child grew within Katya, vigorously striking out at her walls of its shelter, dark forces of guilt began to close in around her, a guilt she had felt when she went first to live with Edward in Lahususu. She thought she had cleared herself with her mother the night Edward had asked her to marry him and she had wrapped herself in the cool sheet reinstating her girlhood, a kind of testimony given to her mother that it was not she who had gone against the mores of her people, but a hunted, tormented girl who could not be held responsible. But now the subterfuge seemed to have been discovered. Had she conceived during those months in Lahususu, the child would have been illegitimate. She began to avoid Madame Mohkov, sitting alone in her own apartment.

One night she dreamed she was on the road leading to her home in Russia. She was not alone, for she carried a newborn babe in her arms. When she came to her home, her mother, stern and white, closed the door against her saying, "The child is illegitimate." In the dream she thought wildly, I must get rid of it, and she laid it in the snow, then knocked on the door, calling for her mother.

She awoke, bathed in perspiration. Pains gripped her, rhythmic and intense. No fancied fears now. All her resources were galvanized into action. She must reach Maria, get to the hospital. She had no telephone. She threw on a heavy robe, half crawled, half walked up the stairs, knocked on the Mohkovs' door. It opened. For the second time that night a gray-haired woman stood waiting, but this time the welcome was certain. "My child!" Madame Mohkov put her arms around Katya, helping her to a chair. "I'll call Maria. We must get you ready at once."

"It's two months early," Madame Mohkov whispered, waking Maria.

"I'll hurry," her daughter answered, divining what her mother meant. "I'll call a taxicab."

But when they came back to Katya, they saw it was too late, too late even to get her to her own apartment. They put her in Maria's warm bed. "Put some water on the stove, Maria," Madame Mohkov commanded; "then see if you can get hold of the doctor."

"I have given birth!" Katya cried. She closed her eyes, indifferent to

Madame Mohkov's cry, "It is a boy!" Performing the services of mid-wife, Madame Mohkov released the child from the mother, carefully lifted the infant. She snatched up a garment of Maria's that lay near and wrapped him in it. Feebly the baby wailed, lying against Madame Mohkov's motherly bosom.

It was a windy March day. San Francisco shone in clear sunlight. The rainy season seemed over, and even the old mansions where the Russians lived looked fresh and clean, washed by the winter rains. On the front of the house where Katya had her apartment a wisteria vine, its gnarled branches twisting themselves into a strong rope which climbed to the third story, had hung out its purple blossoms.

It was evening. The Russian physician had finished his work as doorman at a downtown hotel. He was on his way to see Katya, who was back today from the hospital. The American doctor to whom he had sent her had saved both the premature baby and the mother. But he had not freed Katya from her fear. Until that was done she would not make a wholesome mother. In the hospital her concern for her child had been intense, even morbid.

Madame Mohkov met him at the door. "Andrei Petrovitch, here is a fine little Russian," she cried, as the two leaned over the cradle where the baby lay asleep. "A strong young man is Master Suvorov, even if he did frighten us to death the night he came."

When Madame Mohkov had gone, the doctor lifted the baby from his bed and laid him in his mother's arms. "See, it is better for you both this way. I am an old man, and I have learned some things the young doctors don't always understand." He pulled up a chair to the side of the bed and sat down. "Fondle your baby, carry him. It's a very soft, warm world he has lived in until now. He needs it soft still."

"It's a terrible world he has come to," Katya answered, her eyes filling with tears.

"It will be if you nurture him on fear," the old man replied. "It is for you and this boy to enrich the country that has given you sanctuary."

"Sanctuary!" she exclaimed.

"Yes, hard and bitter as it may seem to you now. Ever since it was discovered, America has been the refuge of countless men and women seeking freedom from fear. It's still a dream, but one worth preserving." Gently he rested his hand on her forehead for a moment.

"I have named him Petya after my brother," she murmured.

"America is Petya's land. Call him Peter," he told her, "and bring him up to be a fine American."

That night Katya dreamed she was walking with Edward through a melon patch on his grandmother's ranch. Curious, she kept thinking, I don't remember its being here. The watermelons lay in rows, and all of them had been cut in half, looking like bells. And then with the inconsistency of dreams, they were the bells of Russia hanging in the domes of the churches, clanging out the hours, the halves, the quarters. Then they seemed to be clanging right in the midst of The Valley, and they were wedding bells announcing her marriage day.

She awoke, but all the next day seemed saturated with her dreams of The Valley. The beautiful valley of California was really America, of which, because of Edward, she was a citizen.

She remembered what the old Russian doctor had said, "This is Petya's land." Now she was willing to accept it. And Petya was not an exile, he was a native of this country. She must see that he took his place in America. She did not guess that her acceptance of Edward's country was intertwined with her desire for him. She thought she had put Edward completely out of her life.

Part Two

THE VALLEY

13

The day had been unseasonably hot for June, but now at five the fog was beginning to come in through the Golden Gate, and the air was fresh and cool. From his father's house, Edward could see it banked like high-piled snow, filling the gap between the land masses to the right and left of the Gate. Soon a mist began creeping over the Bay, penetrated here and there by shafts of sunlight. He watched with concentration, as a person who sees the phenomenon of the afternoon summer fog for the first time. It seemed oddly new and strange to him. He believed he had not been conscious of it since that summer—he stopped there in his thinking, not wishing to remember which summer. Wispy shreds settled over the flat land below him, finally drew in around the house. Etched on the fog were the shadowy forms of the eucalyptus trees. Beauty pierced him like a sword. Once many things had held elements of beauty for him. Was the capacity to discern it coming back to him?

The unprecedented languor which had held him all day, relaxed and happy, he felt certain was the reaction from years of strenuous work. On the evening eight years ago when he had returned to his father's house after a month of dissipation and angry rebellion he had had little faith in his own judgment, convinced it had proved a hundred per cent wrong up to date. He had made up his mind to accept whatever his father proposed. To his surprise he found on his arrival that in his absence his father had undergone the operation on his eyes. This had brought Edward's estimate of himself to an even lower point. His going away had not proved important enough to upset plans for the operation. He felt duped and betrayed. In all those long weeks after his return from China he had never asserted himself for fear of injuring his father's chances, and then when it was too late to save anything out of the wreckage of his life, he found worry over him had not upset his father to anywhere near the degree he had been led to believe it would.

When Edward made his first visit to the hospital his father's eyes were still bandaged and he had evident need to conserve his strength. Yet he had talked over plans with Edward. "You said you didn't want to go on in the office. I've been wondering myself whether it's just the right place for your talents. I've always hoped that one of my sons would go into politics. Of course I don't want to force it on you, but if it interests you at all, what about starting on your law course right away? It's a splendid preparation."

Edward had said nothing at first, bewildered by conflicting emotions—gratitude and the exact opposite. Here was the chance to study law, the thing he had ardently desired, but robbed of the purpose for which he had desired it. Then came the despairing feeling that nothing mattered any more. He supposed law was as good as anything.

He had studied to the point of exhaustion, at first merely to rid himself of the emptiness of his life for which he could find no other relief; then, after a time, ambition to be the first in his class had driven him to even greater effort. He would prove to his father that he had a good, even a brilliant mind. But when he was graduated with the highest honors in his class, his victory seemed empty. He still hadn't proved he was capable of earning his own living. Again he drove himself, this time to build up a law practice large enough to win his father's approval of him as a businessman. But when after three years that goal was in sight, he again sensed his failure in his father's eyes. He needed some public recognition to complete his vindication of himself. His appointment as assistant district attorney a year ago had given him that. But complete satisfaction was denied him because of the knowledge that his father's ambition for him would not be realized until he entered political life.

To accomplish what he had Edward had become almost a recluse, refusing all contacts outside his work. Even family functions he had usually avoided, giving the same reason. And he had not in all these years been back to The Valley. "If Granny wants me, let her send for me," he said when his mother urged him to go. He knew his grandmother would not send for him. He could not meet the terms she had set up for his coming. Her attitude toward him was a sorrow, and yet he was relieved not to have to see her or The Valley.

Jeremy Dodd was disappointed that Edward showed no interest in the family business or in political matters connected with electric power. But in general he felt he had no reason to be dissatisfied, for Edward was making a fine record as assistant district attorney. He had listened to a number of cases in which his son had represented the state. His prosecution was logical and forceful. When the state finally presented the long-discussed water plan, a threat as the power people saw it to their exclusive control, he hoped to press Edward into the role of lobbyist for the power interests.

Beatrice Dodd unlike her husband had never ceased to worry about

Edward, conscious always of the deep lines which led down from the sides of his mouth, and the veiled look in his eyes as if they were on guard against any intrusion into the thoughts which lay behind them. She had not expected him to take the breaking-up of his unfortunate marriage so hard. But within the last few months she, too, had felt less cause to worry. Edward seemed more normal. His step was lighter. Occasionally she heard him whistling about the house, and he had actually volunteered to go to a family dinner tonight celebrating his sisters' return from the East.

This lessening of tension in Edward was not so sudden as it seemed to her. A year ago he had become acquainted with a group of young attorneys who had started lunching together after a morning in court. They discussed every phase of law and politics. They had interesting plans for state control of water and power. The report on the water plan given to the State Assembly, although exhaustive in other ways, failed in that it made no mention of restriction on the use of state waters or whether the electricity generated could be handled by the private companies or by public distribution. Slowly, at first even fearfully, Edward's mind opened to a freer, more imaginative world than he had lived in for many years. It brought back to him how when he was a boy he and John had been excited over many of the same issues.

It was of these new friends and their belief in him that he had been thinking this afternoon as he lay stretched out in a long chair on the sun porch. Yesterday they had asked him if he would allow his name to be put up as state senator at large running on both tickets, with the backing of men from both parties who believed a comprehensive water plan for the state should assure the people that both water and power would benefit all the people of the state, not alone a few powerful private interests.

Hearing his mother's quick step, he glanced at his watch. He supposed it was time to dress.

"I've asked Agnes to come in for cocktails this evening, Edward, before we go over to San Francisco for the dinner," Beatrice Dodd said, standing in the doorway. "You don't mind having her, do you? She's been almost a daughter to me, as you know, since the girls went away."

"Why should I?" Edward wanted to sound indifferent. For six months he had been trying to make up his mind about Agnes Buchanan. He knew his mother wished him to marry her. He liked her; it was just the marriage he should make. And yet so far he had been unable to decide. He was annoyed with his mother for forcing his

hand, for he felt asking Agnes to such an exclusively family party committed him in some way to his mother's plans.

"I think I heard her come in. I asked her to come early," his
mother was saying.

As he rose to greet Agnes, Edward thought, She is exactly the kind
of girl I should marry. She was small with soft brown hair and gentle
brown eyes. Delicate and fragile, a person who needed care and protection. He already had discovered that, when he was with her, he
felt strong and vital.

Jeremy Dodd had insisted they have dinner at the Palace Hotel
because it was there that family parties had always been held in his
father's and mother's day. His own graduation party had been given
here, and the wedding breakfast celebrating his marriage to Beatrice.
It seemed to him the fitting place to celebrate his immediate family's
reunion. They had not been together for several years. Margot, after
her marriage four years ago, had gone to live in Washington, D. C.
This last year Bettie had been away at college. Margot had come
home for a two-weeks' visit, Bettie for the summer vacation.

It took a long table to accommodate them all. Tom and Edward
sat at the right and left of Mrs. Dodd; Mildred, Tom's wife, and
Agnes at Jeremy's right and left. Bettie, Margot and her husband,
Tom's four children, three boys and a girl, all of them now old
enough to behave at a family dinner, were seated down the sides of
the table. Considering how large the family had grown and how much
larger it was destined to become, Jeremy thought of Granny, the
source. There she was at ninety-eight still living amid her ample acres.
He felt her long life gave a solidarity to the family that no rebellious
member could destroy. Edward's unfortunate marriage had left no
lasting mark. Here was the family presenting as solid a front as ever.
He looked leniently on Bettie's defiance of her parents' wishes in going
East to college instead of coming out with the group of debutantes of
the year. It was of minor importance.

This assurance of family solidarity was strengthened in his mind by
the substantial business gains he had made recently. The late twenties
were prosperous years in California. The valley cities were growing.
Hundreds of new users of electricity in the upper valley had all but
exhausted the power he had to offer. He was planning new dams in
regions where he had recently acquired water rights. The final papers
were even now being drawn up to buy out a rival power company in
the district in which he operated. Henceforth he would be evenly
pitted against the biggest power company in the northern part of the

state, whose ambition, he knew, was to buy or squeeze him out. He welcomed the battle ahead.

As the family decorously unfolded their napkins, they sensed Jeremy's satisfaction. It put Tom completely at ease, a thing he seldom was in the presence of his father, to whom he gave blind devotion. Never could he hope to equal Jeremy Dodd's cleverness in his business decisions. Given time, Tom came to sound conclusions, but dealing constantly with his father's quicker mind, as he did in his position as lawyer of the firm, he often felt mentally clumsy, never dreaming that the senior Dodd put forth sudden, even startling ideas, to test them out against his son's good judgment.

Bettie found her defensive attitude toward the head of the family giving way, also the half-understood anger she had had toward Edward ever since he had returned home many years ago without his wife. How silly of her to let her parents' rejection of the Russian— she had always considered it their rejection—interfere with her friendship for her favorite brother! She was far too young at the time to understand. As she looked at Edward, at whose left she was sitting, their eyes met.

"So it's all right between us, Little Sister?" Edward asked. She squeezed his hand, feeling happier, she believed, than she had for years.

Margot was talking with Agnes. Catching fragments of the conversation, Edward gathered that Margot, his proud, aloof sister, so hard to please, was actually accepting Agnes, telling her of recent political happenings in Washington. "A woman plays a great part in her husband's political success," she was saying, "far greater than is generally suspected. She's a listening post for him if she's intelligent." Just why was Margot giving Agnes advice in such matters unless—well, unless she wished him to marry Agnes and go in for politics. He was annoyed. His family seemed to have a corporate will that was stronger than any of its individual wills.

It crossed his mind that Margot knew something about the opportunity which had been offered to him—and yet that was rather far-fetched. She would have little in common with the young politicos who had approached him. Neither would his father. Then he remembered how close was the relationship between Margot and his father, who had always had plans for him politically.

Jeremy Dodd was talking to them now as a group. "The businessman has proved in the last years that, if left alone, he can make the country prosperous. Stocks and bonds are higher than they've ever been in my memory." He looked from one to the other of the men at the table. "Don't you agree with me, Tilbury," he asked Margot's husband, "that our businessmen have the brains of the country?"

For one moment Edward lost his sense of oneness with the family, wondering what was beneath this façade of prosperity his father always presented to them. Did he ever in the dark night awake, find himself alone with himself and ponder any deeper meaning in life? Did he ever experience the sharp stab that beauty gives, as *he* had experienced it this afternoon when the fog had come in? He had no recollection of his father speaking of beauty. Did he ever have compassion for someone less fortunate than himself?

Edward had a sudden vivid picture of his half brother John, the look of compassion and understanding in his eyes the day after he had rescued him from the Doddstown speak-easy. Certainly, thought Edward, the gates of his mind were open today for the intrusion of all sorts of memories. He'd better slam them shut on such unbidden thoughts. He brought his attention back to what the head of the family was saying. But again he found himself a critical outsider. He now took himself sharply to task. Who was he to criticize his father? Sonship was again a blind, uncritical relationship.

He looked at his mother. Her almost pathetic pleasure in having all her children around her touched him. He had a twinge of remorse over the anxiety he had caused her. Well, he'd make it up to her.

At the end of the dinner, as they rose from the table, he drew Agnes' arm through his and walked with her down the corridor that led from the main lobby. It seemed hardly necessary to ask her to marry him. It had been so palpably an accepted fact this evening that she would soon be one of them. And remembering that moment at dinner when his docile devotion to his father had threatened to desert him, Edward hastened to barricade himself behind submission. "Shall we give them the chance to congratulate us?" he asked, bending over Agnes.

She did not answer at once. She loved Edward Dodd, but both her natural honesty and her pride would not let her accept him yet. "Do you really love me, or are you simply doing what your people want?" she said, looking straight into his eyes.

"Of course I love you. You don't think for one moment, do you, that I'm the kind of person who has no mind of his own? You don't think I would marry you just to please Mother and Father?" he demanded.

"There is a strong family feeling among you all," she answered. "I respect it, but it's nothing to marry on."

Edward was determined now that he would marry her. It would be humiliating to be refused on the ground that his family was choosing for him. It roused all his innate manhood, and for the next two weeks he made ardent love to Agnes. That was the limit of her resistance. She confessed to her long-standing love for him. He wanted to be married immediately, know more intimately this lovely, delicately fashioned woman who had made him strong and masculinely aggressive again. He felt himself in love completely, perfectly.

14

GRANDMOTHER DODD's strength was slowly leaving her. First she was too weak to sit up; then too weak to hold the cup with the strong, rich broth that Fu made for her, finally too weak to retain it once it was swallowed. Her frail body seemed to be traitorously lining itself up with the spirit to defeat her. The Valley, which had harbored her life for so long, its sun, its wind, its continuous productivity which season after season she had seen renewed, had come to seem like a guarantee of her own immortality. To leave it was a hazardous undertaking from which her spirit, once strong and venturesome, shrank. For years each autumn she had set herself to live to experience once more the scent of orange blossoms which in the spring drifted through her windows, and each spring she set herself to live until autumn to experience once more the sight of the abundant harvest. But autumn was here again, and the body refused to respond to the proddings of her will. She was very tired.

But one defense still remained to her—the flesh begotten by her flesh, which seemed to guarantee a kind of immortality. The more her family moved before her fading sight, the more secure she felt. She even accepted Beatrice when her son Jeremy was unable to come because of business. One day she asked for Edward. The message reached him as he was leaving court. So at last his grandmother had forgiven him. In a few minutes he was in his car starting his first journey in eight years down The Valley.

It was early October. As he neared the top of the pass a truck loaded with grapes came over the brow. The sun was sinking behind the coastal range. The plain below him was in shadow. His throat tightened, his old love for The Valley reasserting itself.

As it grew dark, he lowered the top of his car, letting the hot valley air flow over him. Toward midnight an old moon rose and light poured slowly into The Valley. No need for haste; he could not see his grandmother until morning. He loitered, caught by the mystery of light, The Valley an unfathomable well of light, depthless, timeless, he a part of the timelessness linked to it through his grandmother, and she linked to it, even in death, through him and those that would come after.

No one was astir when he reached the house except the day nurse just come on duty. Hearing the car, she came to greet him. "She is asking for you," she said, and led the way into the room where his grandmother lay. He took her shaking hand in his.

Her sunken lips quivered. "I . . . wanted to see . . ." She paused, seemingly puzzled. "I thought you'd bring your wife. Once we talked about a boy, my grandson. The family must not die."

"You forget Tom has children," he told her gently.

"It is not enough." Her eyes closed, and she seemed to sleep. An hour Edward sat by her bed. So his grandmother hadn't forgiven him. She was living in the past when she had nothing to forgive. The sound of her breathing grew louder.

"The end is very near. Do you wish to summon the family?" asked the nurse.

Later, when Jeremy and Beatrice Dodd arrived, Jeremy went immediately to old Mrs. Dodd's room. Edward, noticing his mother's distress, put his arm around her. "Edward, I need you," she cried. "Don't ever let anyone else take my place!" This hovering on the very threshold of death, as Grandmother had hovered for many days, brought the idea of mortality too near. Its inevitability shook Beatrice Dodd. She was in panic.

The day drew on to the evening. John drove in from Los Angeles, and Tom and his family from San Francisco. Telegrams had been sent to Margot in Washington and Bettie in New York to take the first plane. They couldn't be expected until late the next day. Restlessly the family moved about the great house. During the night they slept in distorted positions in chairs, feeling they must not leave Granny to cross alone from life to death. The next morning Margot arrived and in the afternoon Bettie. Now the family was complete, a defense against disintegration.

That night it seemed to the old woman as if the harvest of California's vineyards must have reached its peak. Above the hushed voices of her family she heard the trucks loaded with the grapes picked during the day rumbling along the main highway, the volume of sound mounting in a crescendo as day dawned. A hoarse cry came from Grandmother Dodd.

Edward following his mother and father into the room saw that the old woman's face held a startled look, as if at the very end she had been taken unaware. In spite of all her watchfulness death had slipped past her guard. Jeremy Dodd sagged to the floor by his mother's bed, in broken sentences begging the dead woman not to leave them.

Edward went out on the veranda. The birds were singing, and he could hear the trucks moving along the road carrying the grapes to the wine presses. While he stood there in the fresh morning air, he felt an uneasy sense of release, as if his grandmother's death freed him from her disapproval and the last need to remember Katya.

He heard a step behind him. Turning, he saw John coming toward him. For a little they were silent. Then John said, "We can't mourn her too much as it means rest for a very tired but gallant old lady." So John was not shaken into insecurity as the other members of the family were by Granny's death, yet Edward knew that John loved his grandmother more devotedly, perhaps, than any of them, and that hardly a week had passed when he had not found time to come to see her.

Edward felt easier. He studied his older brother. He isn't like the other Dodd men, he was thinking. Not like Tom or Father. John's bigger-boned, more loosely jointed. The faces of the others are thin and long, and the bones in their bodies more neatly joined. With age, as in Father, there's a tenseness as if he had been too tightly put together, thought Edward. Tom's mouth and Father's are thin and straight. "Business ascetic" would be a good name for them, he decided. Everything sacrificed on the altar of business.

He wondered what toll his father's incessant drive had taken of his physical faculties. Was it to put that drive in him that his father had ended his marriage? Was he to be like him in time? It was a disturbing thought. Again, as when he was a boy, he was drawn to John, sensing in the warmth of his personality that freer, more imaginative world the young lawyers had recently opened up to him.

"Well," asked his half brother, "do I measure up? You've been staring at me for some time." He took out a cigarette, passed the pack to Edward.

"I was thinking you look as if you had some pretty good formula for living," Edward answered, a little embarrassed.

John smiled.

Edward had the desire to tell him about the young attorneys and what they wanted of him. Then a sense of decorum in the house of the dead kept him from talking of his plans. Instead he said, "I wonder if it would be any help to Father to have us with him."

When Edward accompanied by his brothers and sisters entered the room where his father was sitting, Jeremy grasped at their young strength to give him the security he so sorely needed.

In these first hours following his mother's death Jeremy Dodd was groping vainly in an unfamiliar world which no longer held the woman who for so many years had represented the prestige and wealth of the family. Shielded as he had been between the old and the young, he had never before known what it meant to have the winds of mortality blow directly upon him. Like an invulnerable breastwork erected against change, the valiant spirit of his mother had in the past, it had always seemed to him, to take into her own person the disintegration of age, leaving him to simulate the indestructible vitality of the Dodds. Now with her passing he felt age with its disintegration bequeathed to him—a shattering experience.

"It is on you I must rely," he told his sons, "to support me in my position as head of the family. There must of necessity be changes. This house——" At this point his voice broke, and he had to wait to regain his self-control before going on to say, "I want your advice on what shall be done with this property and also the ranch. Of course everything depends on your grandmother's will. Out of respect for Mother, I shall not have it read until after——" He stopped, unable to continue, realizing the finality that existed in the word he had been about to speak.

Quietly one by one his children rose and tiptoed from the room, more disturbed by their father's breakdown than by their grandmother's death. To them she had not seemed ageless as she had to their father, but aging—a realization which had prepared them for her death. But the spectacle of their father with trembling lips, asking them to aid him in his decisions, indicated a loss in the cohesive quality of the family much more significant than that brought about by the passing of its most ancient member.

Their reactions were of varying intensity, according to their dependence on their father. John, who had long ago departed from the family pattern, could look at Jeremy Dodd's sudden infirmity of purpose more objectively than the others. Either it was a passing phase brought on by shock, or it meant a definite aging from which the older man would not rally. For Margot it lessened the respect she had for her father which was founded on her admiration of his ruthless drive. Tom was shattered. His father was his idol and also the arbiter of all his life. Never before had he seen him display the weakness of ordinary men.

Bettie's and Edward's reactions were more complex. There was a kind of troubled relief in the sight of their father's dependence on them, giving them a sense of safety in their own strength. No longer could he intimidate them. But this was disloyal! They pushed their relief down deep, putting in its place an upwelling of love. In Edward it was mixed with pity, an emotion which he found more binding than any which had heretofore held him to his father.

It was agreed among them that they would tell their father they did not care to be present when the will was read, nor to know more of its contents than he wished them to know, thus expressing their complete confidence in him. Margot consented in a kind of scornful anger against the man she had always trusted to carry things with a high hand. In the six years since she had married, she had learned how to use her executive abilities to gain recognition for her handsome but mentally somewhat ill-equipped husband. Her drive had carried him into the United States Congress; her brain, working through him, had given him a reputation for astuteness and political know-how and given her a sense of superiority to all men except her father. Now he had proved to be dominated by a woman. She could not forgive him. Let him hear the will read alone if it would give him any satisfaction.

The morning after Jeremy returned to his home in Oakland, he and Beatrice sat in his room opposite the lawyer, who held the will in his hand. In the end Jeremy had decided he needed his wife near him as he listened to his mother's final words. What confidence she must have had in him, he thought, as the lawyer read that he, Jeremy Dodd, her only son, was to inherit—except for a few bequests to charity and dependents—all of her property and was to be the sole executor. His eyes filled with tears. "Read the bequests," he commanded in a choked voice. There was an enumeration of his mother's pet charities, a gift of money to Fu and her nurse, and to Edward's wife Katya one hundred acres of ranch land.

"One hundred acres to that Russian woman!" Jeremy shouted. "Mother couldn't have been responsible when she did that. I'll contest it."

"The will was drawn up seven years ago," the lawyer answered. "There's nothing you can do about it."

"Oh, Jeremy, what shall we do?" Beatrice cried.

"You don't need to worry, Beatrice. This is easily handled," Jeremy answered, all his energies once more galvanized into action. As on that other day, when he saw Katya as a threat to the family, he acted immediately to eliminate her influence. "Hawkins, you'll have to find the woman without advertising. Make a settlement with her. I don't want her around in The Valley. Try any means you think will work. Offer her whatever price you have to, to get her to sell."

After the lawyer had left, Jeremy went over with Beatrice the various angles of their dilemma, evaluating every possible loophole by which information of this bequest might reach Edward. If he knew that his grandmother valued the woman highly enough to leave her property, Edward might take it into his head to go back to her. One thing extremely important was to have Edward marry Agnes as soon as possible. "Beatrice, do you think you can hurry their marriage?" he asked.

"How terrible!" she lamented. "How could your mother have done such a thing."

"It's no use to mourn over what we can't change. The thing for you to do is to go and see Agnes right away. Tell her that Edward needs her especially now to help him bear the loss of his grandmother."

"I can try," said Beatrice.

When Beatrice left on her mission, Jeremy went over in his mind again every possibility of disaster that might grow out of the bequest. Suppose some reporter went to the courthouse and checked the records? Not a very great risk, for he had always seen to it that the family make no public display. He guessed he could count that out. Suppose Edward himself should take a notion to look up the will. But then why should he? He had joined the others in saying he would leave everything in his father's hands. He'd be satisfied with the statement that the property was left wholly to the head of the family, except for one or two small bequests to retainers. However, Jeremy did take Tom into his confidence.

15

PETER SUVOROV, Edward Dodd's seven-year-old son, slid into the chair opposite his mother. His straight, sandy hair was brushed as slick as water and brush could make it. His large eyes were violet-gray like his mother's until he smiled, then golden flecks of light seemed to turn them brown. There was an invincible look about him this morning. He had done what he said he would—got up at five o'clock and helped a bigger boy with his paper route. He wasn't going to tell his mother how another boy had tried to run him off, had hit him over

the head with a cudgel made out of rolled-up newspapers. It had hurt.
He could still feel the sting—but if he told her, he'd have to give up
the coveted display of his manliness and leave paper routes out of his
schedule.

Katya set her son's breakfast before him, saying, "You may do it
only on Saturdays." He smiled a toothless grin, for his two front
teeth were gone. "You must be a gentleman, Petya," she continued.

"Like Baron Kovinsky?" he asked. Then he laughed at the idea
that he could resemble the beribboned Russian nobleman he saw at
occasional functions of the Russian community. No, he wasn't going
to be a queer-looking guy like that. It was better to be an American
and sell papers.

Katya laughed, too, at the absurdity of her freckle-nosed son with
his wide urchinlike grin ever being a solemn, stately old man.

Petya liked them to laugh together. It spread light around them.
He ate ravenously, at the end drinking the glass of hot tea his mother
set before him. All at once his head settled down on his arm, and he
was asleep.

He's just a baby, thought Katya. She lifted him, trying to cuddle
him against her. How angular he was! But she didn't want to face
the fact he was growing up. She laid him on her bed in the corner of
the room and covered him, then washed the dishes and went out
quietly, closing the door behind her. He'd have to take care of himself until she came home at six from the Russian bookshop where
she was working. She had learned too late how inadequate to support herself and her son was the sum the Dodd lawyer had succeeded
in inducing her to accept as a settlement.

She knew little about handling money and at first spent unwisely.
Rent, clothes and food were high in these late 1920's, and there were
so many other things to use money for. There was Madame Mohkov's daughter, for instance, who needed a little money to get to this
country after she learned her husband had died in Russia. And there
was the funeral for her old friend the Russian doctor. In death, if not
in life, it seemed necessary to give him the honor denied him in his
exile. Every ship arriving from China and Japan brought refugees.
There was the Russian Relief Society and an organization to help the
Russian invalids of the World War. Most of all, Katya could not
resist giving to Maria Mohkov's Society for the Care of Russian Children.

She looked back as she reached the corner, longing to see Petya
waving to her from the window and yet hoping she wouldn't see him,
too. Leaving him asleep gave her the feeling she needn't worry

about him for the next hour or two. Saturdays when he was home from school, although Madame Mohkov watched over him, were times of anxiety. Yet that daily last glimpse of him was very precious to her. A year after his birth she had taken rooms in the front of the house so Petya could have sunshine, and since she had started work they had made a custom of waving to each other before she turned the corner.

Peter—as he insisted on being called by all except his mother— awoke. The siren down on the Ferry Building was screeching. It was noon. He thought about the pennies he had earned this morning. He believed he'd go around the corner and get some ice cream, but first he'd eat what his mother had left for him. His luncheon was always under a napkin on the table.

Today was to be his great day. First the paper route and now something he had wanted to do, it seemed to him, all his life. He was going to walk to the top of the great hill up which people and street and motorcars daily climbed. Perhaps Russia was up there, or maybe he would find that that was where his father lived, for he must have a father somewhere. His good friend Mr. Ching, who had a vegetable shop near by, had told him all boys have fathers. He had explained it was necessary to have one, first to be born and then to give the proper balance to a man's life. Peter understood what he meant, even if he did not understand all the words.

He was one man among many women. There was his mother, and the old countess he called, after the Russian, babushka. Then there were Aunt Maria and Madame Mohkov whom he sometimes by mistake called Mother. She often took care of him. When he was little, he loved the warm softness of her lap. Of course he didn't now. In the last year he had come to fear she'd make a sissy out of him. All the rainy season he had never once got away without his rubbers. And she kissed him right out in front of the house if she met him. He'd had a hard time arranging about the newspapers. The women around the big table discussed it for days. His only escape was Mr. Ching. They all approved of his Chinese friend. If Madame Mohkov stopped him today as he was going out, he'd just have to tell her he was going to see Mr. Ching.

However, he reached the corner without her seeing him, safely sped along the blocks across town and started to climb. His heart beat fast, first with the wonder and excitement over his undertaking; then it was pumping hard because of his physical exertion. His short legs ached. Block after block he trudged upward, ignoring the fascinating store windows. He felt very large somewhere inside him. The smell of hot coffee reached him. He followed it down two steps, passed through a swinging door, sat down at a table. He had never tasted coffee before. The waitress, who had a boy of her own, put in plenty of milk and added a sweet roll. He counted out the pennies, feeling very much a man.

Now he was able to walk faster, and then there he was at the top of the hill. Far below him trains, people and trucks looking like toys moved along the labyrinth of streets, tiny steamers nosed into tiny docks, flat-ended ferries shuttled across a blue sheet of water, and beyond were green hills with white houses sparkling in the sunlight— a fabulously new and beautiful world. It made him think of music, the kind played when Russians gathered together.

Peter sighed and sat down on a wide step. When I'm big I'll bring all the people down below up here to live, he said to himself, watching the cable cars climb the hill.

"To the Honorable Small One, greetings. What you do here?"

Peter looked up into the face of his dearest friend, Mr. Ching.

"I came by myself."

"Let us go home together, but first I must fly my kite."

"You haven't any kite, Mr. Ching." Peter always called his friend Mister, and he never shouted after him "Chin Chin Chinaman," as some of the boys did. He shouted it only after an old laundryman he didn't like.

A humorous light gleamed in Mr. Ching's eyes. "Some kites you see. Some you no see."

Peter followed his friend, who took a sudden turn into a narrower street which led even higher. They came to a wall, and beyond it was a bit of grass where Mr. Ching squatted. Peter, squatting beside him, politely waited for Mr. Ching's kite to come down out of the sky. By and by, when nothing happened, he lay flat on the ground and looked straight up into the blue above him. The sun sank low; a slender fold of fog drifted across its red center. The sun sank lower. Across the Bay he saw a light set in every window, a flaming beacon put there by the sun. He clasped his hands and began to sing softly to himself.

Mr. Ching rose, saying, "We go now."

"Why don't you live here?" asked Peter.

"The laws of this honorable country do not allow it. But for what you call dreams, I am allowed here."

"You sleep here?" Peter looked around for Mr. Ching's house.

"The Honorable Little One does not yet comprehend. In day I dream. Long ago my people saw America in dream. It still is dream.

There is a valley——" Ching pointed his delicate forefinger toward the hills across the Bay slowly fading behind an immaculate mantle of fog. "Once your unworthy friend lived there."

"Tell me," demanded Peter, loving above everything else a story.

"Tonight is not the night for long tale—close to darkness—and runaway boy must be returned to home."

How, Peter wondered, did Mr. Ching know he had run away?

Together they started down the steep incline. Petya feared he was stubbing out his best pair of shoes which he wore only on Sundays but which he had put on for this great occasion. Intent on how he would explain matters to his mother, he was silent. Mr. Ching was silent, too, his feet moving mechanically back to the crowded Chinese quarter of the city where he lived, his mind dwelling in Central Valley. He remembered the orchard he had tended. He could feel the trees' bark under his hand, each according to its kind— apricot, pear and peach—and the exquisite pleasure he had known pruning their heavy growth, skeletonizing the trees. Beautiful against the sky and shaped for bearing, the sun and wind touching each minute twig. His delicate, feeling fingers were instinct with the knowledge of man's and nature's interdependence. It was among the trees he had begun his life in America and had meant to end it. Very confused in Mr. Ching's mind was the reason why, in the contest between the big and little landowners, he had been driven out.

He did not know that, like a pageant moving across a stage and into the wings, one race after another supplied labor for the great farms of California, each in time pushed out, the oncoming race treading upon its heels: first Indians in red and black blankets, then Chinese like himself dressed in the common blue of China and peaked coolie hats, Japanese with their kimonos tucked high around their loins, East Indians, Filipinos, Mexicans, all dreaming that some day they would own land, but tolerated by the landowners only as long as they remained rootless people.

As they drew nearer and nearer to the foot of the hill, Peter grew confused. Which was the cross street he must take? He was not used to these heavily traveled thoroughfares, and the lights of motorcars confused him. Now that the glory of his adventure was fading, he was beginning to think of his disobedience. He looked up at his friend's face, which in its immobility made him seem far away. "Mr. Ching, I think maybe we're lost," he said, tugging at the Chinaman's hand.

"Only thoughts lost." Mr. Ching darted across the street, dragging the boy with him, turned the corner, took a short cut through an alleyway, crossed another street, down another alley. Peter gave a sigh of relief. He was on familiar ground.

"Good-by, Mr. Ching," he cried. Letting go the Chinaman's hand, he ran toward his home halfway down the block.

An hour earlier Katya had turned the same corner and seen no Petya leaning out to greet her. He's with Madame Mohkov, she told herself, hurrying along. I'll start dinner, then call him. She had set down her bundles, the week-end supply of groceries and vegetables, and was unlocking the door to her apartment when a man, coming up the stairs behind her, asked, "You are Mrs. Suvorov, are you not?"

She turned, facing him. He seemed vaguely familiar, but she could not remember where she had met him.

"And why do you wish to know?" she asked.

"I am Mr. Hawkins, Mr. Dodd's lawyer, and I have come on business. Do you not remember me?"

Katya's old terror came back to her. It was to get Petya away from her, this man was here. "Will you come in?" she asked in a cool, clear voice. She had learned how to defend herself in these years, how not to betray fear or grief or need. Quietly she turned on the lights, asked him to be seated.

Mr. Hawkins felt considerable surprise. He had expected to see the emotional woman he had met before, the exploiter of the Dodds. This woman seemed to have gained dignity since he had last seen her. In spite of himself he could see nothing about her that bespoke the adventuress. "I have a document here," he began, "which needs your signature. It has to do with your former marriage to Edward Dodd."

"Everything was settled when the court granted the divorce." Katya managed to speak quietly although her heart was pounding. How had Edward found out about his son?

"Yes, but this is of a little different nature. Mrs. Dodd, Senior, in some papers she left, mentions you. She was very old, you know, and evidently did not realize that you were no longer a member of the family. There is in her will a bequest of a piece of land to you as her grandson's wife."

"In The Valley?" Katya asked, her relief and happiness betrayed by her eager tone. Petya was not threatened, and her dream of living in The Valley was to come true!

The lawyer raised his hand. "Please hear me through. In a court of law undoubtedly you would not be given this land. The will could be contested because of Mrs. Dodd's mental condition. However," he went on, "the family are inclined to be generous in the matter. They have instructed me to give you what they feel the land is worth."

Katya felt suddenly sure of herself. The lawyer was too anxious.

"I can scarcely believe Madame Dodd did not know of the divorce. I think she meant me to have the land. I do not want money. I want the land," she answered.

Unaccountable, these foreigners, the lawyer thought. He had found out that she had a child and that her bank account was at the present time very small. Why on earth would she want land instead of money? "I understand you have a child to support. I should think money would be of greater use to you than farm property. You certainly wouldn't want to live on it. And a tenant—besides a small farm, you know, eats up money. If you will accept my advice, I'd like to suggest for your own good that you let Mr. Dodd pay you the worth of the property left to you in the will. It will make you comfortable until your son is grown. If I had a daughter and she was situated as you are, this would be my advice to her."

"I wish to keep the land. I think the grandmother meant me to have it," Katya insisted.

The lawyer was baffled by her monotonous reiteration of the words, "I wish to keep the land." Arguments having failed, slowly, cautiously, he raised the amount Mr. Dodd would pay.

"When the papers are ready, Mr. Hawkins, I will take them to my lawyer," Katya finally said, indicating by rising that there was no need to discuss the matter further.

The row of old houses looked very reassuring to Peter in the half tones of night. He hurried up the dimly lighted stairs, just a little anxious. It was the first time he had ever disobeyed his mother in a big way. She might punish him in a big way. But when he opened the door there was the room with all the lights turned on, something never allowed except on holidays. Katya swept him up into her arms.

"My Petya, it is land that we have. Now do we belong to this country! A good old woman who was your father's grandmother, your great-grandmother, has given it to us."

"And where is my great-grandmother?" Peter, assured of his welcome, wriggled out of his mother's arms, glancing around, expecting to see someone like the old countess as she appeared at night in her black silk dress.

"She has gone to Heaven, bless her soul," murmured Katya.

"Where is my father?" Peter now demanded, sitting down in the nearest chair, for he was very tired. "Mr. Ching says it is necessary to have a father. The forces of strength and weakness are not—I forget what he said, but there must be a father."

Katya knelt before the boy. How could she explain? Edward's desertion and the humiliation that went with it, so long pushed below the conscious level of her mind rose to confront her, bringing to life the old anguish. She bowed her head in the boy's lap and wept.

Peter held his knees close together to bear the weight, feeling an odd sense of discomfiture. His mother's grief embarrassed him. He patted the soft bright strands of her hair. "Don't cry. I guess I don't need a father," he told her.

With his words Katya came back to the present. The renewal of faith in herself, wrought by a wise old woman speaking to her from the grave through the gift of land, took possession of her once more. This evening was not for mourning, nor to burden a little boy with grief long passed; it was for celebration.

She got to her feet, took Peter by the hand exclaiming, "Let us share our happiness!" She ran with him up the stairs, rushed in upon the Mohkovs without stopping to knock, crying in Russian, her English slipping from her in her excitement, "We are here to tell you that good fortune has come to us! Here, I present to you a small farmer, an owner of land—one hundred acres."

Amid questions and congratulatory exclamation, Katya told her story.

"Ah," cried Madame Mohkov, "it is a landowner our little Petya has become!" and she stood him upon a chair. The four women, even the countess letting go her dignity, circled around him laughing and shaking his hand. "A landowner," said the countess, "with great boots striding over the fields."

Peter laughed, excited by the attention he was receiving. Precariously balanced on the chair as he was, he clapped his hands, pounded out a rhythm with his feet. His mother caught him up in her arms, humming a half-forgotten lullaby of the steppes, "When he is big, he'll ride a big horse."

The countess, watching her, thought, How fine and tall and lithe is our Katya! She resembles Catherine the Great with her long straight nose, her large luminous eyes set far apart, her high brow, the perfect oval of her face. There was something about this young woman that answered the desire in the old countess for grandeur of mien. Maria, her granddaughter, was little and dark.

"We are forgetting," cried Katya, setting her son down.

"This demands a celebration. Come, Petya," cried Maria, picking up her hat, forgetting how tired she'd been a few moments before. "We'll go to the Russian shop."

With Maria on one side and his mother on the other, Peter half ran down the street to the Russian confectioners. What a day of wondrous happenings! He had expected to be scolded and instead he was here amid the delightful odors, actually being told by his mother to choose what he liked.

That night after Peter was asleep, Katya lifted him into her bed and held him in a tight embrace. The fright she had had this afternoon, when she believed that his father had come for him, arose to haunt her, and mingled with it was another fear. Petya was growing up. He had gone off today not telling where he was going. In his sleep Peter flung himself from her, wanting to stretch his legs out, lie sprawled across the bed. She drew him back into her arms, burying her head in the curve of his neck, kissing the soft flesh with an overwhelming desire to keep him forever young and dependent on her.

16

DURING the months she waited for the probation of the will, Katya made no further plans. After the first exhilaration over her good fortune, a superstitious fear had taken possession of her that, if she made plans, somehow the Dodds would gain advantage over her and take the land from her. Carefully she avoided mentioning to any of her other friends what she had told Madame Mohkov's family. Whenever she caught herself thinking about her inheritance, she would pretend to herself that she didn't want the property.

But at last one evening on returning from work she found a slip in her mailbox telling her to call for a registered letter as she had not been at home to receive it. At noon the next day she went to the post office and signed her name and received a large envelope. It was a copy of the court decree which confirmed her title to the land willed her by Grandmother Dodd, but until Maria had looked at it she still dared not believe the property was hers.

Again there was a flurry of excitement among the four women. Katya and Maria studied the statements in the papers sent by the lawyer. Katya's hundred acres lay at the southwest corner of the Dodd ranch. It was land bought by Grandmother Dodd's husband many years before. Although it was originally included in the area of a mutual water company, as the will failed to grant her water stock, Katya was entitled to no irrigation water of the company. But a moderately deep well tapped an adequate supply of underground water for irrigation purposes.

The next Saturday the Suvorovs started out to inspect their property. Peter had never been on a train before, but soon the thrill of its novelty was absorbed into the profoundly moving experience of seeing farm land for the first time. Flowing past the window in unending rhythmic patterns were the rain-drenched soil and green growing things. Russian-American that he was, some dim knowledge of man's oneness with the earth woke within him, a confused, ununderstood emotion. He took great bites of the sandwich Katya had brought for him, not taking his eyes from the mysterious stretches of earth half veiled in the heavy downpour.

Late in the afternoon, his legs aching from the long hours of sitting, his eyes red from watching, he followed his mother from the train and then into an automobile she hired at the station, which took them down the main highway for a little and then along an unpeopled road, little more than a lane. It had stopped raining. The sun had broken through the clouds. Its rays fell slantingly across a wide expanse of fields unrelieved by trees or houses. Faintly on the horizon the coastal range was etched. The car stopped. They got out. Peter stood in wonderment at the silence that belongs to the country. Taking his hand, his mother stepped onto the springy surface of the ground. He heard her say in a choked voice, "This is our land, Petya."

Her hundred acres lay on one side of the lane. On the other side the land belonged to a man named Lesly, so the surveyor who had come out to redetermine the boundaries told her. To the east, west and north of her lay the Dodd ranch. "Your land is all on what we call the 'bench,'" the man explained. "On the basis of the wells drilled so far around here, you seem to be on the upper edge of an underlying water basin."

"You say there are some buildings on my property?" she asked. "You said, did you not, you had worked on the Dodd's ranch one summer? Can you take me to see the house?"

He pointed to a row of shacks farther up the road. "Cotton pickers use 'em in the season."

Katya could not conceal her disappointment. "I thought—I understood there was a house where we could live," she murmured as she walked toward the shacks. They looked desolate—unpainted, set on posts a few feet from the ground; the makeshift steps leading to them were not much more than short ladders. The door to one stood open. She could see there was but a single room with a built-in bunk in one corner, a two-holed rusty cookstove in another, the stovepipe extending through the back wall. She'd have to arrange to live in town until she could build a suitable house. A foreman to do the farming would have to live in town, too. All that would mean extra expense.

"You'd better think twice. You aren't going to find it easy. Cotton's tricky business. The saying goes around here, it takes three failures to make a farmer," the surveyor said.

Peter walked away from his mother. The rain-soaked soil was spongy under his feet. It pulled his rubber off. He studied the ground as he retrieved his rubber, puzzled by this strange emotion which gripped him, a kind of love for something that wasn't a mother or a friend.

On the train going home waves of blackness flowed by the window, broken by flashes of light—towns briefly seen. A half-stifled cry startled him. He turned. His mother had her eyes closed, her mouth so tight shut that he was afraid. He picked up the paper she had dropped. There was a picture of a man and woman coming out of a church. He spelled out the words under the picture: "Mr. and Mrs. Edward Dodd." Suddenly he felt a sharp slap. He dropped the paper and edged away from his mother. She had never struck him before. Then she was leaning over him, murmuring, "Petya, Petya, I am sorry, but you frightened me."

How could he have frightened her? He hadn't even touched her. And anyway, why did she have to hit him?

17

WHEN Jeremy Dodd learned of Katya's refusal to sell him her portion of land, he was both angry and worried. Undoubtedly she was intending to use the dead woman's recognition of her connection with the family to identify herself with it. What other reason could she have for keeping the hundred acres? She had a child, his lawyer had learned. Of course, a woman of her kind couldn't prove it was Edward's, but if she went to live in The Valley, she might well spread some tale that the boy was Edward's son. That would stir up a lot of gossip. Just how she would cash in on it, he didn't quite see, as she didn't seem to want money, unless—well he supposed it could be revenge.

Whatever could have possessed his mother to leave property to Edward's divorced wife? She could not have been in her right mind when she did it. Still the will was dated about the time Edward had left the Russian woman. Perhaps his mother hadn't believed it meant divorce. Although she was not a very devout woman, in times of stress in the family she showed her Calvinist background. She did not, he knew, believe in divorce. But surely she had meant to change the will after he had explained to her the necessity for the separation. Uneasily he put out of his mind the years she had never spoken of Edward. But even if she disapproved, why had she given the Russian woman power over the family?

He thought seriously of selling the ranch. His business needed all his attention; also as it expanded he needed to invest more of his capital in it. If he were going to sell the ranch, now was the time. So much of valley land given over to specialty crops had prevented the drop in farm values which had occurred in the grain lands of the Middle West in 1920 and 1921. People had money, and there was a great demand for farm acreage. If somebody other than the Dodds owned the ranch, the Russian woman probably would sell, seeing the game was up.

He talked the matter over with Tom, grew impatient with him when he suggested they wait a little before disposing of such valuable property. "Land is a good investment if we have a depression," Tom argued.

"Well, I don't know about that." Jeremy shifted his cigar from one side of his mouth to the other, a way he had when he prepared to fight. In the process he drew his thin lips back, showing his teeth. "If any of you children would lift a hand to care for the ranch, it would be different. You know none of you wants to assume any responsibility. Would you take it over?" Jeremy demanded, more and more determined to carry out his plan. "Edward's the only one who has ever displayed any interest, and with that Russian woman parked next to us, it would be a nice state of affairs to have him look after the ranch."

"Why don't you sound out the others on it?" Tom retreated behind the family, as he often did in an argument, knowing whatever he said his father would in the end probably do as he pleased.

"I have. Your mother wants it sold. And Agnes—I talked to Agnes. She thought it would be better for Edward, if he ever went into politics, not to get too interested in running a ranch."

"Is that what he wants to do?" Tom asked with surprise.

"Agnes seemed to think he does." A gleam came in Jeremy's eyes. Surprising, he thought: Tom never sees what's right under his nose. Haven't I been working to get Ed in a position where he can eventually run for the State Senate? Anyway, Agnes understood. She'd agreed that if Edward was to succeed in politics, he must give himself completely to that career. Jeremy had convinced her that for Edward to look after a ranch would be too big a distraction. She had promised to point that out to Edward, but only, she had insisted, if Edward asked her advice. "They all agree with me but you," triumphantly Jeremy Dodd ended his answer to Tom.

"This is no time to invest money." Tom stuck stubbornly to his opinion, too honest not to say what he thought. "Stocks and bonds are sky-high."

"Sell at the top; invest at the bottom." Jeremy pleased at having the last word, strode toward the door. He knew now what he meant to do. The idea had taken shape while he was arguing with Tom. He'd get the man on the ranch next to him—Lesly from Alabama, who had come to The Valley fairly recently and started a cotton plantation after the Southern model—to buy his flat, rich valley land, the best possible for cotton growing. Jeremy's two thousand acres, two-thirds of it supplied with flow water and the rest with fine wells, would make Lesly the largest holder in that part of the country. He believed Lesly would jump at such an opportunity. As soon as he was back in his own office, he called Lesly on the telephone.

"Not at your price, Dodd. I'm no speculator." Lesly's voice was smooth and cool.

"It's what acreage is bringing." Jeremy's tone also was smooth and cool. "I thought I'd give you first chance before I broke it up into a number of small ranches. I can get more that way."

But Lesly was not to be intimidated. "If you sell it piecemeal, I can certainly afford to wait," he answered. "At the price you plan to get, the land won't earn enough to meet the payments on the mortgage and give a man a living. No one can farm acreage bought for more than its capacity to produce. When the values drop, which they will, people who buy from you will be glad to get out at almost any price. Better accept only cash, or you'll be caught, too. You know what happened in twenty-one when the farm bubble burst in the Middle West."

"It's entirely up to you, of course. As a neighbor I wanted to give you first chance." Jeremy was nettled over Lesly's refusal, but secretly resolved to take his advice about selling for cash.

He watched the market. He believed the drop in California farm property would not come for some months yet. He figured it would be safe to wait until sometime in the summer to sell. Might as well get the benefit of the potato harvest, so near now. There was something of the gambler in him which enjoyed the chance he was taking, especially seeing his daring speculative mind set against his son Tom's cautious one.

In the matter of what to do with the old homestead, he and Tom had agreed in the main. "If you want Edward eventually to get in the Senate, it might be a good idea to keep hold of a residence he could use in The Valley. Running in that county, with your influence to help him, he'd pretty certainly be elected. If he lived in the house a few months, he could claim residence down there," Tom had suggested when his father told him of his final decision to sell the ranch.

"Just so," said Jeremy, and then he added, "But I intend to sell most of the orchard. I've thought of making the house and, say, two acres a wedding present to Edward. He can't refuse to maintain residence in the county if he hasn't the burden of keeping up an orchard, and I wouldn't have to say why I wanted him to have it. If I told him, he's still pigheaded enough to decide he wouldn't run."

Tom had a moment's feeling of envy for his younger brother. It would have meant a lot to Tom to have the old house for a week-end place for his growing family. But the envy was only for a moment. He had a deep affection for Edward, and of course his father would never think him capable of going into politics.

18

UNTIL Katya had learned through the picture in the paper that Edward Dodd had married again, she had not faced the many problems involved in living in the country. In a woman as young as Katya romance dies slowly, especially in the warm, impulsive soil of Russian emotions. She had loved Edward passionately. The recognition accorded her by Grandmother Dodd had made that love active again. Had she been too impulsive allowing the lawyer to persuade her to apply for a divorce on the ground of desertion? Edward had let it go by default. Had he been convinced by the same lawyer that she really wanted the divorce?

With one generous impulse she had thrust aside the last unhappy days just before they separated and given herself over to the memory of their love for each other. Was not that the meaning of Grandmother Dodd's gift? Edward was very close to his grandmother. Together, she imagined, they had worked out this plan for reconciliation. Katya was to go and live next to the Dodds' estate, and Edward would come down to look after the family ranch, and they would meet. Each would see in the other's eyes how indestructible was love like theirs.

Even when she had seen that there was no house such as she had imagined on her property, she still clung to her romantic dream. It was in the town where Granny herself had lived that she had meant her daughter-in-law to settle.

When on the train she had opened the evening paper and learned that Edward had married again, her illusions had left her in one devastating, terrible moment. With bitterness, almost disgust, she mocked herself for being a romantic girl—after all these years resurrecting her love, imagining Edward had done the same.

And yet she could not immediately stifle her love for him. His picture had revived his image, grown a little dim through the years when she had not seen him. Much as she desired to, she found herself unable to erase that image. She could feel twined around hers his slender, masculine fingers, feel the hard pressure of his lips. Every curve of his body once intimately known to her haunted her now. When she was asleep he entered her dreams with such vividness that she ached for union with him. Day after day the struggle with herself went on. During this time she continued her duties at the Russian bookshop. At one moment she'd decide to sell her heritage; the next she found herself unable to do so.

But gradually a more mature Katya emerged, with the full realization that if Petya were to have the advantages his father could have given him, it must be through her efforts. She began soberly to consider how she could with proper help farm her acres and bring Petya up in the tradition of his American forebears.

Then she found herself faced with another aspect of the question. Did she want Petya to lose touch with her people, forget Russia, her dear motherland? So many of the *émigrés* trained their children with the one idea that sometime Russia would again be their home, the old regime re-established. Against that day they grounded their sons and daughters in the Russian culture which they loved so passionately, the most important elements of which were its literature and its Greek Orthodox religion.

Settled in the very heart of California as Petya would be if they went to live in its Central Valley, her son would be entirely out of touch with the Orthodox Church. Her parents had given only lip service to the Greek Church, but since her flight from Russia, it had been a symbol to her of her country. She could teach Petya the literature of her motherland, but could she make it mean anything to him?

Eventually she knew he would become like the people around him. Even now Petya was American in all his desires, refusing to wear anything that he considered the least Russian, insisting that they talk English even when they were by themselves, in fact refusing to speak Russian to anyone but the old countess, who had never learned English. However, he did have a liking for Russian dishes. She smiled, thinking how very much he appreciated them.

The more she thought of it, the more she too wished him to be a part of his father's country, and not be caught in this backwater of a Russia which no longer existed.

But what about herself? Could she face the separation from her countrymen that going to live in The Valley meant? Never hear the deep yearning voices of her people raised in song? Never discuss the music and art of her own country, give up the daily association with the Mohkovs, her friends and protectors? All this surrendered for Petya? No, not surrendered. It was through Petya she must live and gain a place in society.

Her decision made, she could not wait even an hour to bring about its fulfillment. It was evening and Petya was already in bed, but she lifted him in her strong arms, carrying him with her up the stairs to the Mohkov's apartment.

"How can I find out how to farm?" she demanded of Maria the moment she entered the room where Madame Mohkov and her daughter were sitting. Katya depended on Maria Mohkov, who, although she was about her age, seemed much older. Day after day facing the problems of her stateless countrymen coming on every ship from the Orient, Maria had grown wise and thoughtful beyond her years. Katya trusted her judgment.

Maria ran her hand through her close-cropped hair, took off her glasses as she was wont to do when faced with a problem, studying the impractical Katya who had first seen the gift from her husband's people cloaked in rosy clouds and then had come home from her trip to present Petya with his heritage as depressed as she had been previously elated. Was she now soberly prepared to weigh her chances of success in a new and difficult undertaking?

"You mean," she asked, "you want me to tell you how to run a farm?"

"You are wise, Maria," Katya answered, "and you know the ways of this country as most of us do not. Tell me where to go to find out what to raise and how to get help. Haven't other Russians done any farming in California?"

"Yes."

"And have they been successful?"

Again Maria answered in the affirmative.

"I shall write them, asking them for guidance," said Katya.

Once more, as on the night when she told her friends of her good fortune, she drew them into her plans. With her they poured over reports and advice of all kinds received in answer to her letters. Following the suggestions of Russian farmers, Katya wrote to the government agent in the county where her land was, asking about the best crops for that part of California.

Finally one evening in a moment of inspiration, or so she considered it later, she announced, "I want a good plodding Russian peasant to help me. Surely among all the Russians who are coming into California there must be one."

"Russia keeps her peasants," Maria replied. "But wait," she cried, "there is a Russian settlement over on Potrero Hill. Among them are peasants who came over in nineteen five and eight to avoid conscription. They were Protestants hunting a land where they could escape the ritual of the Church."

"Bad, bad," put in the old countess, who was deeply devoted to the Orthodox Church. "Dissenters against Holy Russia. No!"

"Most of them work in factories now. The younger ones wouldn't know anything about farming. They came over when they were children. No, I guess there's nothing in that," Maria ended.

"But an older man," Katya persisted.

"I'll try and find out for you. I can do that much. You are sure you oughtn't to sell and invest the money, Katya?" Maria asked, seeing too many difficulties ahead.

"It's good to own a bit of the earth, good for Petya," Madame Mohkov put in.

A few days later Maria brought home the name of a man who lived on Potrero Hill and who had left Russia when he was thirty with the idea of farming in America. Because of lack of funds, he had become a boilermaker but still insisted some day he would own a bit of land. Wasn't that what he had come to this country for? For that and for religious liberty? He was fifty-four, still young enough to work hard. He might be willing to be Katya's tenant.

The next Sunday the Suvorovs, accompanied by Maria, set out for the Potrero district. They found it was situated on one of the many hills that made up San Francisco. It lay to the south—a rounded knoll, its streets abruptly ascending the hill. The houses clung to the steep slopes, shallow, three-story affairs with stairs in front leading from floor to floor in a series of switchbacks. Walking about the streets in search of the number given Maria, they came on several churches, plain buildings painted white, without gilded cupola or dome. There was nothing about them which remotely resembled the architecture of Russia whence these people had come, and yet Maria and Katya stopped, caught by some odd feeling that they were in touch with Russia. Men and women who passed them had the good, strong faces of villagers they had known in their childhood. As they stopped before one of the churches, the congregation came out, many of them in their native costumes. All the women wore the Russian shawl over their heads.

The man, Mishka Melekhov, whom they had come to see, they found lived in an apartment two stories up in one of the larger houses. Standing in the center of the room into which he ushered them were a great golden-oak table covered with a cloth of intricate Russian cross-stitch and, filling one side of the room, a sideboard of the same color with a large mirror supported by columns. He motioned his guests to sit down at the table. When Katya stated her errand, he called, "Daria, come, our prayers have been answered."

Followed by a girl about Petya's age, a woman younger than the man came in from an adjoining room and stood by her husband's side.

Tears were running down Mishka's cheeks. "Long ago I dream I become farmer. It is no good. The children come. I do not save."

"I have land," Katya went on, "and I want to hire you to work it."

"The earth—I walk upon it at last," he murmured incredulously. "I teach my little girl to love it?" And he drew the child to him. "Is it black earth, my lady?"

After much talk and several glasses of hot tea, sweetened with strawberry jam, the arrangements were concluded. Mishka would work for Katya, taking as his pay a third of the harvest. He and his wife and daughter—his boys were grown and married—would live in one of the laborers' shacks for the summer which she would make more comfortable for him in the fall when the crops were harvested.

19

FOR Peter Suvorov the months following their visit to the country were filled with surprises, alarms, frustrations and excitement. His mother made him give up the paper route, telling him it was not a fit job for a man of landed people. She insisted on extra hours of study, pressing him for a better record at school. She punished him several times for disobedience—disobedience which he found necessary to establish himself as a man. This rebellion which at times drove him blindly forward, he did not understand. Always before, his mother had been the protector under whose sheltering presence he lived. Now, sometimes, he no longer wanted that protection. And there were moments when he wanted to protect her. With pride he tried to stretch himself to be worthy of her reliance on him. It was then she talked to him of the place they would make for themselves in America. "Landowners," she told him, "are people with responsibilities."

Lying in his cot at night, with the noises of the city lulling him to sleep and flickering lights of automobiles on the ceiling bringing him comfort, Peter thought of the earth of The Valley, resembling in no way the earth of the small grass plots in front of San Francisco houses, or even the parks. How firm it had been when he had touched it with his hand, how spongy and insecure when he had started to walk on it!

He thought also about the strange talk of his friend Mr. Ching. He, Peter Suvorov, now belonged to one of the four classes of society worthy of recognition. At one of the four corners of the social structure stood the farmer—so Mr. Ching had told him. One day he had asked Peter to accompany him to Chinatown where he lived with his wife, his six children and his old mother. If it hadn't been for Mr. Ching's presence, the visit would have been like going to Madame Mohkov's. To Peter's disgust in spite of himself, his newly acquired and carefully maintained status in the world of men had been rudely shaken, for the women had taken him on their laps. All very disillusioning to Peter, who had learned from Mr. Ching himself how important his position was.

But presently Mr. Ching had suggested they retire to a corner away from the family. From the top shelf in a cupboard he lifted a rolled-up picture, spread it out on a table, pointed with his slender forefinger to a little boy astride the broad gray back of a water buffalo. "The water buffalo most powerful and violent of animals, Honorable Little Friend," he said. "You can see the male child on his back has no more strength than your august self, yet he controls the beast he rides. The Honorable Little One must learn first to control himself."

"But I'm going to ride in a truck, or on a big horse," Peter added, remembering his mother's song.

"Water buffalo, like kite, belong many kinds," Mr. Ching admonished gently.

The afternoon before the Suvorovs left for the country, Petya paid his last visit to Mr. Ching. In the room behind the shop, as many times before, they sat side by side sipping tea out of handleless cups. It grew dark. Peter didn't want to say good-by to his old friend, but finally he rose, saying, "I can't come again. Tomorrow the truck's going to take us away. My mother bought it, and she bought a lot of things, and Mishka's going to drive the truck, and we're not coming back." He reached into his pocket. "I brought you this. You can keep it." He laid a white stone before Mr. Ching. "It's a funny stone," he explained. "See, it's got an eye and a mouth."

Suddenly he dashed from the room, through the shop and out of the door, slamming it so hard that the bell above it clanged and reverberated. He was late, and he was to go with his mother to Madame Mohkov's for dinner. He'd been disobedient again. When he rushed up the stairs and into the apartment, amazingly his mother didn't scold him, just hustled him into a clean shirt and his Sunday trousers and up the stairs to the apartment of their friends.

Bit by bit during the evening Madame Mohkov's room began to fill with Russians come to wish Katya good luck and to bring gifts, keepsakes of old Russia, to take with her into what seemed to many the very hinterland of America—copies of Russian poems, a beautiful hand-painted icon, a music score, precious possessions. The countess sat in a high-backed chair holding court, greeting each who came as his rank deserved. To those without rank she gave a friendly nod. But Madame Mohkov, a Liberal at heart as well as through long association with her husband, made no distinction.

Everyone talks as only Russians can, thought Katya. An argument arose over how the Revolution had come about.

Quite as heated a discussion was going on over the races. "Russians will bet even when they are in need," said Madame Mohkov, shaking her head.

"Suppose we bet on Katya's success in her venture," suggested a

dignified older man who had long paid court to Katya without success. "It is the undertaking for a man, not for a frail woman," he said,
turning to her, pursing his lips in disapproval.

A young man just come from Harbin was talking of his work as a
composer. Maria came up, showing him a list of want ads in the
paper.

A middle-aged woman had brought her violin. "Let me try one of
your songs," she said to the new young man. The rest of the evening
was given over to music.

When the last guest had left and she was thanking the Mohkovs,
Katya thought, I'm going out alone to a fight of my own.

When Peter awoke the next morning, he found to his surprise that
his home, which he had not realized would ever be different, was a
strange, unfriendly place. The walls were bare. From his mother's
bed the covers and mattress had been taken. The table where he had
eaten his meals was piled high with dishes and clothes.

As he stood by the sink eating his breakfast, Peter heard a man's
tread coming up the stairs. In a moment Mishka entered the room.
It meant the truck had arrived. Peter dashed to the door, squeezed
around the Russian's great bulk, ran down the stairs to the street. At
the curb stood Mishka's wife and girl, and beyond was the truck—
beautiful, although not new, freshly painted and shining. If only all
the boys on the street weren't at school! If only Mr. Ching could see
the truck! Back and forth Peter went up and down the stairs sweating under the loads he insisted on carrying out. And now here was
his mother coming down with a small basket and their icon. Mishka's
family was stowed away in the back with the furniture, and Mishka
himself climbed up to the driver's seat.

Then out of nowhere a crowd gathered, friends come to say good-by.
Madame Mohkov hugged him right there on the street. As she released him, he looked about to make certain no boy lurking in the
background had seen. None in sight—but there was Mr. Ching coming toward them! Bowing politely, he presented Peter's mother with
a small package. "A most humble, unworthy present from my most
unworthy self." Peter looked anxiously toward his mother, wanting
her to be as polite as Mr. Ching. But now Mr. Ching had turned to
him: "And to my Honorable Friend, a small token. I think water
buffalo nice to go with truck." He placed in Peter's hand a long roll.
Peter didn't know what to say until his mother reminded him to thank
the giver.

"Up you go, Petya!" He felt under his elbow, strong and sure, the hand of the tall, elderly man who had come often to see his mother, hoisting him to the seat beside Mishka. Peter looked down. Everyone was kissing his mother; Madame Mohkov was crying, and Maria was waving to him. Looking up, Peter saw the old countess at the window smiling and waving her little lace handkerchief. Then very gallantly the Russian gentleman assisted his mother to the high seat, and Petya was squeezed between her and Mishka.

Petya's pride grew as they moved into the traffic, going down Van Ness Avenue, along Market, onto the ferry, which took them across the Bay to another city. Soon they were among the hills. Finally the truck labored up the pass that led to California's Central Valley.

He had eaten little for breakfast, although he felt as if he had eaten much. The idea of a truck of their own and his first ride in it had given him a full feeling that made it impossible to eat. Now under the unaccustomed vibration of the motor, which seemed just under him, and the mountains and fields swirling past, he felt he was going to be sick, an ignominious thing for a man of property sitting beside the peasant who was to work his land. He shut his eyes. Soon drowsiness took the place of that heaving sensation within. He settled against his mother and slept.

Katya felt the sudden surrender. Her lips set sternly. This undertaking must not fail. "Mishka, we must plant potatoes as soon as we can plow," she said.

"The earth must be potato earth. We look tomorrow." So did Katya learn, this first morning, that the Russian peasant might not be easily managed. He would put his own knowledge above that of any county agent.

It was a sunny day in late February. All morning they rode through the northern San Joaquin Valley. Barley and alfalfa made great squares of green. The fruit trees were still bare of leaves. The grapevines with their tendrils trimmed away looked like stocky smaller trees. In the midst of orchards and vineyards stood farmhouses near enough together for the people to be friendly, thought Katya. They passed an almond orchard just bursting into blossom. The towns seemed large and prosperous, just as they had when—but no, she would not think of that trip with Edward.

She was grateful when they turned into the highway that led down the west side of The Valley, and the scene began to take on an unfamiliar look. The mountains to the east had disappeared. For a little they could see dimly, far to the west, the coast range. Then it, too, was gone. The towns were fewer and smaller now. Farmhouses became less and less frequent. They were in the country of many large landowners; uninhabited land stretched away for miles on either side of the road. Occasionally they passed a desolate row of laborers' shacks, unoccupied now in the off season. In the distance, breaking the monotony of the leveled fields, other shacks stood close together as if for comfort in the vast expanse. They frightened her a little, because in order to save money she had made up her mind to live in one for the summer. The necessary farm equipment had eaten into her resources alarmingly. Sternly she pushed fear from her. This new Katya, born since learning of Edward's marriage, was determined to show no mercy to the impulsive and impractical woman she had been.

Mishka was growing excited. "The sweet earth!" he exclaimed, pointing to a green field that seemed to have no end. A tractor, tiny in the distance, moved across another field. He stopped the truck, watching the tractor grow larger and larger as it advanced to the edge of the field next the highway, where it turned, laying back a swath of fine rich-looking loam. "Ah," he murmured, "it is good!"

On past giant fields of alfalfa and young barley and far-stretching fields covered with the brown stalks of last year's cotton. But the towns looked poor and lifeless. It was as if their vitality had been sucked up in service to the enormous fields. A store, two or three cafés, a gas station. The houses were small, the paint worn away. Doddstown will be different, Katya told herself, remembering that summer night she had passed through it with Edward—the cars lined up along the lighted street, giving the town an air of festivity. She had not seen it since. The railway station where she had got off when she came to see her land lay to the south of it. She kept looking for towns like the one where Granny had lived, and for comfortable farmhouses scattered through the orchard such as she had seen earlier in the day in the central part of The Valley. But none appeared.

20

LATE in the afternoon they entered Doddstown's main street. "Drive slowly, Mishka," Katya commanded. They passed two or three cafés with dirty curtains sagging on string run across the front windows, a grocery store with fly-specked windowpanes. Every other building appeared to be a poolroom. A plain, unpainted, square building had PENTECOSTAL CHURCH written across its front, and another farther on had printed above its door CHURCH OF GOD. Looking down the side streets, she saw two or three substantial-appearing houses, a number of simple cottages and fringing it all rows of squalid cabins set among weeds. Katya would have been in despair except for the comfortable-looking schoolhouse that stood in the center of a large playground on the southern edge of the town. I'll see that Mishka brings Petya straight home from school, she thought. It won't matter then that there are so many poolrooms.

Petya followed his mother into the one-room structure that was to be their home for the summer. The candle which Mishka had stuck in its own grease and set on the window sill guttered, then flamed up, throwing the man's shadow, huge and black, on the wall as he moved about putting up the bed he had brought in from the truck. When he left them, Peter and his mother sat on the edge of the bed and ate the sandwiches saved from their luncheon. Looking out through the open door, the boy could see into another house where, huddled in a group on a pile of bedding, Mishka and his wife and girl sat munching bread.

"Tomorrow," his mother said, "you must start school." In her new determination to be realistic and face the fact that only by self-denial and hard work could they succeed, Katya was not allowing Peter any respite from school.

It would be strange, Petya thought, dreading its strangeness. He wished he dared leave his mother now, go and sit by Mishka. A kind of comfortable feeling stole over him just looking at the man's broad back. Families were nice.

The night grew black against the window panes. The cheep of insects just outside the door was an unfamiliar sound.

The school building was Spanish in style, red-tiled roof and white-stuccoed walls, a structure common to California. There were yellow stains along its base where during the rains moisture had been absorbed from the ground. Although the rainy season was nearing its end, the playground was still a muddy lake. When a little before nine the next morning Peter entered the grounds, the children were crowded along the walk playing games. Mishka's girl, Peter saw from a corner of his eye, wasn't far behind him. He hurried. He wanted to be American, and Sonya did not look American with her heavy black hair, dark skin and her gaily embroidered dress. A bell rang. He elbowed his way through groups of children running toward the school door—two Chinese holding hands as if for protection, some Japanese, a larger number of Mexicans, one Negro boy walking by himself. On the school steps he saw a half-dozen boys about his own age standing together. Americans, thought Peter. He joined them.

"What does your father do?" a lame boy asked him. "You gotta own land to go in with us."

"My father's dead," Petya explained, "but my mother is an owner. We got lots of land."

"How much?"

"A lot," said Peter.

"As much as twenty acres? That's what my father's got."

Petya saw it wouldn't do to outstrip his interrogator. "About that," he answered. He had learned in school in San Francisco that you didn't put yourself ahead of the leader. And this lame boy bossed the other boys, he decided.

"What's your name?"

"Peter."

"Mine's J. T. Ward."

At recess J. T. and the other American boys made a ring around him. "How old are you?" asked J. T.

" 'Most nine." Peter was a little uneasy about that, but after all in another year he'd be nine.

" 'Most nine," scoffed J. T., "and he's wearing baby pants! Can you beat that!"

Peter wished now he'd said eight.

"A city kid. Don't know what levis is." Again it was the lame boy speaking.

Peter felt the tears coming. He fought them down. He wouldn't cry for a million dollars. "I guess I can wear what I want. It's a free country." He looked J. T. square in the eye, but his hands felt cold and wet.

"What'd you say? You was 'most nine?" asked a boy they called Tuffy, silent until now.

"That's what I said."

"He's young; he's not nine, only 'most nine." Tuffy turned to J. T. "What say we let him stick around?"

J. T. hesitated. "Not in them baby pants. He's got to have real ones tomorrow morning."

It's not just being an American, thought Peter. You've got to be the right kind of one. He had to dress like these boys and not like the ones in San Francisco.

All the rest of the day he kept worrying about Mishka's coming for him. His mother didn't know there was a school bus, and she had sent Mishka with them in the morning. The Russian with his heavy black beard didn't look like an American man. If the American boys saw him ride off with Mishka, maybe tomorrow, even if he had on pants like theirs, they wouldn't let him play with them. He decided he'd ride home in the bus and leave Sonya to go in the truck. And how was he to get the things they called levis by tomorrow? He'd have to persuade his mother to come in town tonight.

After Katya had sent the children to school, she had gone back into the shack determined not to allow herself one weak moment of regret. She had been close to panic during the night. After Petya fell asleep she had lain awake, conscious of the forbidding silence of the unoccupied land around her, and doubt had taken hold of her. She had not realized how much strength she had drawn from the valiant Mohkovs. Was she equal to ruling her household? Mishka had already shown the stubbornness of the Russian peasant, not accepting what the county agent had told her about the soil here being particularly well suited for potatoes. He was going to decide for himself. Could she maintain her position as landowner?

And there was the loneliness. Not a house to be seen. Why had Granny given her acres located so far away from any neighbors? There was a moment in the night when she had doubted whether the old woman had done it out of love for her. She fought hard not to be overcome again by the disapproval of the Dodds, which like a strong undertow had so often threatened to drag her under.

Resolutely she looked around the room, the tumbled bed filling the larger part of the space, the remains of a cold breakfast on the window sill, her footsteps and Petya's showing on the dusty floor.

Again she realized how ignorant she was of the right way to go about her homesteading. She should have had these cabins cleaned before they were occupied. Maybe Mishka's wife Daria wouldn't want to stay.

Then she heard Daria's voice outside, asking permission to enter. Daria was short and plump, and her black eyes sparkled. "By me is pail," she cried, putting a pail full of water, brushes and soap on the floor and pinning her dress skirt around her hips, showing her bright petticoat. Having demonstrated she could speak English, she let herself go in Russian, praising the fields, the sunshine. "First we make Mistress comfortable," she ended.

Katya found that shared work is a great leveler. For the first hour they were mistress and retainer, and then their mutual needs and occupation wiped out the difference between them. Neither woman was satisfied until the shacks were scrubbed from floor to ceiling. It was late in the afternoon when they finished and sat on the steps outside Katya's cabin. Their hands were sore with the disinfectant they had used. They both had kerchiefs tied over their heads. Both wore cheap, cotton dresses.

"Tomorrow we tear down cabin—" Daria pointed to a very dilapidated building—"use boards patch houses."

"Yes," Katya answered, "I can't spare Mishka even one day from the fields." She shaded her eyes. He ought to be back with the children. Yes, there came the truck, but there were only two in it— Mishka and Sonya. "Where is Petya?" cried Katya as Mishka stopped the truck in front of the cabin.

"Peter's riding in the school bus with the boys," Sonya answered before her father could speak. They were almost the first words Katya had heard her utter.

Along the lane that led from the main highway, Katya could see a small, moving figure. She was relieved that they would not have to take Mishka's time to drive the children to school and relieved, too, that Petya had found his place so quickly among the boys.

The Russian began to unload some of the most needed household things from the truck. The women had not allowed him to do it until the houses were clean. In the midst of it Peter arrived. Immediately Mishka put him to work. Back and forth he trudged, hoping there would be time yet to go back for the levis. It was getting dark as he hurried up the steps with the last load. His mother was lighting a candle. The light, flaring up, illumined her face, and he saw she was very tired. That odd, half-disturbing, half-delightful sensation which of late he sometimes had felt of being her protector came over him, and the need to stretch himself to be worthy of her reliance on him.

"No J. T. is going to make me give up my short pants until I get good and ready," he said to himself, throwing out his chest, strutting a little just to convince himself how he'd act tomorrow when he got into the bus.

21

By the end of the week their temporary dwellings had been made livable. Turning carpenter in the evenings after it was too dark for farm work, Mishka had constructed the rudest kind of lean-to at the back of each shack, where they could cook and eat. Daria and Katya had managed to put up shelves for dishes. They'd fastened screens over the windows, and Katya bought a screen door for each house. That was all they could do until late fall after the potatoes and cotton were harvested, for Mishka said he must have Daria to help him in the fields.

They had come to The Valley just as the lifeless winter season was reaching its end, and the first beat of a quickened tempo was beginning. Hardly had they put the houses in order when, early one morning, Katya was awakened by the clear, rapturous call of a bird outside her window. She lay still lest she dissipate the resurgence of hope rising within her at the sound. Suddenly the clatter of machinery broke across the bird's song, drowning it out. She went to the window. On the other side of the road on Lesly's land a man riding a tractor was skillfully guiding a plow hitched behind. And on the Dodd acres the shining blades of a plow were laying back a swath of ground, silken-smooth, penetrated as it was with the recent rains. As if the two had given the signal, from over The Valley, now near, now far, now loud, now faint in the distance, a dozen, fifty, a hundred tractors beat out a clattering tattoo.

Katya had bought a secondhand tractor and plow from an agent who had come to see her the day after her arrival. She wished Mishka would begin his plowing, but when she suggested it, he answered in Russian, "The earth tells me when it wishes to be broken." But at last he evidently received the word, for one morning his tractor's clatter came from just outside her window. He was slow at first in guiding the plow behind the machine. It seemed to Katya that he would never finish the forty acres on which he had decided to raise potatoes. Too, the tractor was often out of order. Then late into the night Mishka would work, repairing it for the next day's use.

Day after day the cacophony of a mechanized countryside echoed and re-echoed over The Valley. At last the earth, as far as Katya could see, had been smoothed and flattened. Scarcely an inch rise from one end of a field to the other, so leveled that none of the precious irrigation water needed later should be lost. The potato fields were furrowed. Now was the earth at last ready to receive the first plantings. Potatoes were cut for seed, the seed dropped into the prepared furrows, the earth drawn over it against the mysterious process of growth.

Mishka and his sturdy wife were in the fields from early morning until dark, for when the potatoes were in the ground the cotton fields had to be prepared. Lacking many of the mechanical aids of the large holdings, the Russian had to accomplish the same results by unending hours of labor. But he was happy. He wanted the earth to control, even break him. He was always its servant and occasionally its master, and maybe sometime he would own a strip for himself. At present he was getting his way with his mistress' land. She was coming to trust his wisdom.

One Sunday he walked the miles to the foothills to see a ranch owned by another Russian. He had been told that five years before it was covered with mesquite and tumbleweed. He didn't expect to see the owner on Sunday, as he lived in a town some distance away. Why he went, Mishka did not know himself. Some faint hope maybe that what one Russian could do another could. As he followed the road west, he was conscious of the growing incline under his feet, but the fields to the side looked as if a carpenter's level had been used in preparing them. Far in the distance a low ridge indicated a step to the next field. In the sun glittered the rounded aluminum-painted surfaces of hydraulic pumps.

Mishka knelt, passing his hand over the perfectly prepared earth, held a bit in his hand, lifted it to his lips, then returned it to the spot from which he had taken it.

"So is a Russian always!" A voice behind him spoke.

Turning, he looked straight into the brooding brown eyes of another Russian. "One can get very emotional over land," the man said, half to himself. "Here, I'll show you what I've done. Get into my car."

For two hours they drove from field to field: fallow fields, fields of lush green barley, a field of dark-green broccoli, the rows leading on into the distance, a field of newly planted potatoes.

"You make this from desert?" Mishka's voice held awe.

"Always I make from new land—once in Russia, once in Palestine and now once here. I plow it, level it, polish it, play with it. And then something happens here." He thumped his chest. "Then I want more untamed land. It is a hunger."

22

In the winter the population of Doddstown shrank, only the permanent residents, of which there were not many, remaining. The great industrialized holdings during these months were like shut-down factories. Only a few maintenance men remained. But as the spring advanced and the work grew heavier, the itinerant workers who had sought employment in the cities or gone on city relief rolls during the slack season began to drift back. After the planting of the early potato crop and its harvesting there was cotton chopping to be done. The schoolrooms began to fill up, but J. T. told Peter it was nothing to what it would be after summer vacation. "Then there'd be loads and loads of dirty people come to pick the cotton."

Peter was learning the ways of this part of The Valley fast. He understood now why he'd been asked whether his people owned land. The children of itinerant laborers kept to themselves. "Damn well they'd better," boasted J. T. "You'd better watch yourself, Pete, hanging round with Sonya, a laborer's kid."

Peter insisted she wasn't. "Her Pa works for my mother all the time."

"How does that make her different?"

"Well, it does, but I don't play with her, so what you got to get mad about?"

Sonya, on the first day at school, had learned that her dark skin made her different from Peter. She had sought out the Mexican girls at recess, and they had been kind to her.

J. T., who even in spite of his lameness had been the acknowledged leader among the boys in his room until Peter came, was disturbed over the challenge in the new boy. Peter had never obeyed him the way the others did. He'd been a week getting into levis, all the time strutting around in his sissy pants. And the other boys had only laughed. Although almost a year younger, Peter was taller, too, and he was whole, and he was smart. "Dumb" was what J. T. had said about the other boys, but he couldn't say that about this boy. And he could run and jump. J. T. turned away from a new game Peter was showing the boys.

"Come on, J. T.," cried Peter, "we got to have an umpire."

"*Me* fall for that kids' stuff?" J. T. limped loftily away. No one followed him. Suppose he should lose his place at school to Peter.

At the last exercises before vacation the teacher chose Peter to represent their grade. 'Cause he ain't got a twisted leg, J. T. told himself. All summer he brooded over the injustice.

Now that vacation had come, Peter became Mishka's shadow. Barefoot and bareheaded, his shirt off—whenever he could avoid his mother's watchful eye—his skin tanned, his hair bleached in the hot sun, he resembled a laborer's child more than the gentleman landowner Katya intended him to be. He had to fight for his right to be with Mishka, a deep necessity with him at present. It was as if some ingredient had been left out of his life until now, and he found it in the powerful man who could do so many things a boy admires. The country, which had held him in such wonder when he first saw it, now often made him feel weak and small. But when he slipped his hand into the peasant's big one, he felt strong, even ready to brag a little.

One day Mishka let him help irrigate. Together they stood on the platform by the hydraulic pump. "Petya, do what I showed you," Mishka commanded.

With his lip caught between his teeth, Peter stretched himself to his full height and pressed the button starting the pump. The water began to fill the irrigation ditch. Then, with his hoe over his shoulder, he followed Mishka into the field, where the peasant showed him how to break the piled earth at the edge of the ditch, letting the water seep out between the cotton rows.

For a time Peter worked opening new runnels, blocking off the areas which had already received the water. He was hungry. He wished they'd stop. Suddenly it came to him that to go home he didn't need to wait for Mishka. He dropped his hoe and ran back through the fields alone.

Katya, hearing his running feet on the steps, shrank deeper into the shack. The hot valley sun at noon, beating down on the thin boards of the roof, turned the room into a veritable oven. Excessive heat, with Katya as with many people, made her apprehensive. And then there was the loneliness. She had not spoken for weeks to any woman but Daria. Loneliness struck down her defenses. This morning her apprehension had taken shape in the old fear of failure which she had determined never to yield to again. Slowly doubt had been growing in her as to the validity of her determination to keep her heritage. Was it not simply another form of her old romantic dreams? It was absurd to think she could ever succeed at farming. This wasn't the place to make Petya into the gentleman he should be.

"Mom," cried Petya, rushing in where she sat, "come, see what I've done."

Mechanically she rose, followed him out to the field where Mishka was at work. As she stood looking at the flow of water and her son's bright eyes, she felt her depression go. Like a black cloud it lifted, leaving her in sunlight. Suddenly she saw the good life did not lie for Petya either in being a Russian gentleman or in what was the equivalent here in America. The good life lay in effort and the need for effort. She thought of the Russian landowner who had come to see her after Mishka's visit to him. "Missus," he had said, looking out over one of Mishka's plowed fields, "a straight furrow is the most beautiful thing on earth." She hadn't understood then, but she did now. It was beautiful to him because it was perfectly fitted to its function.

If Peter's function was to till the land and he did it well, he would be the kind of man she could be proud of. She looked at Petya's straight brown body. In that moment she relinquished the ideal she had been forcing upon him. Why, what I should do is to let him grow naturally, let him choose his own life, she thought, be content to have him work with his hands if he is happy in what he is doing, cast neither in the image of the Dodds nor the Suvorovs.

"If you're going to be a farmer, Petya," she said, "you've got to eat a lot. Come, it's luncheontime."

"I'll race you back," he cried.

When she arrived at the shack yards behind him, he bragged, "I can beat you any time." Complacently he watched her put some of yesterday's meat dumplings on to steam, bring out bread and fruit. It was nice here under the wood awning at the back of the house where they cooked, even if they did have to beat off the flies. Something very nice about his mother, too, the way she smiled at him. He ate and ate, loosening his belt so he could eat more, and she didn't say anything about being a gentleman. He grinned at her.

He didn't seem to need Mishka so much after this. Sometimes he went with him to the fields, and sometimes he liked to be with his mother.

There were days now when he even played with Sonya. She had a family of Russian dolls, smooth lacquered, the costumes painted on in bright color. For some reason he longed to own these dolls. The mother was the largest, and all the others could be enclosed within her, each doll fitting into the next larger size like a nest of boxes. The tiniest was no more than an inch high. Once Petya ran away with them and kept them for a whole day. It gave him a feeling of power akin to the feeling he had had when he let the water into the irrigation ditch.

But at night sometimes he was frightened. Once he dreamed his mother had left him, going away on the truckload of potatoes. He awoke in terror and climbed into her bed.

The next morning as soon as he had had breakfast he ran over to where Mishka was loading potatoes into the truck. "Mishka, I'm going with you."

"Petya! Petya!" It was his mother calling but he made no move to obey.

"You bad boy not listen mother." Mishka with his strong hand slapped him on the shoulder.

"Oh, all right, but you're mean," cried Petya, dashing back to Katya. That need, experienced in the winter, to wrest himself free of her possessed him again. It was intolerable to know he'd acted like a baby last night. But she needn't think she could boss him today because of it. "I'm going with Mishka. I'll hate you if you don't let me."

"Oh, Petya, you mustn't say things like that!" Katya cried.

"Then let me go with Mishka." Their eyes met. He felt his will conquering hers.

Last night when he had clung to her and then fallen asleep, cuddled close against her, there had awakened in her the old fierce need to feel forever that he was her baby. But now, recognizing the independence which foreshadowed the man, she let go, allowing him to be the grown-up boy he thought himself to be.

Peter sat very erect and proud on the driver's seat beside the big Russian. At the washing sheds he was caught up into the excitement around him. It was a great year for potatoes. They were bringing the highest price that had ever been paid in The Valley. Everybody was going to make money. There was a tale going round about a sack of potatoes that fell off a truck a few weeks back near Buttonwillow. It was so valuable that two men got into a fight over it, and one was killed. Round-eyed, Petya told the story to his mother when he came home.

He remembered something else he had heard the men talking about at the sheds, but he decided he wouldn't tell her what they said about a dry cycle due in another year. And something about wells giving out then. It might make her sad again, the way she used to be.

The next time he rode into the washing sheds there was a story about a sack of potatoes falling off a load over by Firebaugh, and this time three men were killed. "Four men got killed," Petya told his mother when he reached home. "A fellow at the sheds said they'd make it a Paul Bunyan story before they got through. What is a Paul Bunyan story?"

For a moment Katya could not answer, remembering Edward the day he had told her of Paul Bunyan. Then she said, "He's an American, I believe, and he does the most wonderful things in the world. He would, if he were an American, wouldn't he?" She laughed, and then Peter laughed, too. He guessed he needn't worry about saying four were killed. He even wished he'd made it five. He wiped the dishes for her that evening, and he kept on chuckling, he felt so good. It was nice to have his mother laugh, the way she often did these days.

It was getting on toward dark when Peter ran out into the field where Mishka had started a second irrigation of the cotton. Water was standing between the furrowed rows. But it wasn't clear and sparkling as it was in the daytime. It was black and mysterious-looking. He didn't feel power over it, the way he had when the sun shone down on it, making it sparkle. Suddenly he started running back to the shack. He ran until there was a sharp pain in his side, but he didn't stop. Holding his side, he ran on, and then there was his home and his mother standing in the doorway. The light from within was shining on her hair, making her look very tall and as if she had a gold crown on her head. Maybe she was a Russian emperor's daughter, and he was an emperor's grandson like the boy in the Russian history they sometimes read in the evenings. He had forgotten the dark water now.

Later he lay in his bed, staring up at the rough boards of the ceiling; then, turning on his side, he looked at his mother sitting by the table figuring on a big sheet of paper.

"I wasn't afraid. I was running because I didn't want you to worry about me," he vouchsafed.

"A good son," Katya murmured. When she had finished adding the column of figures, she came over to him. "Petya, we can make the house nice with what the potatoes have brought in, if the cotton does well."

"Can I have a room to myself? And a dog? Can he sleep on my bed?"

"We'll see."

Katya went back to her column of figures. Yes, she'd build a decent house and buy good furniture. She could pay for it on the installment plan, the way she was buying the tractor.

That night as she undressed she felt serene. Petya looked such a baby, one arm thrown up over his head, on his face the defenseless look that sleep often brings. It was at night when he was asleep that she could indulge herself, making as much a baby of him as she liked —lay a cover over him, smooth his hair back. She smiled. "But you think yourself too much a man for me to do it in the daytime," she whispered. She was beginning to feel confident that life need not be too hard for him. Plans for his room in the new house filtered through her mind as she dropped off to sleep.

Madame Mohkov, Maria and even the countess were coming to visit the Suvorovs. They were to stay two days. Katya and Daria between them had made the preparations. They had scrubbed out an adjoining shack. Katya and Peter were going to sleep there. The Mohkovs were to have their house with its better furnishings.

Katya rose early. The meat dumplings she had made the day before. They'd have some of the newly harvested potatoes, and Daria had baked black bread for them. After breakfast she scrubbed the room her guests were to occupy, moved Petya's and her things to the other shack, where she had put two cots. Still it was not time to go to the train. The hours dragged by, and now in her eagerness she knew how much she had missed her friends.

At the station there was still a half hour to wait, and then at last they saw the train in the distance. It grew larger. She took Peter's hand, fearing in his excitement he'd run out on the track. They could feel the heat of the engine as it steamed past them. Eagerly Katya studied each car, hoping to catch a glimpse of her friends. Had they missed the train? Then she saw the conductor helping the countess down.

Katya, pulling Peter with her, ran forward, choking and laughing at the same time. What deference the man was showing the old lady! There was a regal air about her in her black silk dress that indeed commanded respect. Behind the countess was Madame Mohkov in a new hat and Maria in a light summer suit. Then they were embracing her and kissing Petya over and over. How good it was to be with friends! "Here's my truck," cried Katya. "Do you mind riding in it?" After considerable planning and effort, the countess was installed on the high seat with Madame Mohkov squeezed in between her and Katya. Maria and Petya were seated in chairs behind. Katya was proud when Madame Mohkov praised her driving.

Katya believed she'd never forget the first evening she shared with her friends. The five of them sat around a table in the lean-to. In the west the sun was reaching the mountain ridge. Evening quiet lay over the fields. Madame Mohkov and Maria sat facing the forty acres of cotton growing close up to the lean-to. The last slanting rays of sunlight shone on the dark green leaves and the creamy blossoms set on their red stems.

Katya saw admiration in Maria's eyes, and Madame Mohkov said, "You've done well." She could ask for no better commendation. She had proved herself worthy of their friendship. To offer them hospitality was a rare and beautiful experience. Madame Mohkov told her Tania was arriving on the next steamer from China. Katya did not tell them how, last year, she had sent the passage money, but the knowledge was a warm glow within her.

"And your orphans," she asked Maria, "do they need help?" It was good to press a little money into Maria's hand.

After the others had gone to bed, the two young women lingered. Once they were alone, Maria exclaimed, "You were right, Katya, when you chose to come here with Petya! We will never go back to Russia. Our children should turn their faces toward this country, make it their own. We are the bridge, men and women of our generation."

It was dawn before they knew it. "It is like a Russian to forget to go to bed," Maria said, throwing back her head to look at the fading stars.

"We are hopelessly Russian talking the night through." Katya raised her hands in a pure Russian gesture. But still they lingered, held by the good companionship and the beauty of the coming day. Light was beginning to spread upward from the horizon, but the earth was still dark.

"A grave and quiet land," said Maria half under her breath. "The cities rest on what is here—the serene land."

One morning at the end of August a notice was posted in Doddstown which was repeated in the papers up and down The Valley. It read:

A marvelous opportunity for small farmers. Three thousand acres of the choicest land in the southern San Joaquin Valley for sale. Owner will sell small tracts. Irrigation rights in Mutual Water Company, plus underground water brought to the surface with the latest high-power pumps. Cash deals only.

It wasn't long before everyone knew it was the Dodd ranch that was up for sale.

Men in the neighborhood owning thirty or forty acres counted what they had made on potatoes, took futures on their cotton, speculated on how much they could borrow. Jeremy Dodd was right. When men felt prosperous they would pay almost anything for good farm land, and nothing like this had come their way in years.

All day men and women collected around the billboard. The townspeople were elated. "There'll be a lot more farmers living in The Valley. They'll bring business to the town and a better class of children to the school," they told one another.

The druggist who had been brought up on a farm and the manager of the chain grocery, a farmer once, drove to Fresno to see what kind of loan they could get from the banks. They felt it was an opportunity that might never come to them again to get back into farming, be on their own.

A neighbor stopped for J. T.'s father. "Hey, son, where I find your dad?" he called out to J. T., who was hanging out the week's washing.

"Out workin'," the boy flung over his shoulder.

The neighbor sent up a loud halloo. Ward, far out in the field, dropped his hoe and came quickly toward them.

"Dodd's land is up for sale. You can buy as little or as much as you like," the neighbor shouted as soon as his friend was within earshot. "Come on, jump in! I'm off to see can I get a loan. Now's your chance."

"A hell of a chance I got," the boy heard his father say as he stood, one foot on the running board of his friend's car. "Got a mortgage on what I got now. Who in hell 'ud lend me anything?"

J. T. went into the house. The day after school had closed, his mother had said, "You gotta learn to cook and you gotta keep the house. I'm going to help your Pa." Forthwith she had tied an apron around him. Now he went and sat against the wall far back in the kitchen away from the window where no one could see him. His father and mother secretly despised him. He knew it. He'd seen his mother wince when she looked at his shrunken leg.

He was sure his father blamed him that they were so poor. Unusually strong for his age until he had had infantile paralysis, he had been his father's chief helper. Then they had been able to meet the payments on the mortgage. Since his sickness his father had had to hire labor, which had cut the slender margin of their resources. Now his father said he couldn't afford even that, and he was using his mother to help in the fields.

News spread throughout The Valley, and even to other states, that the Dodds' cultivated acres were for sale—grain, cotton and potato land. And plenty of water. Why, good land like this had not been for sale in moderate acreage for nobody knew when.

Doddstown began to look almost prosperous. Along its main street stood the cars of prospective buyers, and real-estate firms set up temporary quarters in empty buildings. The two cafés had the most thriving business in all their existence. So did the drugstore and grocery. Excitement ran high. With all the new settlers, the town might get a resident doctor and certainly another gas station and surely a movie house.

23

Edward Dodd and Agnes had left immediately for the South after the quiet wedding ceremony. Edward was happy in this new marriage. The doubt which had assailed him occasionally that he might not be able to give of himself completely to any woman as he once had to Katya, he found groundless. There was nothing about Agnes to remind him of Katya whom he had loved so passionately, and who had returned his love so ardently. Agnes' fascination for him lay in her fragile delicacy. It lifted him to heights of pleasure to know intimately her exquisitely modeled small person, but only if she preserved a diffidence.

The first night she had sensed that what he wanted from her was retreat and surrender only after ardent wooing.

At the end of the month he found he had lost the feeling of urgency under which he had lived for the last eight years. Body and mind had acquired a repose which freed him of the old continuous drive. Almost without knowing it, he had decided to allow himself to be put up for state senator at large. But when they returned to Oakland and the flurry of settling their home was over, he found himself unable to tell his friends of his willingness. The gift of his grandmother's house, he knew, was meant by his father to bind him to the kind of political future which he had no intention of undertaking. Why then did he not grasp eagerly at the chance to choose a different course?

Agnes, studying his every reaction, realizing their happiness together was freighted with uncertainty, thought she understood his dilemma, but hesitated to act. Not to speak was to fail him, but to speak might be to fail him also, for she had learned already that in any relationship with her husband she should not appear to take the lead. To assume that role would be in some degree to destroy Edward's ideal of her. But finally she decided she must take the chance. One evening about a week after their return, she asked him if he were going to run.

"I haven't decided one way or the other," he answered.

"Is it because of your family?"

"How do you mean?"

"It means a break with your father politically, doesn't it, to run on the platform your friends want you to?"

"Yes. But in a way I'd welcome coming to grips with Father."
After a pause he added, "If I could——"

"But you'd naturally be at grips with him if you joined another
political group, wouldn't you?"

"Suppose I lose in the election?"

"At least you'd have taken your stand."

"It isn't so simple as that," he answered.

The elation over the opportunity to enter politics he sometimes displayed, followed by periods of depression like tonight, made Agnes
realize what she had not suspected until after their marriage, that the
man she loved was not the self-assured person he appeared to be.
Some deep distrust of himself controlled him. I must help him to
believe that he is the strong man he has let me and others suppose
him. He really could be that man, she thought.

But how could she reach him? She had found already how easily
he mistook interest for interference. She rose and went over to him,
sat down on the arm of his chair. "I happened to run into one of your
lawyer friends on the street today. It's a great evidence of trust, the
way they're all looking to you for guidance in getting the state started
to develop the water resources of Central Valley."

"That doesn't mean anything really. It's just because Grandfather
drilled into me the whole problem of water. I never took a drink
when I was a child that I didn't think what even a glassful of water
meant to The Valley," he answered, slipping his arm around her.

"That's just it! It's second nature to you—and that, coupled with
your fine legal mind, makes you just the man to represent them."

"Oh, I doubt if I'd put it that way. They don't know me very well."

"Why do you always disparage yourself?" she made bold to ask.

"I don't!" he exclaimed. "I just don't want any false ideas to get
around. I've practically decided I'm not fitted to hold such an important post."

"But you are, Edward! These are keen, imaginative men. They
don't make mistakes in choosing whom they want to represent them!"

At Agnes' words and the ring of conviction in her voice, enhanced
somehow by the sense of strength her fingers twined around his gave
him, he felt a new faith pushing his spirit up through the uncertainty
which had for days paralyzed him. With cleansing clarity he saw it
was the old fear of defeat at his father's hand that was holding him
back. He would bring his fear out in the open, rid himself of this
obsession once for all, talk it out with Agnes.

"Do you realize that Father will have the full force of the power
companies and the big landowners back of him? I can stand up

against them as a group. It's impersonal, I understand that. If the state puts in dams they'll have competition. That would break their monopoly. With their point of view they would fight me. But with Father it will be a personal battle between him and me."

"But you have to be true to yourself, dear, even if it does mean an issue between you and your father, don't you? It's a challenge."

Edward did not reply. Agnes felt his hand tighten over hers and then relax.

"I think I'll call the committee now. We've no time to lose if we're going to put on a good campaign." Edward rose and went to the telephone in the hall.

Agnes felt suddenly weak. He believes in himself for the moment, she said to herself, listening to the note of decision in his voice as it reached her from the hall. If he could continue to trust himself, there would no longer be those sudden withdrawals on his part that had so marked his attitude toward her up to now, induced, she felt sure, by uncertainty at the core of his being. She knew she could help to steady him if he would accept her companionship. She was deeply in love, almost too much so, she thought helplessly.

When Edward told his father that he was allowing his name to be put up by a group of men who wanted to see state development of water resources, there was an odd look in the older man's eyes. If Edward read it rightly, it was anger mixed with amusement. "You'll find out what a licking a man can take when he goes against his own class," he said. Then he added, "But I expect you've got to sow your wild oats in politics as you've sown them in other ways."

It hadn't been the battle Edward had expected. It had been a thrust below the belt. "Wild oats." He had a sudden picture of himself sobering up at his grandmother's house after he left Katya. Only by the most rigid guard on his thoughts had he been able to forget that part of his life. And he had been grateful that never during the years since had his unfortunate first marriage been mentioned by either of his parents. He hadn't expected his father to fight on that level. The old necessity to work at fever pitch came back with renewed force.

He welcomed it when his backers told him he would need to stump the state. "People must see you and know you." They were counting a great deal on his ability to make people like him.

It was exciting business, getting his first speeches knocked into shape, setting forth the issues in a way that would appeal to different groups. He knew from his court experience how you could swing people's opinions. "Father's right," he said to Agnes, "in his claim that you can make people believe almost anything if you're clever about it. I'll have to outtalk the propaganda of the big interests if I get myself elected. In the cities I'll have to speak from one viewpoint, in the country another."

Day after day he shut himself in a room upstairs, which Agnes had suggested he take for his own, where he could work undisturbed. Often in the evening the men who were backing him would come in. Agnes was relieved when she saw how willing Edward was to take their criticism. There was a burly fellow named Jim Bricket, with red hair and sandy complexion, blunt and outspoken, the least acceptable to Edward of the group, Agnes would have thought, but he had chosen Bricket for his manager. When there was anything he didn't like in Edward's carefully prepared speeches, he would shout, "That's a phony!"

The night Edward talked over with them what he meant to say in Los Angeles, Bricket was particularly vociferous. "You can't just go on telling them you're working for conservation of all the state's natural resources. You got to get down to brass tacks. Tell 'em you'll fight like hell to get water from the Colorado River for their city water supply, even if you have to rob Arizona and New Mexico to do it."

"Opposition will promise 'em that, Brick," one of the others cut in.

"Well, he's got to talk louder."

"How about using a little more subtle tactics?" one of the others suggested dryly.

Agnes, sitting quietly at one side, noticed there was one thing no one brought out. Edward always talks in terms of the opposition, she thought. Is it just the battle he cares about, or is he really interested in what he is working for? If he'd just begin thinking in terms of human beings! Agnes, who liked people for their own sake, knew how quickly they sensed whether you did or didn't.

24

EDWARD DODD began his campaign in the southern part of Central Valley, where water was particularly scarce. He had never spoken before to any but court audiences. In arguing a case he had the stimulus of the fight to win over the lawyer opposing him; in speaking to an audience which had no comeback he felt the lack of combat. Although he experienced a fine enthusiasm when he prepared a speech, he had a sense of failure when he delivered it. With a good deal of distrust in his ability to interest his would-be constituency, he faced his fourth audience, a gathering of farmers in a schoolhouse.

The night was one of the hottest The Valley had experienced that year. The brilliant desert sun beating down all day on the earth had stored up a reservoir of hot air, released after dark, when the strong wind which had been blowing during the afternoon had died down at sunset. The mountains, near which the town was situated, climbed high into the sky, blocking out any cooling air from the coast.

Hot, tired and a little discouraged, Edward looked down from the platform at his audience. The fat and the long-legged had compressed themselves into the children's seats. Standing in one corner was a group of itinerant laborers—at least that was what they looked like—Mexicans and what the South would call "poor whites." Obviously the people gathered to hear him tonight were the unsuccessful and underprivileged. Their faces, he saw, were lined with care; their under-lying expression was one of resignation. They had learned not to hope for much. After all, a state plan for equal distribution of water had been talked about for years. Yes, when he came to think about it, it went back almost to the state's beginnings. In the last decade a million dollars had been spent in plans and research. These people who had come to hear him speak knew as well as he did that execution of the plan was always defeated in Senate or Assembly. He had a sudden realization of tragedy in the lives of little people, over and over disappointed in the men they chose to lead them, forever forced down into the dark and hampering mold of poverty.

He stepped to the front of the platform and began to speak. "If this is to be the California you dreamed of when you crossed the mountains, or came from overseas to settle here—a place where you can make a home and bring up your children in decency and moderate comfort—two things must happen in this state. You must be able to buy good land and be assured of water. You won't get those two things unless the government helps you. There are many interests in the state that want you to believe the government is your enemy. It needn't be, if you assert yourselves and put into government men who will look after your needs." There was stillness in the room. He paused; at least he had their attention.

Suddenly he was back in Lahususu, and a young girl, her eyes filled with terror, was telling of the Russian Revolution and of the night the laborers on the big estates turned against the owners. It could happen here, he thought, if we allow too much misery. For the first time in his life he had a desire, unmixed with personal ambition, to be of service to his country. "Look here, folks," he said, "what we want to see in California is democracy. That means a strong middle class. The old homestead idea. You—and you—and you—owning enough land for a decent living." At his last "you" he pointed to the group in the corner. "And the waters of the state evenly divided, every man getting his share. No man getting enough of state waters for more than one hundred and sixty acres. That's the Federal Homestead ideal. State power supplementing the private. Cheap power and plenty of it. I promise you, if you elect me I'll do my utmost to see that the state does more than spend your money in planning."

There was an awkward pause when he had finished. "I'll answer any questions you want to ask if I can," he said, stepping down from the teacher's platform.

A man standing at the back burst out, "Maybe you think now you'll do somethin'. I've seen bright young men like you make promises before. We aren't as dumb maybe as we look. I kept a record of fellows calling themselves liberals, friends of the people and a lot of them other high-sounding names. We elected 'em. All right at first, but they give in after a time. Just two had the guts to vote the way they said they'd vote, all the time they was up there in Sacramento."

A murmur of approval broke out. Another man, gaining courage from the first, shouted, "Ain't you a son of them Dodds? Small valley farmers don't like that name."

Had they come only to heckle him, or were they speaking out of a profound lack of faith in their leaders? At least he had some open opposition to combat. He put up his hand for quiet, and even before the buzz of voices died away he began to speak. "All you say is true, and I've no way of convincing you I have the guts you think are needed to stand by my promises." As he spoke he felt that at last he was standing on his own feet, that at last he had found himself, and God help him, he would be true to the mature human being he hoped he was becoming. "I can only ask you to trust me. I'll try to be worthy," he ended.

Listening, the men and women, although made cynical by many unfulfilled promises of their representatives, sensed his sincerity and crowded around him, shaking his hand, promising him their support, only a few holding back.

This oneness with the people stirred Edward deeply. But very quickly, speaking night after night, often tired to the point of exhaustion, he lost that oneness. More and more his attention was centered on the opposition who had the money and evidently the prestige. In spite of the efforts of Edward's supporters there were towns where no one would rent them a building. In other towns where they did succeed in getting a hall, the right to stretch banners across the streets announcing he was to speak was denied by the owners of the stores to which the banners were to be fastened. In still other towns the right would be granted only to be rescinded. The reason was always the same. They had been threatened with loss of business.

For the first time Edward realized that the monopoly he had been talking against was a gigantic superman, its tireless hands working everywhere, its face never seen. What was the controlling brain? "How can I win?" he asked himself.

Bricket, his manager, laughed at his fears. "We've still got the people. What you must do is reach them, and you can." Bricket's stubborn faith in him was the foundation on which Edward now built belief in himself.

One evening as Edward rose to speak, he saw—to his astonishment and a little to his consternation—that his half brother John was sitting in the second row. He began his talk haltingly, but soon he knew that he was speaking well. There was response in John's face. It was an intelligent, almost beautiful face, Edward realized. The play of expression across it was stimulating.

When the meeting was over, a few stragglers came forward to ask questions. John stood at the edge of the group. "How about coming home with me for the night?" he asked as soon as Edward was free. Bricket was not with him this evening and Edward was glad to accept, but when the gates of the industrial school closed behind them, he half regretted his acceptance.

Once they were seated in John's living room, he felt more comfortable. However grim John's work might be, this room was a pleasant place. John's wife had died several years before, but her personality still pervaded the room, Edward was thinking as he looked up at her picture over the mantel. There were both gaiety and wisdom in the face that looked down on him to which he felt himself responding.

John brought in a bottle of red wine. They sat sipping it and talking of John's work, of Edward's campaign, of the family. Edward realized in his brother's eager questions that he, too, felt separated from the family. Were all men who thought for themselves lonely men? he asked himself.

"John," Edward said at last, speaking with diffidence, "I've wanted all evening to ask you a question. If you don't feel like answering, don't."

"Go to it!" John smiled, leaning back in his chair, his hands behind his head.

"I don't know how to put it exactly. I guess I'll just have to blurt it out. What satisfaction do you get out of your job here? I don't know what the pay is, but it can't be enough to make up for the unpleasantness of the work—or isn't it unpleasant? You don't give the impression of sacrificing yourself."

John made a slight grimace. "I'm not fond of the word sacrifice," he said. "Let me ask you something. What satisfaction do you get out of running for a minority group? It would pay you a whole lot better financially to go in with Father if you want money, and a whole lot more in prestige if you supported his side politically."

"When I went in, I was spoiling for a good fight."

"You aren't now?"

"Yes, but once or twice it's been something deeper."

"I think you are on the verge of answering your own question. But I'll tell you as best I can why I'm here. I hate waste and destruction. Here I have a chance to rebuild human beings. Why do I want to do it? Philosophers and religious teachers have tried for centuries to explain the desire. It's only the initiated, though, who understand why it's the good life."

"But why," Edward persisted, "did you choose to work among the degraded?"

"Why do you use the word 'degraded'?" demanded John. "If you mean 'degenerate' I don't grant you its accuracy. Most of these boys have good minds—just not properly used, like their bodies, impoverished. What kind of a person do you think you or I would be if we'd been brought up in one of Doddstown's camps—or the town itself for that matter?"

John rose, walked around the room. He looked disturbed and unhappy. "Towns like Doddstown," he said at last. "All that they imply. This is a kind of compensation. Maybe it's a superstition that somebody in the family must pay the debt."

25

A FEW DAYS later, looking over his schedule, Edward saw that he had not been booked for an appearance in the county in which his father's old ranch was situated.

"We've tried our best around there, but it's the old story," Bricket told him. "Solid opposition. No buildings available. We decided we'd better let it go; it's not a large voting population. Mostly big ranches. And we know we can't win the owners over. Anyway, most of them live in San Francisco."

"Well, there's one town I want to speak in," Edward answered. "It's near my father's old ranch. A lot of small farmers are coming in there. I believe it's worth while. I have a spare evening. Suppose I go over and see what I can do. I know the man who's been the political boss there for years."

"O.K.," answered Bricket, "if you want to try. But I bet he's nailed to the mast of the opposition."

As Edward struck the Doddstown shanty district, he began to wish he hadn't come. He felt the old sense of shame, even though his father had broken up the ranch. He understood that a hundred family farms had been made out of it. After a while that should make a different kind of town. For the thousandth time he asked himself why his father had been in such a hurry to sell the ranch, why he had broken it up into small holdings—something that would eventually lessen the chances of control of the county by the large owners.

Edward drew up before the house of the man he had come to see, stepped out of his car, went up the steps and rang the bell. "Hello, Jake," he said to the man who opened the door.

"Well, if it ain't one of them Dodds!"

"Ed Dodd," Edward prompted him.

"You're sure the spittin' image of your grandfather. Hope you're as good as him. He got me my job. Been janitor at the school ever since."

Surprised him, thought Edward, as Jake Bodkin ran on about the elder Dodd, evidently trying to gain a little time. He believed he had me blocked. He wasn't expecting to have to meet me face to face.

"Perhaps if you felt that way toward my grandfather, you'll help his grandson out. May I come in? I want to talk to you," Edward said when at last Jake gave him the chance to speak.

"Yeh, sure. Always glad to do what I can to help a Dodd." He stepped back, allowing Edward to enter the house. Edward sat down in an overstuffed chair that flanked one side of the front window. Jake stood. He would have been extraordinarily tall, had not his rounded shoulders shortened him. His head was pushed forward, which seemed to throw his long nose out in front of him, giving him the look of a razor-backed hog, Edward thought.

"I've come about this fall's election. I'd like to speak here."

"What I've been hearing, you won't be very welcome around these parts. Lesly's not for yuh."

"How about all these new families that are coming in? They ought to be interested in the state's efforts to develop water and power."

"These-here new farmers your father's sold to, they ain't moved in yet."

"I've spent a good deal of time around here off and on—doesn't that rate me a chance to say something for myself to the people I know?"

"There ain't ten people left in town that 'ud remember you. This-here town don't hold its people more 'n two or three years. They move on. Laborers don't get no roots down."

"So Lesly's your boss?" Edward's voice carried more than a modicum of scorn.

"There ain't nobody my boss. I've been the boss around here for years."

"You don't act like it." Edward stood up. "I'll do a little doorbell ringing if you won't give me a hearing."

Jake looked scared. He and his bosses thought they had sold the small farmers and townspeople the idea that Edward Dodd was interested in plans that would raise their taxes without giving them anything in return. Jake scratched his head. If he gave this young upstart his support, he was sure to lose the backing of Lesly and his kind. If he didn't give it, he might lose his hold on the new people coming in. Here he was with the father on one side and the son on the other. He'd have to manage 'em both.

"The best thing you can do, and it'll save you time, 'ud be to come to the school tomorrow and speak to the kids. I guess I could fix that for yuh." When Edward hesitated, he added, "Pass out stuff for 'em to take home if yuh wanted to."

"You think you can arrange it?" asked Edward. It was better than nothing. It would be an opening wedge. Maybe some of the workers in his campaign could use that start to get a meeting later on.

Jake gave him a baleful look. "Don't you suppose Miliken knows who keeps him in his job? Ain't you got it through your head yet that I'm boss here?"

"Tomorrow afternoon I could take the school in on my way north," said Edward rising.

"How about tomorrow morning?" Jake figured most of the leaflets given out would be destroyed by the time the kids went home. They'd drop 'em around the schoolyard at noon, and he'd get rid of them.

"Can't make it until about three in the afternoon," Edward insisted, aware of Jake's duplicity. Too, a plan had been growing in his mind ever since he left John. He wanted to drive over to his grandmother's old home. So far it had stood closed except for Fu's room at the back. Jeremy Dodd had stipulated when he gave the old homestead to Edward that Fu should stay on as caretaker. Edward had done nothing with the place so far but now, longing to lay all the ghosts of the past, he was thinking of redecorating the house and using it week ends. He'd wire Agnes to come down on the afternoon train. They'd need tomorrow morning to go over the house and grounds and decide what should be done.

"No, it has to be afternoon—about closing time," he said with a grin.

As he drove east, filled with the warm memory of a new understanding growing up between John and him and the sense of victory he felt in going to Doddstown, he gave himself over to The Valley. As darkness came on he drove slowly through the orchard country, taking back roads he had known as a boy, anticipating as never before his meeting tonight with his wife. Around him, coal-black in the pale light of the moon, fruit trees and grapevines, heavily weighted, bent to the ground. In the vineyards where the grapes had been gathered, freeing the trailing, delicate branches of weight, an all but imperceptible breeze lifted them in graceful, dipping movements. He passed a low farmhouse. Through the trees shone a shaft of moonlight, with one bell-shaped white flower caught in it turned upward as if to receive the light. He felt the intensification of reality that recognition of beauty brings. He was beginning to expect such moments when he freed himself from the urgency of personal striving. "Letting go" was how he thought of it.

He stopped his car, giving himself over to the beauty of the evening. He remembered a film a naturalist had shown him once of the unfolding of seed into plant, buds forming into flowers, flowers into seed. So was all The Valley at this moment filled with the throbbing growth of trees, vines and grain.

It was like the night he had driven down The Valley to say good-by to his grandmother—he living through her, she through him and the children he hoped for—perhaps to be realized now.

He looked at his watch. The train would be in soon. He started his car.

The doors of his grandmother's house stood open as he drove Agnes up to it. Coming down the steps to greet them, white-clad Fu, looking like a wraith in the moonlight, said, "This your new missie?" He bowed again and led them to the back of the house and to Grandmother Dodd's room which he had made ready for them.

26

THE NEXT afternoon, standing outside the superintendent's office in the Doddstown school, Edward heard Jake say, "Nothing for you to worry about, Miliken." A moment later a dapper little man opened the door and hurried forward. With difficulty Edward suppressed a smile—the man gave so much the impression of a small boy being driven forward by tall Jake following on behind.

"I declare, Mr. Dodd," Miliken began, not waiting for an introduction, "this is most unusual. Politics are not really a part of a school curriculum, but, ah . . . after all . . . this will be a lesson in practical government. If you can wait a few moments—as you no doubt know, we have no auditorium—I suggest that we gather the pupils at the foot of the steps. The steps will . . . ah . . . be more, ah . . . like a platform, I dare say."

Jake winked at Edward. "You follow the superintendent. I got my work to do."

"Most of the children of the laborers are picking cotton at this season," the superintendent said to Edward as they stood watching the children file down the steps. "The only ones in attendance now are children of townspeople and those living on the few small farms around here, native Americans mostly. Like those boys coming out now."

Edward liked children and remembered his own boyhood and how difficult the first weeks at school were after the summer's freedom. Ignoring the noise of shuffling feet, he said, "I understand a man got killed around here because you've raised potatoes that turned out to be as valuable as gold."

"It wasn't here, mister," a small boy called out.

A giggle ran like a ripple over the group. They felt at home with him, now that they were all in on the same joke.

"It's having potatoes as valuable as that all the time I want to talk to you about, and I want you to tell your fathers what I say when you go home. I'm going to tell you a true story about water," he went on.

All of them were listening now. Water they knew as something more precious than gold. A boy in the front row attracted Edward's attention. His gray eyes had grown suddenly somber, then bright with happiness when Edward explained the plenty of water which was to be brought to their farms if their fathers voted for him.

When he had finished speaking and the children filed past to receive the leaflets, J. T. was first in the line, Peter second.

"Tell him your names," the superintendent called out.

"Ward," said J. T.

"Some good American settlers by that name," Edward said, noticing with pity the boy's shriveled leg.

Next came the boy with the appealing gray eyes. "Suvorov's my name," he said, "Peter Suvorov."

"Well, Peter, don't forget to tell your father what I said. I think you must be the first Russians in here. They make good farmers, good citizens. Petaluma in Sonoma County has found that out."

"My father is dead, and I'm an American." Petya's answer came in an angry spurt, and he did not hold out his hand for a leaflet. As soon as he had reached the edge of the group of children he started running as fast as he could for the school bus so as to be first in the front seat where the American children always sat. If only J. T. hadn't heard! Ever since school opened J. T. had been mean to him. With a hoot and a rush the others came crowding after him, flapping the leaflets. As he entered the bus, J. T. stood guard over the front seat. "Peter's a Ruski," he called out. "Sonya's beau! Sonya's beau! Bolshevik!" The Japanese and Mexican children, Sonya among them, took their regular places; the American children filed into the coveted front seats. Proudly Peter stood in the aisle looking straight ahead. Sonya pulled on his coat sleeve. There was room beside her. Peter wrenched himself free.

The bus stopped to let Petya and Sonya off. They stood watching it start, pick up speed, roar itself down the flat, treeless highway. As the sound and sight diminished in the distance, Peter turned, picked up a stone, threw it at Sonya, then ran out into the Dodd fields that bordered the road. He wanted to hide, but there wasn't any place to hide in all the level stretch of land. Everywhere he turned, there seemed to be cotton pickers, trailing their white bags behind them. On and on he ran. At last he was alone. He threw himself down among the low-growing cotton plants.

How he hated that silly man who'd called him a Russian just because his name was Suvorov! In Peter's mind Americans had white skins. His own skin was very white except in the summer. But now J. T. had told him he wasn't an American and that he couldn't play with the American boys. What was he to do? For a long time he lay with his face pressed into the earth, alternately sobbing and beating his fists against the ground in an angry tattoo. He must have fallen asleep, for it was nearly dark when he heard voices calling him— Mishka's from one side, his mother's from another. At first he made no move. He didn't want them to find him, but when the voices drew nearer he got up, walked nonchalantly toward his mother.

"Petya, you frightened us," she cried.

"I've just been looking over the cotton."

In the dim light Katya saw he'd been crying. His tears and the dirt of the field had left gray blotches on his face, and his eyes were swollen. She ignored it, knowing how humiliating tears were to him. "Come," she said, "the carpenter's almost finished your room. I thought maybe you'd like to move your things in tonight."

He did not answer, but when they were in the house and he saw the room he had dreamed about so long, with his bed in one corner and a desk and chair by the window, stifling a sob he gasped, "It's really mine?" He began to arrange on the window sill the stones he had been collecting.

Whatever happened to upset him he's forgotten it, thought Katya.

"Suppose we hang Mr. Ching's scroll," she suggested. She was further assured when he ran to get it from the drawer where they had put it for safekeeping.

"It's the most beautiful thing we have, except our icon," she said, studying it. "Do you know what it means?" When he did not answer, she turned and saw he was sitting in the chair by his new desk, his shoulders hunched up and shaking.

"Could you tell me what's wrong?" she asked, going over to him. "No."

I can't force him, she thought. At bedtime, she helped him to undress, something he usually did not permit.

27

EDWARD DODD drove his car at top speed along the highway. The events of the afternoon had roused some sleeping memory. The boy's eyes haunted him. Suvorov was Katya's maiden name. Surely she couldn't have bought any of the Dodd acreage. Too much of a coincidence. Things didn't happen like that. The idea was preposterous. It simply couldn't be that she was living around Doddstown. Could that boy be hers? But he couldn't be. Katya still bore the Dodd name—at least he supposed she did. Or had she preferred to use her own? Or had his father arranged for her to give up their name? If he had, it had been without consulting Edward. He should have tended to the details of the divorce himself, not left it to his father's lawyer to talk to her, thought Edward with an uneasy feeling bordering on remorse.

His son? Edward jerked his mind away from such an idea. The past was past. Let it stay dead. Or was there no such thing as a dead past? Did some part of a former marriage always remain?

Darkness had come almost unnoticed. Mechanically he switched on the headlights. The weeds along the side of the highway swayed under the rush of air made by the car. A gopher scuttling across the road, hypnotized by the glare of the headlights, froze into immobility, its small, brown body poised on its hind legs, its tail erect, touching its pointed head. With the brakes grinding, Edward stopped a foot from the tiny creature. In a moment it had skittered away to safety.

In the sudden silence Edward's thoughts grew loud within him. Suppose this boy was his son and growing up in the mean little village of Doddstown with its record of truancy and petty crime? But the boy he had seen was younger than a son of his would be, he assured himself. Then the thought struck him that Katya might have settled there in order to make trouble for him. If his opponents were given by her the story of their marriage, what kind of tale might she and they twist it into! How often he had heard his father say how careful anybody in politics had to be that not the slightest hint of scandal be raised against him. The memory of those drunken weeks just after he left Katya came back. What had he done to his life by marrying her?

By a great effort Edward got hold of himself. But gradually the suspicion that something had been kept from him in the matter of his grandmother's will grew into a near certainty. Odd events which puzzled him before now fitted together in a pattern—his mother's determination to have him marry the very week after his grandmother's death, his father's hasty decision to sell the ranch. Could it possibly be that Granny had left property to Katya, thinking that she would bring them together again? That was preposterous, too, but there had to be some explanation why Katya was there—if she were there. Well, he'd find out for himself, look up the will tomorrow at the courthouse in the county seat farther south where the will had been probated. Turning south he stopped at a hotel along the way, giving up his original plan to spend the night at home.

The will lay before him. He was back in the old cul-de-sac wherein his family decided what was best for him. Would he ever manage to get the direction of his own life? He felt a mad desire to break out somehow, some way, from this trap which always, no matter how he tried to circumvent it, seemed set for him. If his father had only told him about the will, he'd never have gone into politics, risked the publicity that might be given to his first marriage. Could it be that his father was using the terms of the will to frighten him into follow-ing his lead in politics? He should never have departed from his original intention to be a good trial lawyer. He'd be safe from his father there. He should never have let his barriers down.

Even taking Agnes into his life had weakened his position. It was she who had persuaded him to oppose his father in politics. No, he should never have let down the barriers to admit anyone into his private life. For eight years he had kept everyone out. Well, he'd raise the barriers never to be let down again. And he'd win in this election and on his own terms and in his own way.

Late in the afternoon he crossed the pass that led into Contra Costa County. The bold mass of Mount Diablo rose in the distance. Winding through the Contra Costa hills, he looked with unseeing eyes on the live oaks throwing black shadows onto the yellow sun-baked mountains—a sight in which he usually took intense pleasure. He glanced at the clock on the dashboard. He could just make it—reach the women's headquarters of his party at the hour he had promised to be there.

As he entered headquarters, several women gathered about him, in their excitement laughing and talking all at once. "We know you'll win. You can't help it," they chorused. "The reports that are coming in are beyond anything we hoped for."

"Your wife is certainly pulling for you!" exclaimed one of the women.

Edward felt a sudden withdrawal. So Agnes was trying to take over his life.

"Nonsense!" cried Agnes. "I haven't done anything of importance. It's Edward's talks that have put him over."

"Now, now, don't be too modest. We women are helping and you especially," the woman insisted.

For a long time that night Agnes lay awake, struggling to come to a decision. She liked politics; she liked the fight. But finally she told herself that she must get out and stay out, or she would ruin their marriage. She had thought until now she could work with the women's committee. But the look in Edward's eyes when his attention had been drawn to her efforts was enough to warn her of impending disaster. Edward's trust in her had seemed so complete just two nights ago when they were together at the old family home in The Valley. How could he lose it so quickly? Her work with the committee must threaten him in some way she couldn't understand.

The next morning as soon as Edward had left the house, she called the chairman of the women's committee.

"Jane," she said, "I'm afraid I'll have to drop out of the final campaign."

"What on earth has come over you, Agnes! You just can't. Why, it might cost Edward the election!"

"Nonsense," answered Agnes, laughing lightly. "Edward could do it, I think, without any of us."

"That's a wife's faith and very laudable, but you know as well as I that he can't. It's nothing against Edward Dodd. It's just that there's a good strong opposition, and it's going to take all everyone can do to get out the vote if he is to win."

Agnes hesitated a minute. He *must* win. This was the turning point in his life. Failure—what would failure do to him? And yet she was convinced she must sit with folded hands. It was a difficult role she had set for herself. Into the telephone she said, "It's a matter of health. But I'd rather you didn't tell the others this. It might reach Edward. I don't want to worry him right now when things are so critical."

"Well, of course, if it's that." Reluctantly the chairman of the committee gave in.

Agnes put down the receiver. She really wasn't very strong. This was enough to justify her stand. And she would need all her strength for the round of entertaining she'd like to do this winter in Sacramento when the legislature convened.

28

It was a still November day such as preceded rain in the valleys of California. Katya was looking at the shrubs around their remodeled house. Both the potato and cotton crops had been good. Her ideas for the house had grown with each check that came in. Money to her was something to enjoy. The garden had perhaps been a trifle foolish. Mishka had not openly disapproved of it, but he kept talking about the danger of a drought if the unbroken procession of brilliant days continued throughout the winter. But today the air was soft and moist with the prophecy of rain. As she stood fingering the leaves of the oleanders she had just finished planting, a drop of rain fell on her hand. Then came a brief, quick shower, so mistlike Katya felt no need to go in. She knelt, gathering the earth around a rosebush, drawing deep into her lungs the earth scent released by the rain. Russia, she felt, was loosening its hold on her. She belonged to this new striving America, hard, even cruel at times, but good, too.

"I must speak!" Katya started. She had not heard Mishka's tread on the soft ground.

"Young master——" Mishka began.

"What is it, Mishka? Quick! Petya—nothing has happened to Petya?" Katya rose from her knees, holding the trowel in her hand.

"Petya, he well. Please not to be distressed. Petya go not to the school."

"Sonya tells you this. Mishka, if the children cannot get along, it is not for you to bring the matter to me."

"Mistress, not Sonya who tells me this thing. I have come today from the town. The police he says he must see you. Now he is here."

Katya turned to see Petya and a man coming toward her. "There," the policeman said, taking Peter by the shoulder, pushing him forward. "Tell your mother what you've been doing. Hanging around the back alleys." He turned to Katya. "I've told him a half-dozen times to get back to school. He promises me as glib as you please, but he don't go." He stopped. He was about to tell her where the boy spent his time, but he wasn't supposed to know about the speakeasies in the back of the poolrooms. "I'm the truant officer, ma'am. Because the boy has no father, I'll give him one more chance."

The officer had gone. Petya stood by the front window, his back against it, facing his mother. His lips were tightly pressed together; his eyes had a hard, stubborn look. "I won't go back to school," he told her.

"But, Petya, you must. If you don't, they'll lock you up."

"We could go to San Francisco to live. This is just an old hole, anyway."

"Why, Petya! Just after we've built the house? You've liked the house, and your own room. Besides, we can't afford to go away. You know that."

"I could live with Madame Mohkov till next summer."

"Petya, what's happened to make you like this?"

"Nothing's happened. Just Doddstown's a dirty old hole. I want to go to San Francisco."

"I don't believe you stayed away from school just to be naughty. Can't you tell me what's the matter?" Katya pleaded, remembering the day two weeks ago when he had hidden in the cotton.

When he would not answer, she left him, went into the kitchen, set about preparing their dinner. Katya believed in the value of food. She came from a people who loved food. They knew how to use it to fortify themselves in emergency. She was glad she had made her son's favorite dish for him earlier in the day.

"Come, Petya," she called. She placed a large bowl of borsch before him.

Silently the boy joined her, picked up his spoon, then laid it down. "I don't want any old Russian food," he cried, gulping down his tears.

It's something about Russia, she thought. I wonder if the children have been teasing him. But Sonya is Russian too, and everything seems to be all right with her. No, it can't be that. Besides, he wouldn't give way like this to a little teasing.

"I think, Petya, if I were you I'd go to bed," she said gently. "You've had a long day. You know what the officer told you, that you must be at school tomorrow morning. You needn't go to school alone. I'll take you."

Petya felt driven into a corner. To have his mother go to the school. His mother calling him Petya—J. T. would never forget that name. "No! I told you, I'm not going! You can't make me," he cried and ran into his room, slamming the door behind him.

Katya washed the dishes, prepared his luncheon for the next day, more and more disturbed. Never before had he lied to her, but for two weeks now he had deliberately planned to deceive her. Each morning he had taken his lunch pail, gone down the road with Sonya and had come back in the afternoon with her. Sonya must know what had happened. Katya threw a shawl over her head and, leaving the door open so she could find her way by the light streaming out, went across to Mishka's house. Daria was clearing the table. Sonya was helping her. It was evident she had been crying. "I want Sonya to tell me why Petya hasn't been going to school," Katya began.

Daria and Mishka had been trying for an hour to get Sonya to speak. Angry that Sonya would not answer even the mistress, Daria, so gentle usually with this child born late to her, administered a sharp slap. "You speak. It is not good this way."

Sonya backed away, her head flung high, her black eyes shining with tears. Her security was shaken by her mother's desertion of her here before the mistress, whom she must also defy. And yet she would not desert Petya.

She had never resented the fact that the American girls did not include her in their games. She liked the Mexican girls better anyway. They seemed nearer to her with their quick laughter and their easy tears, one minute happy, the next terribly sad. But Petya—to have Petya excluded at school roused her anger, Petya who was nicer than anybody else in the whole world. She had been proud and happy that he needed her to help him and had delightedly sworn herself to secrecy in the matter of his truancy.

"Petya is good," she cried. "I'm his friend. You can't make me talk against him."

"It isn't that," Katya explained. "If you'd only tell me what made him stay away from school maybe I could help."

Sonya shook her head, sending her long black braids flying.

Back in her own house, Katya waited, hoping Petya would call her, as he always did before going to sleep. She could hear him moving about. Finally all was quiet. The small clock on the shelf over the table said midnight. Her eyes traveled from closed door to ticking clock, from ticking clock to closed door. She must go in and see that he was covered. Perhaps he was even awake waiting for her to come in.

She opened the door. The bed was untouched, the window wide open! "Petya, Petya," she cried, leaning out. There was only the sound of insects, shrill after the rain.

Hurriedly she crossed again to Mishka's house, dark now, knocked on the door. No one answered. "Mishka," she called.

At last came his muffled voice. "I come." Half dressed, he appeared at the door, his wife and Sonya peering out from beneath his arms, raised as he shouldered his way into his shirt. "Don't worry, mistress, boy soon we catch."

He started the truck. Katya climbed into the seat beside him. "Turn north on the highway," she commanded. "He'll try to get to San Francisco. I'll watch my side of the road. You watch yours. He can't have gone far unless——" Surely no one would pick him up. "Mishka, would anyone——" Slowly the truck moved down the road. "Drive faster, Mishka." Katya's voice shook in spite of all she could do.

"If mistress will look there ahead—something, maybe a little boy."

Mishka pulled the truck to the side of the road and stopped. Peter shrank away from the path of light made by the headlights of the truck, stiff with terror. Maybe it was the policeman come after him. But all around him now was the night world, he alone in it with the frightening shadows and fearful squeaking noises of little animals. A furry body brushed his bare leg!

Quickly Katya climbed down from the high seat, ran calling, "Petya, Petya!" She couldn't see him now. Had they only thought they saw him? "Petya!" She ran faster, calling louder.

His name, he heard it! It was his mother calling. He ran back along the road toward the light. His mother's arms were around him.

They were home. Rain beat down on the roof, close over their heads. Katya took Petya onto her lap. He didn't feel too big to be cuddled and kissed tonight. It made him feel safe, and then all at once he remembered that morning was very near, and the school and J. T.'s jeers and all the boys joining in. He put his head on his mother's breast and between sobs he told her why he couldn't live in Doddstown.

"You're ashamed to be a Russian? Your mother is Russian, you know. And the countess and Madame Mohkov." Katya only dimly comprehended how cruelly these children inflicted upon one another their parents' prejudices, how barbed with ridicule J. T.'s taunts were, how ruthless his attacks, for he was fighting for the final remnant of his own self-respect. He must destroy his rival, or his rival would destroy him.

"J. T. says Russians are bad people. Nobody would ever let anyone be an American who had a name like Suvorov. J. T. says it's a bad name. What J. T. says goes," he ended. He nuzzled his head between his mother's breasts, locking his arms around her neck.

"But J. T. didn't think you were bad last year. Why does he now?"

"Please go to San Francisco," begged Peter, weary of trying to explain what he didn't understand himself.

She unlocked his arms, raised his head, looking deep into his eyes. "Listen, Petya. You are truly an American. And you have an American name, but for reasons you wouldn't understand, you use mine."

"What is my real name?" Peter demanded eagerly.

Too late Katya realized that unless he could use it, it would mean nothing to him. She wished she hadn't spoken. She had done it impulsively, thinking to rid him of the feeling that his name made him bad. "Isn't it enough just to know you are an American with an American name?"

Peter was silent. He seemed to be thinking it over. "Please, let's go to San Francisco," he pleaded.

How could she break down this stubborn demand?

Suddenly she saw a way out. "If you'll go to bed and sleep, Petya,

I'll send a note to school tomorrow with Sonya, asking that you be excused until Monday. Maybe by that time we can arrange so you may have your American name." A plan was forming in her mind. She would write to Edward Dodd and tell him she intended using her rightful name. Although, according to Maria, she had been defrauded of it, because she had promised not to use it she felt in honor bound to notify him that she had changed her mind. There was no reason to explain why she wanted to take the name at this late date.

But when she sat down to write the letter, she was troubled. Wasn't Petya's unhappiness her fault? What right had she to deprive him of his father? She had a sharp, hard struggle with herself, but in the end, for Peter's sake, she wrote Edward of his son, saying simply that so far he had borne her name, but that she felt it would be better for him from now on to use his father's. If Edward wanted to see his son, she would bring him to San Francisco.

29

Two weeks remained until the end of the campaign. Looking at Edward sitting across the breakfast table from her this morning, Agnes was satisfied she had been wise in taking no active part in the campaign. He was not on the defensive with her any more as he had been for a day or two after their meeting at the women's headquarters. But why was he like a tightly wound spring? She had seen him this way before they were married when he had had an important case. She wondered if such tension were necessary to him whenever he was struggling to win.

Bricket had wondered much the same thing on the quick swing around the northern part of the state they had just completed. Edward had driven himself and his manager to an inhuman pace. Bricket had to concede that the results had been gratifying, but the more leisurely, kindlier man whom he had accompanied south he liked better.

"Listen to this, Agnes." Edward began reading aloud from a letter come on the morning mail. "This man has evidently done a lot of thinking and reading. He says he's a retired professor who came west a few years ago. He had a farm background, and he bought forty acres of land over on the east side of The Valley. He calls the farms of two to ten thousand acres a leftover of feudal Europe, something alien to our tradition. He's for me because he believes I stand for progress.

"Here's another. Wonder what Father would say to what this man says. He's a small farmer, owns about fifty acres of orchard land. Listen: 'Me and my neighbors have been trying for years to get electricity brought to us. We hope you can do something for us when you're elected. Give us public power. The small, out-of-the way farmer can't compete with the big fellows unless we have electricity to run our pumps.'

"That's the kind of thing I'm going to fight Father on." Edward's mouth shut in a hard line strangely like his father's.

The maid entered, laid a special-delivery letter beside his plate. "Your father sent it over," she explained. Edward picked it up, quickly slit open the cheap-looking envelope.

"It isn't bad news, is it?" Agnes asked, noticing his startled expression when he opened the letter.

"Obviously a crank of some sort," he replied, rising and gathering his letters together. "I've a lot of business to tend to this morning. I must be off."

"But, Edward, you haven't eaten any breakfast!"

"Don't worry about me. I'm all right," he answered shortly, hurrying out of the room.

What could there have been in the letter to disturb him? Agnes watched him from the window as he entered his car that stood at the curb. Usually he drove at a leisurely pace, but not this morning. Evidently something critical had occurred which demanded immediate action. If only he would confide in her! How complex he was, needing so much, refusing so much, asking so much. She felt unaccountably tired as she went slowly up the stairs to her room. It had seemed only an excuse when she had told the chairman of the women's committee that she was not well. She must have had some premonition that day, for truly she was not well. But maybe, could it be . . . She wanted a child badly. She felt a sudden lifting of her spirit. Almost blithely she went about unpacking Edward's suitcases used on his last trip, putting away his clothes. A child would draw them together, strengthen what she felt more and more was too frail a link binding them together.

Edward stopped his car before a drugstore which had a telephone booth out of hearing of eavesdroppers. He sat looking out through the glass door of the telephone booth. Whom was there to call? What good would it do to demand an explanation from his father of why he had not been told that Katya was living in The Valley on land left to her in Grandmother Dodd's will? Even his mother had joined in the conspiracy of silence, treating him like a child, not letting him know how his grandmother and father had both in their way plotted against him. There would be no use appealing to Katya, who had taken this moment for revenge. She had chosen his most vulnerable moment to blackmail him. He was driven into a corner.

That he was only experiencing the fear of everyone who enters politics, the fear that a not-too-scrupulous rival will construe some act of his past to discredit him—whether guilty or innocent made little difference—he failed to realize. All he could see was that on the eve of his election his family's secret machinations had worked together to his undoing. And he had nowhere to turn.

Then he remembered John. John believed in what he was doing. John would help him. He'd ask him to go and see the woman, pay her money if necessary to keep her still. He picked up the receiver, asked for long distance.

John was just leaving his house for a full morning's work at the school when Edward's call came through. He recognized immediately that Edward was in trouble, but it took a few minutes for him to grasp the almost bizarre circumstances which had worked together to place his brother in his present position—a conspiracy of silence, unrelated in fact but related in outcome—his grandmother, his father and his first wife, each hiding something from Edward the victim but also the cause of the entanglement as he had assumed no responsibility in arrangements with Katya over the divorce and no interest in his grandmother's will.

Despite what Edward said, John doubted if any of the three had acted with malicious intent, certainly not Granny, although it was childish of her to think she could set things right by a gift of property. His father had kept silent only from fear, he was certain. As for Katya, he could not guess her motive. Her appeal at just this time looked suspicious, but there was nothing in her letter, which Edward read him, to indicate any malicious intention. Edward's present distress, John felt certain, had its roots in his father's ruthless breaking up of his first marriage.

Someone must see Katya and make her understand the harm to everyone including herself which probably would ensue if she took the Dodd name just now. Doddstown, with its meager, stunted life, feeding as it did on gossip, especially gossip about the Dodds, might turn against her if her connection with the family became known. Also it might well prove a bitter experience for the boy to be told he was Edward's son and yet not be recognized as such. And in Edward's present state of mind John believed it impossible for Edward to feel any affection for the child. Also it would jeopardize Edward's development if he lost the election through his opponent's interpretation of Katya's relationship to him. John believed Edward had built well since that day, years ago, when he had been found, disheveled and thoroughly demoralized, in one of Doddstown's speak-easies. It would be a pity for him to lose his battle as he probably would if he were publicly discredited. All these things passed through John's mind as he listened to Edward's plea that he leave at once to see Katya.

"If you can wait until this evening, I'll go. I can't get away before."

"For God's sake! What are a lot of half-criminal boys worth compared with my defeat?" Edward shouted.

For a moment John felt like hanging up the receiver and leaving his brother to whatever fate held in store for him. Then, realizing what delay meant in terms of anxiety for him, John's anger changed into compassion for this brother closest to him of all his family, caught now in the crosscurrents of family scheming. He must do what he could for him.

"Look here, Edward, you're overdistressed. There's no such need for haste," he said. "Katya told you she'd wait for your answer. Tomorrow morning is about the earliest she could expect to hear. Suppose you put the matter in my hands. I am sure I can arrange something. I'll wire you tomorrow morning as soon as I have seen her. In the meantime, remember that plenty of public men have had to meet some such crisis as this. It is not necessarily disastrous. Gossip is apt to rebound, and I am not at all certain there is as much to this as you think." He was about to ring off when he realized neither of them had thought of credentials. "Edward, you'll have to get a letter of identification to me."

"I'll send one to my headquarters in Fresno. You can pick it up there tomorrow morning. Name the time you'll be in Fresno, and I'll have it there," Edward answered. This time his voice was crisp and businesslike.

But he turned away from the telephone with his faith in his undertaking shaken. Did he not always find in the end that his father was right? "Wild oats" his father had called his adoption of what had seemed to him sound social philosophy. Was not his departure from the family norm yielding the harvest wild oats could be expected to yield?

Having started soon after midnight, by eight the next morning John was well up the west side of The Valley. Every foot of the way was familiar ground. He drove his car along one back road after another, gaining time, undelayed by the heavy produce trucks that clogged the main highways, scarcely conscious of his choice of roads, so absorbed was he in what he was going to say to the Russian woman. She might, of course, prove to be an adventuress. He had not believed it before, and neither had Granny. He still believed Granny was too keen to be taken in. However, what Katya was doing indicated an expert knowledge of the effective time to strike. Well, he'd have to wait until he saw her. He must try to withhold judgment until then.

He was almost there now. He recognized the special type of fence Lesly used. As he passed the great steel gates guarding Lesly's entrance, he thought how un-American such an establishment was— locked gates, no one going in without permission, the owner himself living in San Francisco and fighting every improvement in labor conditions on the ranches. A senator's proposal for government labor camps that would give the itinerant laborers and their families decent housing hadn't had a chance with Lesly and men of his sort fighting it. Here was an issue Edward could well take on. Yes, Edward must be saved for the work ahead of him, if possible.

John hoped he'd come on the Suvorov mailbox south of the town. That would mean he'd not have to drive through town and possibly be recognized, which might start talk. Nonsense, he told himself. Edward has communicated his fears to me. There were new boxes along the highway, new names he'd never seen before. The long stretch of land, in his grandmother's time unbroken except for clusters of laborers' shacks, today showed the skeleton framework of houses under construction here and there. It gave the landscape a more personal look. Homes were what this part of the state needed, not shifting tribes of laborers and absentee landlords. Into Los Angeles every winter poured the itinerant farm laborers with their families, most of them on relief. Crowded living conditions, inadequate food, no real homes—the end product, delinquency.

John took himself sharply to task. He must not see everything in terms of his work. The scene before him was lovely. It was late October, and the cotton bolls had burst. In the midst of a sea of white foam the pickers, men, women and children, waded, trailing behind them huge canvas bags looking like water wings.

None of the mailboxes bore the name of Suvorov, and there was the town just ahead, as bleak and forlorn-looking as ever. If the boy Katya had mentioned in her letter really was Edward's son, what irony that he should be growing up here! John was out of the town now, following the highway north. At the northern boundary of the old Dodd ranch he had to acknowledge he'd missed the place. Slowly he retraced his route, coming finally to the road separating the Dodd and Lesly properties. Suvorov he read in black letters on the side of a homemade wooden letter box set on a post. How had he missed it before?

He turned into the road, looking for a row of shacks which had stood somewhere along it in the past. Evidently they had been torn down. No, they'd been moved back from the road. Two of them had been used as wings to a newly built section. Quite ingenious, he thought. At a little distance two more had been made into one. As he drove his car up in front of the larger house, he saw oleanders had been planted in a square, making an enclosed garden around it. Everything was neat and carefully planned. He realized he had expected to meet shiftlessness and a need for money. Of all the unpleasant things he had ever been asked to do, he decided that the interview with Edward's former wife was going to be the most unpleasant.

30

JOHN knocked. The door was immediately opened. Before him stood a woman above average height, wearing a plain blue house dress like dozens he had seen in small-town store windows. It makes her look slightly awkward, he thought. She needs clothes especially made for her, which would set off her long-limbed body and finely modeled head, was his quick appraisal. She must have been beautiful when Edward met her, was his next thought; her face is classic with its long straight nose, large eyes set far apart, high well-shaped brow. It occurred to him that her hair, drawn severely back, was as golden as the wild barley on California's summer hills. It seemed incongruous that her hands should be rough and red. Undoubtedly she didn't shirk hard tasks. "Are you Mrs. Suvorov?" he asked.

"Yes," she replied. "May I know your errand?" There was the faintest suspicion of something foreign in her speech, more a matter of emphasis than pronunciation.

"I have come in answer to your letter to Edward Dodd." Frankness and directness would be the best approach, he decided, for he was pretty well convinced already that he was dealing with a sincere person.

Katya led the way into what was evidently a combined living and dining room, asking him to be seated. The room was plain almost to bareness, which the rich blues and golds of the icon in the corner seemed to emphasize.

"I am his brother John," he said, handing her Edward's letter of introduction. Noticing how nervous she was when she opened it, he wondered if, after all, she was hiding something. Perhaps she was being exploited by someone more designing than herself.

"Could you give me your reasons for wishing to take the Dodd name now?" he asked after she had finished the letter. "You have used your own for a long time and quite successfully, I judge. Unless you have some good reason, it would seem unnecessary to embarrass my brother with such a declaration at the present time." John realized he was plunging rather abruptly into the purpose of his mission.

"Embarrass him! I see no reason why giving his son his name should embarrass him." Her nervousness was gone now. She appeared to have wrapped herself about with the dignity and reserve the socially trained know how to assume under attack.

"It is not you or the boy who would embarrass him," John hastened to explain. "It is the misinterpretation that might be made if a heretofore undeclared Mrs. Dodd and her son should suddenly appear here in this part of The Valley where he is so well known. The gossip that would spring up might be just the thing that would defeat Edward in the election. I doubt if you wish to do that." He felt distaste in putting it so bluntly, but he knew no other way to set the unpleasant facts before her.

"I do not understand."

It had not occurred to him until now that Edward's wife knew nothing of his prominence in the coming election. She was probably completely ignorant of American democratic procedure. Anyway, in Doddstown she would have heard only of Edward's opponent. Every store, as he had passed through the main street, had had the opposing candidate's picture in the window, but none of Edward. He concluded there had been no clever timing in presenting her request at just this moment. There must be some more personal reason. He realized, also, that whatever it was, she had decided to take the Dodd name, and it would be difficult to make her change her mind unless the need for her request could be answered in some other way.

"If you thought it would benefit Peter to take his father's name, why did you not arrange for it when he was born?" he asked.

"I wasn't living in The Valley then, I was living in San Francisco.

I was afraid to tell Edward he had a son. He might take him away from me. And I was using my own name because Mr. Dodd's lawyer told me I couldn't have any money if I didn't give up the name, and I had to have money. I didn't know much about America when Edward left me. The lawyer said I had to give up the name."

John was too shocked for a moment to speak. He had not believed his father could be so hard. It was his father, he was certain, who had driven the bargain. In all fairness he felt Edward was not capable of such an act.

"But now I see I was wrong," Katya went on. "Edward has a right to his son. And I am keeping from Peter benefits his father could give him."

John saw it would be a shock to her to know that Edward did not wish to claim Peter, that he was not convinced, perhaps never would be, that the boy was his son, although there was no further doubt in John's mind.

"You must remember he's never seen the boy, never guessed he had a son. Isn't it natural that he does not immediately have a sense of fatherhood?" he asked as gently as he could.

No longer could Katya sit here talking of Petya as if he were any little boy. He was hers and Edward's son, and he was in trouble with the law. Impetuously she began to tell him what had happened to Petya, occasional Russian words slipping in unnoticed. In these solitary months in the country with only Mishka and Daria to speak to all day, she had come to think again in her mother tongue. "In school Petya—Peter I mean—must be Monday morning," she ended, "or the policeman do something dreadful to him. He won't go and be called a Russian! He's not a Russian. He's an American. Edward owes him his name."

Although evidently her motive in demanding of Edward the right to his name was a perfectly innocent one John doubted he could convince Edward that there was nothing sinister in her request. Again he tried to explain Edward's position.

"I'll put it as simply as I can, Mrs. Suvorov," he began. "Edward is about to become a public officer, to be one of those who make the laws of the state of California. He is under fire as such——"

"You mean he hasn't time?" Katya interrupted, her face lighting up. "But it is not necessary for him to come. His name would protect Peter."

"It isn't as simple as that, Mrs. Suvorov. To have Peter suddenly proclaimed as his son might defeat Edward. His enemies would misconstrue the facts."

"But Peter *is* his son."

Katya's eyes lighted with amber specks revealed to him her stubborn determination to set things right for her son. The larger issue. Edward's public value, he realized she did not grasp. What he had to deal with, he saw, was a lonely woman whose whole life was channeled into one emotion—love for her son. What he had to do was try to make her understand why if her request was granted it would harm Peter.

"I have mentioned my brother's campaign, to help you to see that at such a time to insist on your demand might harm your son. Edward fears that his enemies will try to prove that the boy is illegitimate. The boys who are teasing him now would certainly use that against him."

"So my son, just a baby yet, must suffer instead of Edward." Katya spoke bitterly, ignoring the possibility that what she demanded would hurt Petya. She did not believe it would.

"I do not see that suffering can be avoided for Peter, even if he were given his father's name, while he continues to live here in The Valley. The children would still regard you as a Russian. If the school children have determined to ostracize Peter, they won't be put off by a new name. He'll have to make them accept him. It seems hard to put it like this, but I think no purpose will be served by subterfuge. There has been too much of that already. You are the victim of the same prejudices that are hurting your son."

"How do you mean?"

"Wasn't it race prejudice that ended your marriage to Edward? To his parents you were a foreigner. That they could not overlook."

Could it be that Edward had rejected her and was now rejecting Petya for the same reason the children at school were rejecting him? Was there, in the eyes of Americans, some stigma in being a Russian? Had Petya no place in society because of her? She clasped and unclasped her hands, unable to speak.

John realized he had hurt her, but had not helped her to see the issues. He must break through her misconceptions, reach her somehow. "What I have to suggest is a man's way of solving this problem," he said gently. "A man's way to supplement your woman's way. Both are needed."

His words gave her the first indication that someone in the Dodd family cared what happened to Petya. Edward's brother was speaking as if he believed in her and believed that together they could straighten things out for her son. Could she really count on him to help her? "How?" she asked.

"Would you trust him to me for a couple of days? Let me see if I can straighten things out for him?"

She drew back. "You mean without me? He's never been away from me."

"I'll take good care of him," he assured her. "After all, he's my nephew," he ended with a smile.

I must trust someone, she thought. There is no other way. She rose and went to the door. "I will speak to Petya—Peter," she said, correcting herself.

John walked over to the window, thinking he had won the first round, got past the mother's guards. Now if he could only win the boy's confidence! He caught a glimpse of him as he stood at the foot of the steps looking up at his mother. He had a frank and open face. His eyes were like his mother's, he had her good brow. But in spite of his slightly flattened Slavic cheekbones, there was something about him that reminded John of Edward when he was a little boy. It's that sensitive expression of the mouth, he thought. Too sensitive, perhaps, for the fight he's going to have to put up. The boy's chin is like his father's, too, long and a little pointed. It gives his face a fragile quality.

For one moment John wondered if the best thing wasn't to send him away to school. He should be able to persuade Edward to do that much for the boy. But immediately he gave up the idea. Peter's mother wouldn't consent, he was certain. Besides, he didn't believe the boy could stand being parted from her very long at present. There was an air of strain about him.

As Peter entered the room, a mask settled over his face. Such a withdrawal is unusual in a child of his age, thought John. With all his knowledge of boys, he felt at a loss how to reach this lad. Of one thing he was convinced. He couldn't talk to him about going back to school here and now. If he could interest the boy in going with him for the week end, take him to a cabin he had in the Sierras, he might by degrees win his confidence. Two years ago he had persuaded the authorities of the institution to let him take honor boys on short camping trips. The effect on them had been startlingly good and had greatly improved his position with them. Perhaps something of that sort would happen with Peter. Regretfully he gave up the prospect of being alone there for two days as he had planned.

"Petya, I want you to meet Mr. Dodd, an old friend of mine," said Katya.

John shook hands with the boy. "I'm getting up some skiing trips for this winter," he said. "It occurred to me your mother and you could help me out. I thought you might be interested in getting a group together here."

Petya smiled. The change was startling. His mask of indifference lifted. His eyes danced. The smile grew into a wide grin. "Gee!" Then suddenly he seemed to remember something. "No, I guess not."

"I thought," John went on, ignoring Peter's refusal, "I'd like you to come along with me now just to see the site. You'd know better then just what the setup is."

"You mean today? Go to the mountains?"

"Yes. This is Saturday. I could get you back home by tomorrow evening."

"Could I?" Peter turned, looking eagerly up at his mother.

Katya hesitated. He was so little to go away with a stranger, even if the man was his father's brother. And then all at once she consented.

31

JAKE was just leaving the school as John and Peter drove past. If that ain't one of them Dodds! Wonder what he's got to do with the Suvorov kid, Jake communed with himself. Widow Suvorov—she's got too much looks to get along without a man.

John Dodd headed his car for the Sierras, driving straight across The Valley, stopping on the east side to get food and to telegraph Edward that things were going well, promising a letter on Monday. That was the best he could do for Edward just now.

Then he turned his attention to Peter, for whom already he was beginning to feel something close to affection. I wish I could tell him I'm his uncle, he thought. He looks as if he could do with a male relative or two to help fight his battles.

"Ever been on the mountains, Pete?" he asked.

"No, sir."

"Ever camped out?"

"No, sir."

"How'd you like using a sleeping bag? Make a fire and sleep outdoors by it?" It was something John loved to do.

Peter remembered the wild, uncharted darkness the night he had run away, but he wouldn't want this man to think he was afraid. "Sure!"

John, conscious of a strained note in the boy's voice, said to himself, I mustn't ask too much of him. It's pretty plucky of him to come with me at all. It's the first time he's spent the night away from his mother in his life. Aloud he said, "As a matter of fact, I haven't enough gear for both of us, and it's too late to pick up any. I guess, after all, we'd better bed down in my cabin tonight."

Peter didn't answer, but he felt safer—safer than he had felt for a long time. Now that Doddstown was behind him, it didn't menace him so much. The present enveloped him. He felt important. Wasn't he going to see about a place to take kids camping? When they reached the mountains and began circling their great sides, climbing higher and higher, and he looked down into deep canyons beneath them lined with dark green pines, clear sunlit streams at the bottom, wonder and awe claimed him. He leaned out the window, humming softly to himself.

Good, thought John. But when they drew up before the cabin set among a forest of great firs, Peter shivered, whether from the sudden cold or from the somber touch of the forest on his spirit, John did not know.

"We'll have to hustle around to get ourselves warm," he said, opening the door to the cabin as he spoke. "Bring the food and stuff in. I'll have a fire started in a minute." Watching Peter's hurried efforts to get everything in as quickly as possible, John feared he'd made a mistake to expose him to so many changes all at once. But soon the boy seemed to have lost his fear and for the rest of the short afternoon worked contentedly at John's side, doing little things about the camp.

When darkness began to settle down among the trees, they went inside and built the fire higher. John set about preparing their dinner. The long sticks the boys used to toast their wienies stood point upward, leaning against the stones of the chimney. "What are those for?" asked Peter.

John explained. "You can toast the rolls for us if you will."

It was fun, holding out the long stick, bringing the roll in contact with just enough of the blaze to brown it. Peter was proud when his new-found friend praised him for the nicely browned roll he presented to him. Not since his friendship with Mr. Ching had Peter felt so grown-up. It was great to have a man like Mr. Dodd choose him from all the boys to help him. Then slowly his pride oozed away. If Mr. Dodd knew how the boys felt about him! If Mr. Dodd knew he ran away from school and about the policeman, there wouldn't be any other times like this. Well, he wasn't going to tell. What business was it of Mr. Dodd's, anyway? He toasted another roll, carefully placed a wienie inside, took a big bite, found it hard to swallow.

Later when they had washed the dishes, made up the bunks and were again sitting by the fire, Peter burst out, "Look, Mr. Dodd. They don't like me at school."

"Think you could tell me about it?" John tamped down the tobacco in his pipe, settled back in his chair.

"No." Petya's childish mouth set in unnatural firmness.

"Well, I don't know but what I admire you for that. A boy has his own battles to fight."

Peter gave him a surprised look. New idea to him, John was thinking, that he can change the hostility directed against him. "Perhaps you'll have to fight it out first," he said. "Then you'll be in a position to choose a few boys. It's too early yet for us to come up here. We have to have a fair fall of snow first for skiing. By the time the snow is hard, I'd be willing to bet you have your boys."

"You mean that, Mr. Dodd?"

"Certainly I mean it. Now we'd better be getting to bed. We have a lot ahead of us tomorrow."

Peter was too excited to sleep. Maybe he *could* change things at school, and it was nice here in the cabin. Was it like this when you had a father? Maybe this man was his father, and he'd tell him so in the morning, or sometime. His mother had said things would be right by Monday. He tried out the name—Peter Dodd. With a good American name he'd teach J. T. where to get off. But he hadn't told the man about the policeman and running away from school. That bothered him.

Hearing Peter twisting about his bunk, John rose, put some wood on the fire, fussed around a bit. Maybe the boy was frightened or lonely. "Need another blanket?" he asked.

Peter's defenses went down. "Mr. Dodd, I gotta tell you something. The policeman came after me." Peter sat up in his bunk looking miserable and frightened.

"Maybe I could help if you'd tell me the whole story," John said, sitting down on the bunk.

It was told at last: all the things Peter had kept from his mother, how it had started when the man came to speak at the school, how J. T. told the boys they'd get in trouble if they had anything to do with him because he was a Bolshevik—he stumbled over the word— how the policemen were after Bolsheviks, how he had tried for a week to explain, then decided not to go to school any more, how he'd persuaded Sonya to help him, how he'd spent his time in one of the poolrooms until school was out in the afternoon, how he always met Sonya at the crossroads and walked home with her so his mother wouldn't know about his not going to school.

John asked his first question. "What did you do in the poolroom?"

Peter drew his legs up, clasped his arms around them, lowered his head until it touched his knees. "Please don't make me tell," came in a muffled voice. "I promised. They said I'd get in trouble with the law, terrible trouble, me toting——" He stopped. He had nearly told.

Things were a little worse than John had supposed. Yet what should he have expected? How often he had heard the same story—kids helping out in poolrooms, passing drinks. Some men thinking it funny to make them taste the stuff. Small offenses against the law, finally the reformatory. But today it was brought home to his own door. He thought of the mean, stunted life of the town named in bitter jest after his family. Well, the jest has now come full circle today, he said to himself bitterly. What would be the family's shame if Peter's story were known! But there was no danger. The truth about these towns near the great holdings was never told. He came back with a start to the immediate problem, roused from his thoughts by a small, muffled voice saying, "I guess you don't want me now."

"Want you? Of course I want you. But let's get a few things settled. You must be the kind of boy I can trust. If you promise me, I believe you'll keep your word."

"Yes, I will," Peter answered eagerly. The promise not to go to the poolroom he gave easily, but on the promise to go back to school he hedged. "If I had my American name——"

"What do you mean your American name?"

"My mother said I had one. She was going to get it for me."

For a moment John did not know what to say. He thought Peter was in complete ignorance that he had any other name than Suvorov. How now to save the boy from the sense of rejection in knowing Edward did not want him? Quickly he decided to gamble on persuading Edward after the strain of the election was over to accept his son.

"You want to be a real American, don't you, Peter?" he asked.

"Yes."

"Suppose I should tell you that you could be a better American just now by not insisting on your American name?"

"I guess I'd think you were crazy."

"Sometimes when a man is doing something for his country, he has to keep all his personal affairs to himself. If he doesn't, he loses out," John went on. "Let's say your father is in that position, and——"

"Is my father really like that?"

"I think he's going to do something pretty fine for America."

"If you know my father, then you can tell me his name," Peter suddenly demanded. What was this man up to? Peter's childish trust in him was shaken.

John realized this and answered frankly, "I wish I could tell you, Pete, but I can't. It's not my business to tell you. But what I honestly believe is that some day not too far off, your father will tell you himself. Just now he asks you to wait to use his name."

"On account of what he's doing?" asked Peter.

"Something like that," John answered.

Peter fought a hard battle with himself. Always before he had been shielded. This man asked hard things of him. It would be so much nicer if his father would let him help some other way, maybe go around with him. At last he said, "Tell him it's O.K."

"And you'll go back to school? May I tell him that?"

There was an even longer pause. "I guess he'd want me to, wouldn't he?"

At dusk the next day they drew up at the Suvorov cottage. Katya came running out. "Petya, are you all right?" she exclaimed. She knelt, gathering him into her arms, feeling him as if to make certain he was intact. "Is everything—did you have a good time, darling?"

Peter wriggled free. "Of course, Mom. I want to find Mishka."

"Good-by, Pete," John called after his vanishing form. "Let me know when you have your boys."

Katya came to the side of the car. "Thank you," she said. "He looks happy."

"It's not going to be easy for him, but I think he'll see things through. He wants to tell you himself about the plan we worked out." He hesitated a moment, then started his car. There seemed nothing more he could say.

32

EDWARD, who was learning that to hold public office one must be all things to all men, was attempting to strengthen his position in the cities these last two weeks before election by shaping his talks to the interests of the city-bred. Not one resident in ten of San Francisco, Alameda, Oakland, Berkeley or Richmond, the cities of the Bay area, he reflected, ever thought how precarious was the productive life of the semiarid valleys on which he depended for food. In the cities the eucalyptus, redwood and deodar trees were always cloaked in perpetual green. The gardens, watered by sprinkler systems, were as green in summer as in winter. Always a shrub or a flower was bursting into bloom. Only an occasional vacant lot made the citizens aware how dry and parched their cities would be without adequate water. Nor did many of them realize that both water and power for their use must be drawn from the state's limited water supplies.

The Tuesday after John's visit to Katya, Edward had spoken before a men's luncheon club in San Francisco, explaining that his party's platform for developing the state water resources did not mean, as his opponents contended, a heavy burden of taxation on the cities for improvements from which they would get no benefit. Quite the opposite. Money spent in The Valley will reward the city businessmen twofold, he contended. Only as the great Central Valley flourishes will their cities flourish. The country is the lifeblood of the cities. The semiarid valleys cannot reach their full production with insufficient water, nor can California's cities develop their industries without the state to help with water and power.

He felt he had never spoken with greater clarity or been more at ease. The logical presentation of economic facts he found more in harmony with his nature than the presentation of social problems, for such facts were always an implicit, if not an actual, part of his valley speeches. The response had been enthusiastic, and now, driving home, he allowed himself a moment's indulgence planning his future career—something pretty well shattered, he had feared, until he had received John's telegram on Saturday morning.

As he entered the hall of his house, the telephone was ringing. There were a hundred last-minute campaign details to see to. He had but an hour before starting for downtown Oakland, where a dinner was being given for him by the women's auxiliary. For the first time Agnes would hear him speak. He wanted his speech to be good. He picked up a pile of mail lying on the hall table. Shuffling it through, he saw there was a fat letter from John. Why was John bothering him with details? All he needed to know was what the money settlement came to.

Standing by his desk in his room upstairs, he glanced through the closely written pages, catching a sentence here and there. Of course, he was grateful to his brother, but certainly John had been easily taken in. Imagine believing that Katya knew nothing about his campaign! Hardly possible with all the publicity.

A line farther down the page caught his eye. "After the election I hope you will arrange to see your son." My son! How naïve John was to swallow that hoax! Edward tore the letter in two. He scratched a match and held the pieces to the flame. From an unburned bit the words stood out: "It's a serious handicap to be brought up in a place like Doddstown." Well, wasn't he getting himself elected to improve such conditions? Absorbed in his thoughts, he held the burning paper until the flame touched his fingers. Quickly he dropped the charred fragments into an ash receiver, went into the bathroom, held his slightly burned fingers under the tap.

The night of the election Jeremy Dodd had insisted on a family dinner at the hotel where the two parties were to gather to hear election returns. Edward could not understand why his father wanted to mark the event with a display of family solidarity.

Edward could see his father was excited. Almost as if I were *his* candidate, thought Edward, as they gathered round the table.

"We'll drink to your future success, Ed," his father said.

There were only two, Edward felt, who drank the toast with pleasure—Bettie and her fiancé, a free-lance writer who ran a column in a number of the valley papers. Edward liked him, but he believed his father did not want him in the family. Bettie looked at her brother and smiled. We're both a little out of the family picture, he thought.

"I swung you a few votes today" was his father's next surprising remark.

"I thought you were working to defeat me," Edward said.

"I don't know that I'd put it that way," Jeremy answered. "Better say I want to see the views you represent defeated."

What sort of a game was his father playing? Edward wondered. He should by all rights be angry over his youngest son's political position. Tom was. His older brother would gladly have picked a fight with him, he could see, if they had been alone. He could understand why Tom was angry. He was an apostle of the power companies' interpretation of individual enterprise. But so was his father. "The initiative we Americans pride ourselves on is at stake in this election," he was saying even now. "It's for private business to say where water is to go, where power lines should be run. It pays to put them only in thickly populated districts." Jeremy looked at Edward. "Well, what have you to say to that?" he demanded.

"Only that the small farmer doesn't have much chance at personal enterprise the way you play it. He's caught."

"Nonsense!" Jeremy spoke with impatience. "You're going to let the small man who hasn't the initiative to get anywhere himself hamstring the man with brains."

"I'll never grant you that," Edward answered.

"Well, we'll see when you get into the Senate."

"Do you think I'm going to?" Edward asked in some surprise.

"I hope so. I'd hate to see a son of mine defeated."

Feeling that the fine strands of a web of his father's weaving were throttling him, Edward excused himself before the dessert was served, pleading that he was due upstairs where the men backing him had taken a room for the evening to listen to the returns.

When Edward and Agnes left them, Jeremy turned to Tom. "Cheer up! You don't need to think Ed's always going to take the stand he's taking now. A man changes his mind a dozen times a session at Sacramento. The worst thing would be to have him licked. He'd be finished politically. You never come back, once you're defeated. He'll be with us yet. Perhaps more valuable for having put over the kind of campaign he has. It makes the people believe in him."

How well everything was coming out! Beatrice was thinking. It was she who had pointed out to her husband that if he wished to influence Edward in his public life, he should not quarrel with him. That would only strengthen Edward in his attitude. "He is at heart a loving son," she had reminded her husband. "The way to rule him is through sympathetic understanding." To rule you, too, she thought, smiling at Jeremy across the table.

The room upstairs taken by Edward's supporters was a large one. A dining table covered with a white cloth was pushed to one side. A ticker-tape machine had been set up. Over in a corner a group of men were smoking. A strong odor of rich cigars filled the air. Bricket, seeing Edward and his wife enter, took his feet off a chair and came over to them. "Not much in yet. Two or three small precincts."

"How'd they go?" asked Edward.

"For your opponent!" Bricket grinned. "I was just about to put it up on the blackboard."

A group of women came in. The head of the Oakland Women's Organization stopped to speak to Edward. "This little wife of yours looks very beautiful tonight, so I suppose we'll have to forgive her for running out on us. That is, if we win."

"Of course Edward will win," Agnes answered, feeling again that threat to her marriage in the woman's assumption that her efforts could in any way tip the scales for Edward.

"And you're feeling quite well again, I hope." The chairwoman's words held a little sting. She hadn't meant to mention Agnes' health before her husband. It had been an unpremeditated statement, but she was tired from weeks of hard work and hadn't taken time tonight to get up her own dinner party as most of the others had. Instead she had worked at headquarters until the last moment. To come upon Agnes looking rested and happy, exquisitely gowned in a black dinner dress, her hair obviously done for the occasion, had been too much. The instant she spoke she regretted it. Why did I do it? she asked herself, seeing the scrutinizing glance Edward gave his wife.

"Is anything wrong, dear?" he asked her, anxiety in his voice.

"No, not really." At her words she saw a shadow of doubt had crossed his mind. Maybe he thinks I didn't care enough about his winning to work for him. "I'm well, Edward, if I take care of myself. But I mustn't do anything very active," she said, answering the doubt in his eyes.

Their conversation had taken only a minute as they stood there in the middle of the room with the ticker tape working rapidly and the returns going up on the blackboard, but Agnes realized that in that moment she had committed herself to a role she must continue to fill if she gave Edward the assurance he seemingly possessed only when there was little or no self-assertion on her part. But have I not, in assuring him, she thought, given sickness power over myself? The idea was gone almost as it entered her mind.

"Looks better, doesn't it?" It was Bricket speaking, pointing at the blackboard. The excitement rose and fell like waves on the shore. The air grew thicker with tobacco smoke. Gradually they all drew in around the blackboard. The returns from San Francisco were in. Edward had won by a slight margin. He was winning in Los Angeles! The impossible had happened.

It was two in the morning when Edward's opponent entered, strode across the room and shook his rival's hand. "I'll have to concede my defeat. Congratulations! It's been a good fight. Good night." He was gone quickly to hide his disappointment.

The young lawyers, Edward's old friends, closed in around him. "This is the biggest victory the water project has ever had," said one very tired-looking young man. He added, "I'd like to sleep for a week."

"Senator Jones won't have to carry the whole fight from now on," Bricket rejoiced.

The lobby was almost deserted when Edward and Agnes stopped at the checkroom for their coats. "You look tired, my dear. I'm going to take better care of you from now on." Edward stooped, fastening his wife's coat at the neck. "It's cold this time of the night."

It was good to take care of her. He realized by her words tonight that she had leaned on him and did not, as he had feared, want to join with his parents in shaping him. On the ride home he told her of his growing ambitions—first state senator, then congressman. It was good to talk freely. Released from the necessity to hold her at a distance he sought for words to express his conflicting emotions, the uncertainty he felt over the various pressures his father was putting on him—yes, he wanted to tell her about his grandmother's will— yes, suddenly he believed he wanted to tell her of John's letter and explain about Peter, who perhaps did have a claim on him. He hesitated. Suppose in giving her his confidence he gave her some power over him. Wasn't it better, as he had decided after he learned about the will, not to let his barriers down? Not even before the woman he loved.

Agnes waited for him to go on, wishing she dared take the initiative but fearing to. Never until tonight since the evening he had first discussed with her his stand politically had he taken her into his confidence. That one time she had dared to take the initiative, and it had succeeded, but of late at the slightest show even of wanting his confidence he had drawn back. Perhaps if she did not urge herself on him, he would again open his heart and mind to her.

Suddenly he leaned over and kissed her, saying, "I mustn't tire you." Relief swept over him. How near he had come to putting himself in his wife's gentle hands! Gentleness! He distrusted it. His mother had always used it to rule him. Even his father was beginning to use it.

Agnes felt both baffled and defeated.

33

THE morning after Peter returned from his trip with John Dodd, Katya awoke with a start to the strident sound of her alarm clock, to which she had never been able to accustom herself, less so in these short November days. Hurriedly she dressed, then went to waken Peter, a little fearful even yet that he might refuse to go back to school.

·She turned on the light and studied him, and as always seeing how defenseless he looked in sleep, she longed with all her being to save him today's ordeal. But there was nothing she could do. Gently she shook him. "You'll have to hurry, Peter, to catch the bus," she said, steeling herself against any appeal he might make. But he made none. Silently he got out of bed, began to dress.

Still anxious, Katya watched him trudge down the road. He had assured both her and Mr. Dodd he would not play truant again. She had to trust him.

A few days later going into town for supplies, she saw a big yellow sign had been erected on one of the empty lots. Her heart seemed to jump into her throat, choking her. In the center was a picture of Edward. She stood before it for a moment, staring up at this man she had once known so intimately. After a little she read the caption underneath.

EDWARD DODD
FRIEND OF THE PEOPLE
WATER FOR EVERY FARM
CHEAP ELECTRICITY

Was Edward Dodd guarding hers and Petya's future welfare, or was Petya guarding Edward's? There was an ironic twist to Katya's lips as she turned away. She had a vision of her son, his small sensitive face set in a stiff grin each morning when he started for school.

By the middle of November both color and activity had gone from The Valley. No trucks filled with purple grapes or brown-skinned potatoes rumbled along the roads. Tardily opening cotton bolls looked like bits of dirty snow in the stretches of dead brown stalks. The itinerant workers and their broken-down cars had disappeared. They had gone to the cities, some to find work, more to swell the relief rolls. Those of them who had managed to gain a foothold in The Valley, mostly Japanese and Mexicans, were settling down to a season of unemployment and a meager winter living. Some of them would go on local relief. Doddstown looked dead even on Saturday nights.

There was little rain this winter, little moisture except the tulle fogs blanketing the earth morning after morning. Katya was lonely. She had made no friends. She had no entree with the town's elite—the members of the Boosters Club, Mr. Lesly's manager, employees of the utility and oil companies, retired farmers. Her English, although correct, was definitely marked with a foreign intonation. Had she been known to these people as Mrs. Dodd of the prominent Dodd family, this difference in speech would have seemed thrillingly exotic; as Mrs. Suvorov it placed her as a foreigner. Peter's ostracism at school branded her as a foreigner among the small farmers.

For long hours of the day she sat by the window reading the Russian books she had brought with her, marking parts she thought Peter would understand and enjoy. She must see that he was given his Russian heritage. Watching the quiet, unresponsive boy who had taken the place of the carefree child of the summer, she began to think of returning to San Francisco. And yet with every month that passed the road back was more difficult. Mishka had given up his job as boilermaker to come with her. With the ranch paying, she had no reason to sell and leave him without occupation. Too, her apartment in San Francisco was occupied and her place at the Russian bookshop had been filled. Her loneliness had developed its own inertia, which made taking up the new an impossible effort.

Gradually Katya, having within her the seeds of introspection and mysticism common to her countrymen, began to draw strength from her solitude. The unbroken hours of the winter days, with no sound coming from the expanse of earth broodingly awaiting the returning cycle of creative life, brought her a stillness of heart gratefully accepted, healing her wounds. As broodingly quiet as the earth outside her windows, she knelt before the icon lost in contemplation of the beautiful Mother of God.

The trickle of newcomers—the buyers of Dodd's land—ceased. Jim Ward, J. T.'s father, never set foot in the town that he didn't find at least one chance to sneer at the progress talked about in the summer. "Health program," he would say to anyone who would listen. "Resident doctor, my eye! As much health program going to be here as was hereabout when J. T. got paralysis. All the county ever does if there's an epidemic is to drive the itinerants out, spread their dirt and disease into other towns."

He had gone into the drugstore one foggy afternoon to get some liniment. "Where's all this change we going to have in Doddstown?" he demanded of the clerk, a woman about forty.

"I guess you don't want it to come, Mr. Ward."

Ward's face took on its most belligerent expression. "What you trying to say? You mean I'm one of Lesly's laborers that daren't call my soul my own, let alone my vote?"

"Now, Mr. Ward, I was just meaning you seem to get pleasure out of saying this town won't be different when we get more people living

here. It's mostly that people don't feel permanent here, why we
haven't done anything before. I don't mean you," she hastened to
add, seeing Ward's face getting stormy again. "You got land, even
if you do have to work for Lesly now and then. You aren't beholden
to him. Why don't you go along with the new farmers? At least help
see this town is incorporated?"

"And how'd I know any of 'em going to live here more 'n a year or
two? I learned one thing and the hard way—if you pay more for land
than it earns, you're sunk before you begin. That's what that skunk
Dodd did. Sold his land for more 'n it'll bring in. Lesly'll have it in
the end. If I help get the town incorporated, where'll I be then?
Lesly don't want it incorporated any more 'n Dodd did or does. Lesly
'ud be after me in no time then. How'd I get work? Answer me that."

'You make me tired. Here's your liniment." With a flip of the
wrist she gave a twist to the paper wrapping around the top of the
bottle and handed it to him, tapped impatiently the keys of the cash
register, gave him his change. "Your boy and mine soon be big enough
to louse around the pool halls if we don't get something better started.
The men who bought Dodd's property—if they work their land themselves, they got a chance. You'll see, come spring, when their houses
is built. Then if we all get together we could make things hum in this
town." She flung the last sentence at his retreating form. She wanted
to shout after him, "J. T.'s the worst boy in town. It's mean what he's
doing to that Suvorov kid," but she didn't dare.

Now that the school was no longer crowded with pupils, now that
the laborers had for the most part left The Valley, neither on the
playground nor in the bus did Peter find a place to get away from
J. T.'s barbs. Every way he had tried to reinstate himself at school had
failed. He had gone back believing that when he told Tuffy—who
had defended him, the previous spring, over the short pants—that he
could get him a free chance to go skiing, the boy would make J. T.
lay off him. Why, any boy would jump at a chance to go to the
Sierras! But it hadn't worked.

The opposition to Peter under J. T.'s taunts had become an un-
reasoned mass emotion which swept the boys up into a high state of
excitement, both terrifying and pleasurable. They had felt cheated
of their prey when Peter played truant. Now at his return they were
in full cry after their victim, massing themselves behind their leader.
If Peter could have fought the leader, he might have won their respect,
but you couldn't fight a cripple. Peter knew that.

The antagonism to Russians was even extending to their elders.

What was a black-bearded Russian doing in The Valley? Mishka had a threatening letter telling him he'd better get out. At the church he and his family attended one or two of the members questioned whether the Russians were true Protestant Christians.

After a time Peter thought of another plan. He, like others in the town, had come to believe that the breaking up of the big ranch was to bring the millennium. When the new boys whose fathers owned land came to school, he'd make a crowd of his own, and he'd be the leader. Then, when Peter took his crowd skiing, J. T. would wish he hadn't been so mean!

But the new boys didn't materialize. Most of the houses would not be finished before spring. However, the people who had bought forty acres next to the Suvorovs on the east got their house done late in November. Peter's hopes rose to fever pitch when, coming back in the school bus one afternoon, he saw a truck standing before the new house unloading furniture. After the bus had dropped him, he ran back along the road. Perhaps he could help. That would be a good way to get acquainted with a new boy. There was a car just driving up to the house. He slowed to a walk, a little nervous now at his own temerity. He watched from a distance a man get out of the car, then a woman with a baby in her arms. Then two girls!

A few other children entered the school, a couple of boys for the first grade, one boy several years older than Peter in another room. Then even this trickle of children ceased.

By early December Peter was again reaching the limit of his endurance. Even thinking about the man who was his father, whom he was helping, didn't mean very much. And then came awful moments when he wondered if maybe his being Russian made his father ashamed to have anyone know about him. John Dodd's letters didn't seem to help any more either. There wasn't a chance of getting even one boy for the skiing trip, and there were the continual gibes of the American boys. One afternoon, as he entered the bus, J. T.'s crowd started chanting:

> "Peter's a Red.
> We got to sit on his head.
> Peter's a Red.
> Peter's a Red."

Peter stood in the aisle, his mouth set. A pull on his sleeve made him turn. A Mexican boy, a grade in advance of him in school, motioned to a place beside him. Peter hesitated, and then all at once something seemed to burst within him. He didn't want to be one of the American boys! He was sick and tired of J. T. and everything that had to do with him. He sat down by Pedro.

"We got a fiesta next week. You wanta come?"

"Sure," said Peter. In spite of himself, he was gratified at an older boy's attention, even if he was a Mexican. He had a sudden, startling thought. Why weren't Russians and Mexicans just as good as anybody else? Sonya was a nice girl, and she was a Russian, and Pedro was kind to him.

He ran up the path to his house, feeling happier than he had felt for a long time. Maybe he could get Pedro to go skiing. "Mom, can I go to Mexican Town with a kid tomorrow after school?" he asked almost before he was inside the door.

Katya looked into his shining eyes. They hadn't been like that for a long time. But Mexican Town—she couldn't let him go there. It had a bad name. They couldn't afford to get mixed up with such people. They were on the margin of discrimination themselves.

At his mother's refusal, all Peter's happiness left him. Probably Mr. Dodd wouldn't want a Mexican boy either. He'd be on his mother's side. Still he must try.

Painstakingly he wrote his letter: "Dear Mr. Dodd, I got a boy might go, but I guess he won't do. He's a Mexican. Maybe I could get two. I don't think my mother will let me go if two Mexicans go along."

Before he left for school the next morning, he took some pennies from his bank; at recess he ran all the way to the post office. The next day was Saturday. He hung around the mailbox at the end of the lane, waiting for the carrier to drive past. Well, he guessed Mr. Dodd didn't like what he wrote him. It did not occur to him that his friend had not yet received the letter. By Tuesday he had lost hope, but nevertheless he opened the box as he passed it coming home from school. It was empty. Guess he couldn't get Pedro to go skiing anyway now. He had been hurt because Peter hadn't accepted his invitation to the fiesta.

There had been a slow drizzle all day. The ground was sticky and stuck to his feet, making them almost too heavy to lift. Slowly he entered the house, dutifully took his shoes off, set them to dry by the kitchen fire. Without a word to his mother he walked in his stocking feet into his own room and shut the door. There, propped against his inkwell, was a letter!

"Mom," shouted Peter, his tousled head appearing around the door, "Mr. Dodd likes Mexicans! He says he'll take two. You gotta let me go. You promised once."

"But not to the fiesta," she insisted.

Peter retreated again into his own room to think. Pedro wouldn't go skiing, he was sure, if he, Peter, didn't go to the fiesta. Tomorrow was its last day. He simply had to go. Bit by bit he worked out a way. He'd get kept after school and miss the bus; he'd go to Pedro's house just for a minute. The plan bothered him a little, but he had to be friends with Pedro.

The next afternoon Peter ran down the street toward Mexican Town on the ragged, weed-grown fringe of Doddstown. The short December day was almost done. He ought to be home by dark, or his mother would worry. She'd ask questions of Sonya, who'd tell her that he had been kept after school. He knew he could depend on Sonya. It would be all right if he reached home by dark.

At the corner leading to Mexican Town he hesitated, caught up into the fear all the other children had for Mexicans—dangerous people who got drunk and carried knives. The shacks huddled together along the unpaved, unlighted streets looked sinister. Peter started running. Ahead was the church where Pedro said he would wait for him. It was not much larger than the surrounding houses, but he knew it by the cross on its roof standing out clearly in the dusk. And then as he ran toward it he saw its door swing open and the altar aflame with candles.

Turning a corner, advancing toward the church was a candlelit procession of women bearing on a litter images Peter understood— the Holy Family, the Christ Child in the manger. Peter heard the women's soft Mexican voices raised in song. The Spanish words were strange to him, but the tone of reverence was not. Now he was not afraid. And there by the steps of the church stood Pedro. Peter drew up panting, "Am I late?"

"We're not to go in," said Pedro. "It's just for the women, but afterward we'll go to my house." Quietly they waited among the group of children growing larger as the minutes passed.

When the women came out, a stout, comfortable-looking one stopped and spoke to Peter. "You Pedro's friend. Come." She led the way toward a house at the end of the street.

The ritual of worship was over, the ritual of play was about to begin. Strumming of guitars seemed to come from every corner of Mexican Town as they passed along. The two-room house entered was soon crowded with men, women and children, laughing and singing. Great platters of steaming food were handed about. Peter forgot everything except that it was fun to be here with people laughing and singing and eating.

It was eight o'clock and very dark. With the old night terror taking hold of him, Peter dashed along the streets of Mexican Town, passing a couple of drunken men, then out into the highway and almost into the headlights of his mother's truck. There was Mishka peering down at him from its high seat. And for the first time Mishka spoke to him harshly.

"You should a father have to whip you. You make us trouble."

Peter's hands felt wet and cold. He could feel stubbornness growing up within him. Mishka says I'm bad. So will my mother. And the teacher does. They say I'm bad, he kept repeating to himself. Only Sonya didn't think him bad. It was through her friend Maria that she had maneuvered to get the Mexican boys to accept Petya.

The days dragged on. Peter discovered he sometimes gained immunity from the insults of J. T.'s crowd if he made himself inconspicuous. He grew listless, took no interest in his schoolwork, letting J. T. excel him in reading and arithmetic. Even his handwriting, of which he had been proud, he allowed to become slipshod. In the bus he lost himself as quickly as possible among the Mexican children. At recess, in a corner of the school yard, quietly Pedro and he discussed plans for the skiing trip. They decided to talk to Pedro's friend Manuel. But Manuel had a job cleaning the Sunshine Café very early every morning. His mother needed the money. It wouldn't do for him to go.

One morning at school there were two new boys standing by the teacher's desk. Peter's old plan came back to him. J. T. would probably be mean to them. Peter would be their friend. They'd like him, and——

"Peter, you may go on from here." It was the teacher's voice! Where was the place?

"Daydreaming again, Peter? You may read to me during recess."

I'll be too late, he thought desperately, sitting in the empty classroom listening to the shouts and laughter coming in at the open window. The recess was half over when at last the teacher let him go, and he raced down the steps and onto the playground. He saw a knot of boys gathered at the far end. Probably picking on the new boys. He'd see about that! He elbowed his way into the knot. Why, the big boy was a bully! He was advancing on J. T.! He'd knocked his cap off.

A wild joy took hold of Peter, a sense of release. All the anger and hate he had felt for J. T. were transferred to this new boy. This bully! The fat lummox pitching into a cripple! With a flying leap Peter landed upon him, hitting him with his fist. "Get to hell out of here!" he shouted. The new boy dealt him a blow on the nose. The blood spurted out, but Peter didn't even know it. With a fierce joy he grappled his opponent, tripped him. He had him down. He knelt on him. "Say you're licked," Peter cried, his voice choked with anger and blood, as he punched his knees into the boy's stomach. "Say I'm your boss!"

Sullenly the boy complied. "Now get up," Peter commanded, rising. "This guy here—" he pointed to J. T.—"what he says goes!" He looked around at the circle of boys no longer his enemies.

The bell rang, calling them in. Peter tried to stop his bleeding nose. His handkerchief was soaked. Somebody handed him another. He was the center of an admiring crowd racing toward the school door.

Only the teacher didn't admire him, kept him after school for pitching into the new boy. But Peter didn't mind staying this time. He had defended J. T., who was now his friend.

All J. T.'s warped and twisted hatred of Peter had turned into a half-agonizing, half-healing acceptance of him. He was still the leader, but he had to have Peter for his defender.

The teacher sat at her desk fidgeting with a pile of papers. These spring afternoons were short. She longed to catch a little of the day's freshness, escape the stale odor of too many bodies packed for hours into the room. And the chalk dust—sometimes it seemed almost to choke her. But where would she go? Nothing but a cheap second-rate movie house in this Godforsaken town. She would not come back next year. Teachers seldom did come back to Doddstown. There had been a long succession of them.

Peter, well versed in the signs of weariness in teachers, asked, "Can I go now?"

She was about to say he could, desiring of all things to be rid of him, and then looking at this stupid boy, for so she regarded him, seeing his swollen upper lip, his shirt stained with blood, she felt disgust rise in her against the drab town and its drab people. "Not after the way you've behaved," she answered sharply.

Peter's head ached. He could not hold it up any more. It sagged, finally dropped on his arm.

"Sit up," commanded the teacher. So the two sat until daylight was gone and the shadows began to fill the room.

Peter stumbled along the road, hoping to thumb a ride, but everyone seemed occupied with his own business. He was trying to hurry, but his head ached, and his body felt sore all over. He didn't care. Only he cared that his mother shouldn't think him bad. It was important she should understand.

An hour before Sonya had left the bus, run along the stretch of road to the two houses. The sun was topping the mountains. Ordinarily she would have noticed the sunset glow. Sonya loved color and enjoyed it wherever she saw it. She liked the bright yellow of the school bus, the red dress her teacher sometimes wore, Mrs. Suvorov's shining hair, the sunlight in summer setting the fields shimmering with light. But today she was in too much of a hurry to notice how the sinking sun tipped numerous small clouds with pink. She hurried toward the Suvorov house, but when she reached the hedge that shut off the garden plot, she hesitated a moment. Her mother had taught her never to go to the mistress' house unless invited.

Then resolutely she lifted the latch of the gate, crossed the few yards to the house, went up the steps. She must see Mrs. Suvorov. Peter was being kept after school, and he'd promised all the grownups it shouldn't happen again. But grownups didn't understand that sometimes you can't help being kept. She tapped timidly on the door.

Katya opened it, stood looking down on Sonya. This daughter of Mishka's had grown from a child into a girl very suddenly, it seemed to her, and pretty with her black hair and warm brown skin, a lovely color coming and going in her cheeks. Her vivacious black eyes were lighted now with excitement.

"Petya's going to be late, Mrs. Suvorov. I thought he'd like me to tell you, so you wouldn't worry."

"You mean he's being kept after school?"

"Not really. He hasn't broken his word. It really isn't his fault."

"Then why is he being kept in?" asked Katya, holding open the screen door for her small guest.

Sonya forgot she meant to tell only a little. Putting her books down on the kitchen table, she burst out, "After all J. T.'s done to Peter, Peter fought the new boy off for picking on him. The teacher didn't seem to know it. She kept Peter after school instead of that big bully of a new boy," Sonya ended scornfully. Then she added, looking anxiously at Peter's mother, "I think when he gets home maybe he'll be a little dirty, but I guess you won't mind."

"You can trust me," said Katya, grateful that through Sonya she had been admitted to some of the hard realities of Peter's childhood— or wasn't he a child any longer? Sonya had told more than she realized, for she had revealed that she loved Peter, loved him with the fierceness of foreshadowed adolescence, but humbly as it befitted just a girl. Katya didn't know whether or not she liked this.

Sonya's eyes wandered again to the window as they often had during their talk. "I've got to go! Peter's coming." He wouldn't like it if he found she'd been explaining. He'd have no girl messing into his affairs.

34

AT LAST Peter was able to write John Dodd that he had two boys to go with him on the skiing trip. In order to give them time to get to their camping ground before dark, it had been agreed that Mishka should bring the boys over to the east side of The Valley to Merced, where John would meet them. This would shorten John's ride by several hours. It was certainly an odd assortment of small boys John saw standing on the sidewalk by the gas station at the edge of the town when he drove up to the prearranged meeting place. The fair-haired, fair-skinned son of his brother, a dark, thick-set Mexican, the third an undersized youth with a withered leg. "Here's J. T.," Peter shouted triumphantly, and with almost as much pride, "and Pedro." Getting J. T.'s consent to Pedro's coming had been a great victory.

How Peter had won over his enemy, making him into a friend, John could not guess. That there was a special alliance between the two was immediately evident. "Who's going to sit in the front with me?" John asked, but he knew it would be Pedro.

"You hist in our duds," J. T. commanded the Mexican boy, as he and Peter climbed into the back seat.

There was a good deal of shifting about and horseplay on the part of the two boys in the back. Occasionally Pedro tried to join in, leaning over the front seat, but as the road began to lead upward, his whole attention was on the mountains. When they reached the snow line all three grew quiet, awed or a little frightened—John couldn't tell which—by the white sheet that lay everywhere. Experience had taught him that one emotion or the other was common to boys seeing snow for the first time. But whichever it was, he had found, lifting them as the sight did so suddenly out of their drab environment, it sometimes gave them the needed jolt to slough off their past and make a new start.

He turned the car into a narrow side road. Immediately they were deep among the giant pines with their long, black shadows stretching across the snow. Peter leaned forward, putting his hand on John's shoulder. How thin and light the hand was!

As they got out of the car, John caught a glimpse of J. T.'s face.

"Illumined" was the only word he could think of, but immediately the lame boy saw he was observed, his expression changed to one of cynicism and contempt. "Long way to come to look at trees," he scoffed.

"Come, boys, I'll show you the slide," said John, leading them around behind the cabin.

"Whoopee!" cried Peter, and with one accord the three boys began to clamor for sleds, skis, anything to slide down the sloping white way.

"There's a big sled in the shed. Here take the key." John handed it to Peter. "We've time for one or two trips before it's dark."

It wasn't a big slide, but very satisfactory for beginners, built by Jeremy Dodd for his children when they were little. Grandmother Dodd, like many other valley people, had secured a land use permit to this mountain retreat from the Forest Service in order to have a private recreation ground. John had persuaded her to make over the permit to him so he could have the camp for the use of his boys.

"Get on, J. T. I'll pull you up," cried Pedro, dragging the long sled to the foot of the slide.

"You, too, Pete," J. T. commanded. "Pedro's strong."

John started to object. He wasn't going to let them make a truck horse out of Pedro. He realized just in time that to have Pete on the sled was the only thing that made the necessity for his ride tolerable to J. T. "Come on, Pedro!" John took hold of the rope alongside the docile Mexican.

"How'd you like to steer?" he asked J. T. when they reached the top.

"You kiddin' me?" The lame boy's expression was one of incredulity.

"A little practice and you can do it," John answered, then proceeded to show him how. The boy was an apt pupil, quick with his hands and his brain. But despite his unconcealed delight in his prowess, and later his little-boy happiness in helping to prepare their supper over the open fire, John sensed a deep hostility in him. Even toward Peter, he decided with sudden insight.

He was a little uneasy over the friendship between the two. Perhaps the course he had taken with his brother's son was not the right one, but what else could he do? He wished he had more time to give Peter. He had planned to drive up to Doddstown occasionally through the winter to see him, but it had been a particularly busy season. In the last months of 1929 a good many men had been thrown out of employment. The crime wave among children had risen sharply.

He must keep a closer watch on the boy in the future, as Edward would do nothing. John had come to sharp words with his brother over Peter. It was inconceivable to him that Edward should continue to insist the boy was not his child. He could not doubt it if he would only consent to see him. Peter's pale-yellow hair was streaked with darker strands just as Edward's had been in childhood, before it turned dark. His face was beginning to take on the Dodd cast. His hands were long and narrow, a peculiarity of all the Dodds.

He seemed much older than the little boy who had confided in him in the early fall. He was uncommunicative now and several times during the evening he seemed ill at ease in John's presence. After the three boys were in bed, John sat by the fire wondering if it would be of any use to make another appeal to Edward to accept his son. If he wouldn't, some day Peter would awake to the fact that the role John had suggested to him in the fall of helping his father by laying no claim to him was the role of the unwanted child.

John looked across at the tousled heads of the sleeping boys. All three underprivileged in lesser or greater degree. According to his record of underprivileged boys, it would be a fair bet that one of the three would in time become a delinquent. There was Pedro; his thick, close-growing mat of black hair marked him as Mexican—he had only half a chance. J. T.? Undoubtedly the boy had brains, but his chances, too, were slim. And there was Peter, cast in the image of his own family, and already guilty of a misdemeanor.

John had promised that he would deliver each boy to his own home sometime on Sunday afternoon so that there would be no chance of any of them missing school on Monday morning. Their first stop was at the farm of J. T.'s father, situated on a side road south of Dodds-town. When the car drew up before a small, neat house, J. T. got out hurriedly, limped away toward the back door with hardly a good-by or a thank-you. John thought he saw a curtain lifted ever so slightly at the front window, as if someone were peering out, but he could not be sure.

At Pedro's, although the house could hardly be dignified by the name, so dilapidated it was, they were urged to come in, and Pedro was welcomed as if he had been away for weeks instead of two days. That the father was a little tipsy did not destroy Pedro's evident pride in his family.

"Now your guests are delivered, how's for getting you home?" John turned to Peter.

"I could get off at our road," Peter answered. "You've been awful good to take us. I guess you got a long way to go yet."

John was touched by the boy's thoughtfulness. He could see Peter was so tired with the two days of unaccustomed exercise that any walk ing would be a difficult chore. He fell asleep even before they turned in from the highway. John roused him as they neared the house.

"There's Mother!" cried Peter trying to act as if he had not been asleep. "And Mishka!"

In the lighted doorways of the two houses John could see figures, and then in the headlights of the car he saw the boy's mother running forward and behind her Mishka's family.

"You must come in and have something to eat before you go on," urged Katya, once she had hugged her son, who now had run on to the group behind. John walked beside her toward the house, all the rest trailing, bringing Peter's things into the kitchen. To Mishka's dark, animated wife and the no less animated little girl Peter was talking in long bursts of Russian.

Then they were all in the kitchen. Katya was stirring something fragrant on the stove. Daria, the wife, disappeared, but soon returned bringing a plate covered with a white napkin. "Petya, for you!" she cried. Her black eyes snapped, her laugh rang out gaily.

"How is the snow, Petya, deep to the earth?" asked Mishka.

Peter sobered. "I think not very deep, Mishka. Wait!" He darted off, returning with a piece of knotted string. "This deep." He gave the string to the older man.

John, watching, saw that Mishka made a point of sharing the responsibility for the ranch with Peter. He was not so concerned about the boy as he had been. Here were the ingredients of a good life. With better conditions promised for the town, Peter surely would be all right. A hundred new families scheduled to take over the Dodd property ought to mean a town as good as the one he had been brought up in, on the east side of The Valley.

In a little while Mishka and his family left, and Peter, after proudly displaying his room to John, willingly went to bed. John knew he should start. He had a long ride home tonight, and he must be up early in the morning. And yet he could not find the will to go.

"You have been very good to us," Katya, sitting across the room from him, said. "Before, I thought you hard on my son, but I see he grows from within."

Grows from within, thought John. It could be applied to her also. You could not sit with her, as he had for the last half hour, without realizing her richness of spirit.

He rose, taking her hand for a moment before parting. "If I can be of help to you any time, will you call on me?"

"Sometime if you would come to see us and tell me if I—— I am not strong with him, the way a father would be."

After he had gone, Katya moved about putting the kitchen in order for their early breakfast. When this brother of Edward had first come to see her and ever since until this evening, she had resented his interference, resented the gratitude she owed him. He was enough like Edward to seem the man who had not wanted her. Only tonight had she been able to see him as separate from Edward.

35

THE quickening pace of spring—the birds' early morning song, the mechanized cacophony of the tractors, a renewed bustle in the town—did not stir Katya as they had last spring. Without protest she allowed Mishka to decide on the proportion of land to lie fallow this season. Eighty acres were to be divided between cotton and potatoes. Twenty he insisted should lie fallow. But given good crops and good prices they would more than break even, he assured her.

Neither did she take any interest in the new people moving into The Valley, nor in the roads being built to give access to the hinterland of the Dodds' three thousand acres, nor in the farmhouses going up here and there on the once empty stretches. She had come to accept her isolation. Fate made her belong to America; fate decreed also she should not be a part of it.

Peter's departure for school in the morning, his return in the afternoon marked the days. She was not aware that Peter, determined to be a part of America, was helping to impose isolation on the less fortunate. Dysentery had broken out in one of the camps. A rumor went around that two of the children had died. At school the pupils, frightened by their parents, imposed a quarantine of their own on the itinerants.

J. T. told his crowd that if any of them went near the dirty Mexicans or other laborers, they could no longer play with the American children. Peter was his henchman, running all foreigners off the section of the school walk J. T. had pre-empted for his crowd. Only Pedro, Peter insisted, shouldn't be excluded. Pedro quietly settled the matter by staying off. But on Saturdays he and Peter often played together. Then a case of diphtheria was discovered in one of the cabins at the edge of town, and the county health officer ordered all migrant laborers out of the county—three hundred families in all. "It is my duty," he said, "to protect the health of our people."

"There, I told you so," said J. T. "Pete, you got to stop going round with Pedro. Mexicans are dirty." This time Peter consented.

Sonya escaped J. T.'s watchful eye by maintaining an attitude of self-effacement. Ever since she had come to The Valley she had attained immunity from all badgering by quietly taking her place among the Mexican girls and never attempting to associate with Peter away from home. But she had until J. T.'s vitriolic attack on foreigners walked along the lane with him. Now she lagged behind.

For a little after the going of the itinerants the school assumed its winter status, and then boys and girls of all ages began trickling in, members of the hundred new families who had bought sections of the Dodd ranch. The boys Peter had once longed for in vain had come. Landowners indeed, and not to be looked down on by J. T. A rival group was formed even as Peter had foreseen, only now he was on J. T.'s side. All the rest of the school year the groups formed and re-formed, and J. T. learned he could hold his supremacy only so long as he dealt justly. Even Peter once threatened to go over to the other group—in fact, he did for one thrilling afternoon.

Now suddenly Sonya emerged from obscurity. One noon she came through the wide doors of the school, lunch pail in hand, bent on securing her favorite corner in an ell of the building. Here she ate her lunch alone each day, as the Mexican girls went home for their luncheon. She felt an arm around her waist, and a voice in her ear whispered, "Can't we be friends—you know, special friends?" It was one of the new girls in her class whom she had admired at a distance. The new girl was pretty in a doll-like way that pleased Sonya, and every day she wore socks to match her freshly ironed dress. "Your name's Song, isn't it? I heard the teacher say it."

"It's really Sonya. My people came from Russia."

"I *said* Song, didn't I? My people came here from Iowa. My name is Bertha."

"Song." Sonya said it over and over going up the lane that afternoon. "I'm always going to be Song.

> "Song, Song, I can walk to the name!
> Song, Song, I can dance to the name!
> I can swing my books to it."

She twirled the strap in her hand, experimenting with the rhythm. A perplexed look crossed her face as she came into the kitchen of her house. Her mother had just come in from the fields. She had on men's shoes, and she wore a shawl around her head, the ends tied

behind. For the first time the girl was conscious of differences between herself and her mother.

One warm April afternoon Katya was working in her garden plot,
stirring the earth around her two rosebushes, intending to water them
while Mishka was still in the fields. The unwonted sound of a motor-
car coming to a stop very close made her look up. A stout, middle-
aged woman was getting out of the car. "You are Mrs. Suvorov?" she
asked. When Katya answered in the affirmative, she continued,
"You're just the person I want to see. I'm one of the new people who
bought a piece of the Dodd ranch." She was in the garden enclosure
now. "I'm your neighbor down the road apiece. May Roberts is my
name. Some of us are planning to do things together. You know,
make a few improvements in the town. We hoped you'd like to join
us."

Katya hesitated a moment. The doors of communication so long
closed seemed to creak on their hinges. She wanted to open her heart
to this stranger, let friendship in, but she didn't know how.

"Won't you come in?" she said at last.

May Roberts was a comfortable woman, long used to town activities. She'd hardly noticed Katya's hesitation, her mind full of all the
things she wanted to talk about. Organization was the breath of life
to her. "We have a lot of things to do," she said as soon as she was
seated. "There's no parent-teacher association here, not even a ladies'
aid, I hear. The men want to get a cotton co-operative going so they
can gin their cotton. But all of this can wait. What we must do first
is to back the state up on this water business."

Until Mrs. Roberts had reached the last sentence, Katya had stared
at her blankly, unable to take in so much activity. But water was
something she understood. The shadow of its going hung over her.
Mishka was having to irrigate the fields a month earlier than last year.
That meant an extra irrigation for the season. Next year would be
worse, for so little rain had fallen to seep down and replenish the
underground basin and in the mountains there was no heavy snow
pack. The late-fallen powdery snow would give but a small percentage
of water to sink into the ground. As Katya had no flow water she
might have to deepen her wells, even get higher-powered pumps if the
underground water level sank much lower. That would mean an
expense which would reduce her bank account almost to the vanishing point.

Now Katya realized her anxiety could be shared with neighbors. "If
there is anything to do about water, I'd like to join you."

"Just so!" triumphantly exclaimed May Roberts. "Of course you know about the state plan to distribute water. It will be up before the legislature in Sacramento this fall. Power companies and big fellows like Lesly are trying to keep the matter from coming up. We want to get up a petition signed by a lot of us and send it to our representatives, especially Dodd, the senator at large." Katya caught her breath.

"How do I sign?" asked Katya when May Roberts laid the petition before her.

"Why, here, right after the last name put down. Evidently you don't know about petitions. I hope you voted at the last election," said Mrs. Roberts. "You didn't!" she exclaimed when Katya answered in the negative. "Probably not even registered. Where have you been all your life? I declare the American people don't deserve democracy." She was off on her favorite subject. Crossing her legs, she drew out her knitting and started to make one good American this afternoon.

All through this lesson in civics Katya's heart was singing, She's scolding me as one of the American people. Petya doesn't need to be ashamed of me any more. If she thinks I'm an American, all the others will, too.

It was almost time for Petya to come home from school when Mrs. Roberts rose, stuffed her knitting into her sweater pocket, saying, "Well, I'm coming around for you tomorrow to get you registered." She was halfway down the steps when she turned. "Oh, I almost forgot. We're fixin' up a couple of trucks with seats to take us over east aways tomorrow night to hear a man explain about water. Can I pick you up?"

Having gained Katya's consent, May Roberts drove away with the warm sense of the evangelist who has made a convert. Her creed was *organization*—women's clubs, ladies'-aid societies, men's rotary clubs and co-operatives. Most of all, just now, a close group of the small farmers who by co-operation would help one another to prosperity. "Get together" was her slogan, a chant that went through her mind as she washed dishes and hustled her children off to school and her husband off to his newly acquired cotton patch. It brought her a mystic satisfaction to have won this isolated woman farmer into the fold.

Riding across The Valley to hear her first political speech, Katya sat wedged in between May on one side and Jed Roberts on the other. All around were friendly faces, men and women drawn together in a common need—the need for water.

As the truck rumbled along, Mrs. Roberts harangued them all.

"You got to stick together. Somebody's telling the people it means higher taxes." Katya's mind reached out to take in the complicated problem of being a good citizen. Once, long ago, Edward had said she couldn't understand. Now she must. And in making the effort, she felt the lethargy of the winter slip from her.

They were passing through orchard country now. Acres of blossoming plum floated like a pure white cloud let down from the sky, the black tree trunks lost in the failing light. Above them—for they were riding in an open truck—the sky was an intense blue. As darkness came on, the blue was studded with stars. And there in the night amid laughter, an occasional earthy joke, May Roberts' voice proclaiming salvation through organization, Katya for the first time felt herself an American. She made a silent vow to work for the good of her community.

As they grew acquainted with one another, other voices were raised expressing hopes or fears.

"The piece of land I bought," said a quiet man named Miller, "has flow-water rights, but I don't get the first water."

"I'm one of the fellows that's got that, I guess," called out a man sitting at the other end of the truck.

"What we need to do is to all get together," said May Roberts, the apostle of organization.

"You're goldarn right!" It was the ex-druggist of the town speaking. "I've lived around here for a long time, and you can be mighty sure that the Dodds had plenty of rights to protect themselves. They're keen as mustard when it comes to business. We own all their stock in the water company but Lesly is in it too. What we've got to do is stick together and vote solid for what we want. The way the land is split up now with all the ditches and things, we're going to have a hell of a lot of trouble unless we do."

"Speaking of Dodds," said the father of the little girl from Iowa, "I'd hate to have a town like Doddstown called after me. It's as full of vice as a dog with fleas. And it looks like a shanty town." He had been lured to The Valley by Iowans who had settled in numbers in California and told him the climate would do away with his wife's chronic cough. Doddstown offended him. Only in the South had he thought to see such a slumlike aspect. "No respectable town looks like Doddstown," he ended.

Katya felt her cheeks grow red. She was thankful for the darkness, thankful at last that she and her son did not bear the Dodd name as she had once so vehemently desired.

"Well, we'll have to clean it up. We ought to get it incorporated first of all. The county runs it now, and that means the big fellows. If we get it incorporated, we could run things ourselves and make a good town," May Roberts put in. "I'll get up a petition."

"You ain't got a fourth of the new farmers represented here tonight. Maybe some of them won't be interested, except maybe in a cotton gin of our own that'll gin our cotton cheaper than taking it to an outside gin—they ought to be interested in that, and they ought to be interested in getting cheap electric power for their farms." Like a Greek chorus reduced to one voice the speaker kept murmuring, "Most of them won't care anything about the town, just theirselves."

When they returned from the meeting Katya felt that their community was tied into all the communities of The Valley, bound together to work for water. She kept thinking of the map of The Valley displayed at the meeting. The Valley was colored a pale-yellow entirely rimmed with purple mountains. At its northern end a great dam had been drawn and a blue lake behind it making a fountainhead of water to be poured into rivers, streams, canals, gathering together the waters moving south, touching with life each separate farm like her own.

36

LESLY had left his home in San Francisco early to visit his ranch. He was driving his car himself today, leaving the chauffeur in town for Mrs. Lesly. His Southern gallantry would not let him do less with his wife burdened with so many last preparations for their trip east—getting the children off to suitable camps, arranging for a complete renovation of their house while they were all away, collecting a fit wardrobe to visit her people in the South while he was attending to his business in New York. She was to join him in New York after his business was finished. Later they'd go down to Washington. These Eastern directorates he had recently assumed, enlarging his influence as they did, made it necessary for him to get the lay of the national political scene.

Lesly hoped to do his errand in The Valley and get back to San Francisco in time for a late dinner. He hated a night at the ranch, avoided it whenever possible, for it in no way appealed to him as a home. Neither did he care for land as land. He would mistreat it if by so doing he could make more money out of it. He had exhausted the soil of his plantation in Alabama during the years when cotton was high-priced, then sold out and started over in California. The ranch was simply one of his most lucrative ventures. He thought of it as that overflow of his growing fortune which provided the luxuries of his life. The "velvet" he called it. Certainly from his looks there was plenty of velvet. His fleshy cheeks merging into his fleshy neck indicated he lived very well indeed. His chin stood out like a promontory of decision in the midst of his pink flesh. Together they made a face that his competitors feared. He was soft with the need for luxury and he had the will to get it whatever it cost his neighbor.

It was barely noon when he came to the northern boundary of what was once the Dodd ranch. He slowed his car. A lot of houses going up. A lot of money going into them. Adds just that much to their high-priced land. Give them three years to fold up, he said to himself, now the recession has begun. He'd have them by that time. But the itch to increase his acreage immediately he could not entirely resist. He had decided to play his first card today. He'd written his manager, Butterfield, to get in touch with the Widow Suvorov, whose small holding bordered his ranch on the north. A woman wouldn't know much about business. He ought to be able to maneuver her into a position where she'd sell.

As Lesly's car had reached the edge of Doddstown, he felt a fastidious withdrawal. "Almost as bad as a nigger town in the South," he said to himself. "It goes to show you can't make a silk purse out of a sow's ear. If people want to live like that, they're going to do it. Talk about labor camps set up by the government. Just waste a lot of money on no-'count people." He increased his speed.

When Lesly's manager had called Katya on the telephone, asking her to come over this morning and meet Mr. Lesly, she had hesitated at first. A few months before, Mishka had told her Lesly had tried to hire him. She guessed that he had offered Mishka higher wages. "I do not go," said Mishka. Worried that she could not do as much for him as Lesly, Katya had deeded ten acres to him. She had done it on an impulse of generosity, but Mishka's gratitude, she soon saw, was one of the best investments she had ever made.

Listening to Butterfield's gentlemanly voice over the phone, she wondered what Lesly wanted of her now. She was about to refuse his invitation when she remembered May Roberts' remark, the day they had organized the parent-teacher association. "We ought to get hold of the mothers at Lesly's labor camps." Here was a chance, Katya realized, to do her part. "Yes," she said, "I'll come," and put down the telephone.

She was a little frightened as she drove her truck up to the aluminum-painted gates of Lesly's place. Did one get down and knock, or was there a bell? As if by magic, the gates swung open. Someone must have been watching for her, but there was no one in sight. Slowly she drove her truck along a drive covered with fine white crushed rock bordered with whitewashed, rounded stones shining in the brilliant sunlight. To one side was a group of low moderate-sized houses freshly painted dark-green. Some distance away a group of whitewashed cabins. Still farther away another group just discernible, white specks in a sea of growing cotton.

Just ahead was a larger building. White letters on the front read: ADMINISTRATION BUILDING. In a great shed to the side women were sorting potatoes. Through an open door at the back she could see a railroad spur and boxcars, into which men were loading sacks of potatoes. There was a store, too, with the kind of things in the window working people need—a company store where the laborers could charge against their wages. Katya had heard of it. The merchants in Doddstown complained it took business away from them.

As Katya stepped down from her truck, a man came out of the main building. "I'm Butterfield, Mr. Lesly's manager, and you—you are our neighbor to the north, I believe. It's nice of you to come in response to my telephone call. Mr. Lesly ought to be here very soon. Won't you come in?"

The room into which he ushered her was at the end of the company store, evidently his office. "You'll have a Coca-Cola? It's pretty hot today." He rose, went to a small refrigerator standing in the corner, and took out two bottles. As she sipped the refreshing ice-cold drink, she tried to decide whether to ask him about the laborers' wives, or to wait and talk to Mr. Lesly.

Embarrassed under the man's gaze, an appraisal not altogether impersonal, she hastened to say, "I came a little early, Mr. Butterfield, to ask if you'd let me talk to the women in your camps about the parent-teacher association we're trying to form."

"You're sure you're not a Red come in to stir up our laborers?"

"Oh, no," gasped Katya, then detected the amusement in his eyes. Was he trying to make her a little ridiculous? With dignity she went on: "Now we're a community, we think we can do something for our children."

"Who is we?" he asked in a bantering tone.

"Why, all the small farmers who have just come here from other parts of the country. They want things right for their children, and so do I. I should think it would interest you, too. You might have children some day."

Butterfield threw back his head and laughed. "Frankly it doesn't. I'm a bachelor. I have been manager here for five years now. We give our office force more than most companies. Let me show you." As they stood up, their eyes met in challenge. Putting his hand under her elbow, he directed her steps toward the door. On the wide balcony outside he stopped. "You see," he said, waving his hand toward the houses of his overseers. "Nice, aren't they?"

His implication, Katya felt, was that his helpers were housed better than Mishka, and honesty made her admit he was right.

"As to our laborers," he went on, "we give them everything they need. We are a self-sustaining, efficient unit."

Katya could see he was proud of what he had done and loyal to the man he served, but she, a recent convert to civic responsibility, could not give up what she had come to do. "But the school! Your laborers' children come to the school. We want their parents to take part in things we're planning."

"I'd have to talk it over with Mr. Lesly, or perhaps you had better. I can't decide such questions myself."

"Maybe you'd be interested in helping personally. You could act for yourself without asking, couldn't you?"

A guarded look that seemed to rob him of all individuality settled over his face. "I am too busy to take on any outside work. I'm putting all the energy I have into my job."

She did not know what to answer and was relieved to see the gates swing open again to admit, to her surprise, not Mr. Lesly but Jake Bodkin, who she had recently learned from Mrs. Roberts was political boss of the town. "Lesly here yet, Butterfield?" he called out as he climbed out of his rattling old Ford. "It don't matter. This is the coolest place I've found. All them sprinklers going and green grass. We're all dried-up in town."

Butterfield introduced them. "I'd like you to meet Mrs. Suvorov."

"Mother of that kid Peter, aren't you? If I was you, I'd keep him away from that Ward boy."

Just then Lesly's car shot through the open gateway and stopped before the building. Jake made no move to go and greet him. "Better get in out of the heat," he called. I come over to meet him just as he wired me to do, he was thinking, but he can do the coming now.

Should come to meet me, thought Lesly, but he knows his power in the town. Even Lesly walked softly before Jake.

Butterfield held the car door open. Lesly climbed out, mopping the perspiration from his cheeks and neck with a fine linen handkerchief.

"Valley heat too much for you?" Jake looked down from his great height on short, overweight Lesly, thinking, He ain't got a pint of red blood in him, even if he does look like the inside of a watermelon. Cold as stone. But he admired Lesly. In fact, they admired each other. "We kinda jibe," Jake had once gone so far as to tell Lesly.

Lesly was annoyed that Jake had come an hour early. He'd have to get rid of him while he talked to Mrs. Suvorov. "Whom have I the pleasure of meeting?" he asked, going toward her.

"Oh, excuse me!" Butterfield hastened forward. "I forgot you hadn't met."

"Mrs. Suvorov, I've waited for a long time for this pleasure, but pressure of business . . . As neighbors we have problems in common."

"It's because of that I really came!" exclaimed Katya. "It's a question of school. We want to get all the parents together. Mr. Butterfield said to speak to you about the women here joining us. We want to get more entertainment for the children."

Jake Bodkin was enjoying himself. Hadn't expected to run into anything like this.

Lesly's eyes narrowed. "Mrs. Suvorov, I hope you're not going to be one of those people who foment trouble among laborers. That's not the kind of neighbor I'm looking for. You've had bad advice. You can't educate people out of their class. If you do, you won't have any dependable labor."

"You mean *you* won't! I have dependable labor," Katya retorted, remembering how he had tried to get Mishka away from her.

"Suppose we go inside to my office and talk this over. You don't mind waiting a little, do you, Jake? See that Jake gets a cool drink while I discuss plans with Mrs. Suvorov," he said over his shoulder to Butterfield.

Once he and Katya were in his office out of earshot, he went on: "Small places like yours tend to disappear all over America today. They can't be efficient. You've shown me how bad they are in another way, bad for our youth. Your son, for instance, shouldn't be associating with a lot of laborers' children. What you propose won't work among such people. Take my advice. Sell out. I'll give you a good price for your land. Take your boy back to San Francisco. That's where you said you used to live, didn't you? It's to your interest."

"You mean you *want* people to live the way they do around the town?" Katya asked, her distaste for him growing. His hands seemed to typify the man. His right one, plump and white, spread out on the green blotter of his desk, was a womanish hand with short fingers, the tips cushioned with pads as soft as those on a cat's paw.

"I didn't say 'want.' No matter what we did, they'd soon sink back to their way of life," Lesly replied.

Suddenly Katya was very angry indeed. Time seemed to be welded together, the past and the present and the future. The past seemed to be the present. "Some day they won't accept the little you give them," she said.

Lesly lifted his eyebrows. "By any chance are you a Russian, Mrs. Suvorov?"

"Yes, and once I stood where you do, and we lost."

"As to my offer, Mrs. Suvorov? You know there's a depression in the country. A woman alone——" As he spoke he rose and, moving quickly and lightly for such a heavy man, circled the desk and came up behind her. Before she realized his intention, he had laid the hands she so much detested on her shoulders, began sliding them down her arms.

His very touch seemed to contaminate her, but she managed to control her shivering sense of revulsion. "Please," she said with dignity, rising and moving toward the door. "I have to go now, and I'll report what you've said to the other women."

"Quite a gal," Lesly remarked later to Jake and Butterfield as they watched her drive away. "A woman like that must have a past. I'd like to see her dressed up in good clothes."

With a sense of impending disaster Katya drove home. Almost with the detachment of a stranger she surveyed her own farm. Her fields looked as well cared for as Lesly's, thanks to Mishka's untiring labor. There was no paint on Mishka's house, to be sure. Even her own house looked a makeshift affair. Farm machinery stood about. She didn't have sheds for it yet. And then she remembered the face of Lesly's manager when she asked that he help in town activities. He was afraid, too.

Mishka was sitting in his doorway. Strange he did not come to help her down from the truck, nor even rise when she went toward him. "Mishka, the farmers meet soon to plan for a co-operative to market the cotton. Will you go and speak for me?"

"I go," Mishka answered, "but I speak the thoughts I think. You want speak your thoughts, you speak them. I speak you some thoughts. This Lesly, he just thief."

"What are you talking about, Mishka?"

"You see." He looked off over Lesly's acres, his huge work-worn hands clasped in front of him. "Ours the earth that is not filled with water—sometime."

"But how, Mishka?" Katya spoke bravely, but she was afraid. Lesly had the advantage over her in owning the deepest part of the water basin. If he wanted her land and he found a way to pull the water out of her shallower part of the basin, he'd show her no mercy. He had made very plain to her the only means a woman had of getting mercy from him. She shivered, feeling again his soft fleshy hands on her bare arms.

As the summer progressed, the men and women who had bought the Dodd ranch found that for the most part they were doing well. May Roberts bit by bit was hammering them into a cohesive body. Together they owned as many acres as Lesly, and in the water company in which he was a member, their votes outweighed his. It was only when they did not stand together that he won over them in water matters.

Katya's friendship with the Roberts was an ever-increasing wonder to her. It seemed never to occur to May Roberts that Katya's background was different from hers. Their friendship was further cemented by a growing friendship between Hal, the Roberts boy, and Peter. It started in the spring when Mrs. Roberts had proposed that on Saturdays the children of the two families—she always included Sonya in the Suvorov family—share their work. It would be more fun for them if half the day they spent together helping Mishka cut up the potatoes for seed and the other half helping Jed. The two boys, a little scornful of the girl's ability, worked together to prove their greater prowess. At school Hal began to single out the younger boy. It was Hal's crowd that Peter joined on that one thrilling afternoon of rebellion from J. T.'s domineering.

By fall the Dodd farmers, as they were called, were beginning to share May Roberts' enthusiasm for a cotton gin of their own. Their yield per acre on cotton had averaged a bale and a half. It needed at that rate about three thousand acres to support a cotton gin. If they could interest the small farmers within a radius of twenty-five miles to join them, they hoped they could raise enough money so they could go to the bank and borrow enough more to finance the construction of a gin.

It had not all been as peaceful as May Roberts had envisioned it. There were two Negro farmers who wished to join and offered to put up more than their share of the money, but a number of the other farmers insisted they didn't want Negroes in any co-operative they belonged to. They were finally convinced that the Negroes' money was as good as theirs when it came to putting it up for collateral at the bank.

Some little difficulty occurred, too, in the new parent-teacher association when Katya suggested weekly dances. To Katya's consternation May Roberts opposed the suggestion with the vigor usually attendant upon religious scruples. To Katya's further astonishment she found Daria siding against her, too. Dancing was not allowed by the sect of Protestant Russians to which she belonged. It was all very confusing to Katya, who thought of dancing and music as expressions of joy. Finally the matter was settled by calling the weekly entertainments sociables and devoting the evening to games.

But the greatest innovation at school was the organization of rival baseball teams by the professor-farmer. Peter was on Hal's team and so was Pedro. J. T. was made manager. At first he had refused, suspicious of the fact that he had been chosen out of pity for his lameness. But in the end he was swept up into the general enthusiasm. Peter without being conscious of it shifted his allegiance from J. T. to Hal.

37

THREE years passed. The dread dirge of depression beating out its slow rhythm in the cities of America—New York, Pittsburgh, Detroit, Los Angeles, San Francisco—in time had brought rural America into its fateful harmony. As the buying power of the big cities dropped lower and lower and employment decreased, lower and lower fell the price of corn and wheat from the Mississippi Valley, lower and lower the price of luxury crops of California. The second summer of the depression the fruit trees, overburdened with pears, peaches, apricots and oranges, awaited the pickers who never were hired. Cheaper to let the fruit rot. Even potatoes and cotton hit an all-time low.

In Doddstown there was an ominous tension. It was as if it waited for a time clock to sound out its doom, a doom made real by the sight of the last migration to come to The Valley—farmers driven out of Arkansas and Oklahoma valleys by drought and dust. Day by day, week by week, a drab procession of old cars moved into the town. Roadside camps sprang up filled with hungry, dejected people, augmenting the rows of laborers' shacks already edging the town also filled with hungry, dejected people. Children went scantily clad to school, sometimes carrying dry bread to eat at noon, sometimes taking nothing and making it known they were not hungry. The county could not feed them all, the state said it had no authority to feed them, and the big companies who depended on them to harvest their crops, finding labor plentiful and therefore cheap, claimed hunger was not their responsibility. The newly formed parent-teacher organization tried to do what it could. But it could spare so little. Some of the members were so hard-pressed that they feared they too might soon be among the homeless throng. Men who had bought the Dodd land at boom prices, counting on continued bumper crops and bumper prices to pay their mortgages, were facing the specter of defeat. Depression had pulled down the price of their products; a dry cycle had pulled down their water supply. Their one chance of winning, they felt, lay in a quick passage of the state's long-delayed Central Valley Project. If they could find temporary work in the building of the great dams and canals, thus eke out the scanty returns from their ranches, they hoped to meet the interest on their mortgages when they fell due. All eyes were upon the State Building in Sacramento, where at last the plan was to be voted on.

The passage of the act would be a high moment in the history of California. In bold type it carried the words: *for the welfare and benefit of the people of the state, for the improvement of their property and their living conditions.* The Federal Government, in accordance with its recovery program to advance thirty per cent on all construction of public works in the country, would take much of the financial burden off the state.

In Doddstown and a hundred other towns and in the countryside the people of the state began to hope. In the offices of the power companies men hoped, too, but for a different outcome. Although there was little likelihood of defeating the bill, there was a chance to have it so worded that it would allow the private companies to control the distribution of all power generated in the great dams. Astute lobbyists were detailed to present the case of the private interests to assemblymen and senators. At informal luncheons and dinners company officials discussed ways and means of approaching the men they knew in the legislature.

Just before the opening of the regular session Jeremy Dodd invited a number of his colleagues and a couple of executives of large land companies to an informal dinner. It was given at the Palace, his favorite hotel, in a private dining room. He had taken great care in ordering the meal. It began with a crab cocktail, not minced-up tiny pieces but large ones a man could taste. followed by juicy filet steaks of corn-fed beef and the best white and red wines of California. When the waiter brought in the dessert, he paused a moment so all might see the chef's creation, a pyramid of ice cream surrounded by large California peaches, blue flames of rum encircling it all.

Throughout the dinner there had been considerable talk about the coming bill, the chance of introducing amendments, and how various members of Assembly or Senate would probably vote. As the men pushed back their chairs and settled down with cigars, cigarettes and pipes, Jeremy asked the question he had brought them together to ask: "How many votes do we lack to make our position secure in the Senate?"

"Three," said a stout little man sitting at his right.

"Two," said his neighbor.

"I'd cut it down to one," said Jeremy.

"How do you make that out?" asked the man who had said "two," leaning forward. It was significant that Dodd should say this. It was his own son of whom all the men were in doubt.

The implication behind the question was not lost on Jeremy. It was a constant humiliation to him that these men regarded him with some suspicion—some flaw in him to have a son who in their estimation betrayed his class, something irregular in the family somewhere.

"Of course Edward is pledged to vote for the project as a whole," Jeremy answered. "It is on that platform he was elected, but I see no reason why he should oppose certain adjustments which would make the plan more acceptable to us."

"Suppose we appoint you a committee of one to see that he does not."

"I consider it my responsibility," Jeremy answered.

The conversation became general. But later he spoke directly to the man at his right. "My company has been thinking of buying up some land—" he mentioned the region almost in a whisper—"It would give us certain water rights. Might build a dam later——" He did not complete the sentence.

"I don't see why it couldn't be managed if this bill goes through as we wish it, Dodd. My company certainly would make no protest."

These two men, the heads of rival companies, understood each other. If Jeremy delivered his son's vote, his rival would not interfere with the expansion of Jeremy's business.

In the closing hours of the regular session the bill passed by a comfortable margin in line with what the power companies wanted. But the fight was not ended. A special session was eventually called to write into the bill four provisions, among them one giving the people of the state the right to form utility districts which could compete directly with the privately owned corporations for the purchase of the power generated at the government dams. This would be a great boon to the small and isolated farmers whom the private electric companies did not supply, and to groups of small owners, even towns, wishing to join together to get power cheaper than the private companies offered it.

The voting would be closer than it had been in the regular session. Many of the senators had already expressed their intention to vote for the provisions, as the Federal Government had declared against appropriating money to help if the provisions "safeguarding the rights of the people" were not accepted.

This July morning official Sacramento was tense with the coming struggle. Usually the city at this season drowsed in its summer heat, no longer the focus of interest for the state, senators, assemblymen and lobbyists having all alike gone home.

But this year of 1933 the legislature had only recessed from its regular session and had returned this morning to settle finally, or so it hoped, the fight over water and power for The Valley. In the hotel lobbies and the halls of the Capitol the power men were making last-minute appeals for support.

Many eyes followed Edward Dodd as he crossed the lobby of the Senator Hotel. He was not unaware of the interested glances. He knew he was a keyman in what happened today in the Senate chamber. On how he played his hand might depend not only the whole future of the state, but also his own career. The voting would be close—his vote possibly deciding it.

All very well what he had promised his constituency in his original campaign speeches. Conditions had changed since then. Experience had taught him many things—one that he was not the representative of a particular group of people, but of the whole state. During the regular session he had come to the conclusion that originally he had oversimplified the water problem, seeing it somewhat emotionally because of his early attachment to The Valley. He had a better perspective now. He no longer had any personal connection with The Valley.

Telling himself that he should not be identified even with Sacramento, a valley city, he had not rented a house in Sacramento for the past session; instead he had taken rooms at the hotel. This arrangement gave him greater freedom of action and the opportunity to accept a type of entertaining he could not when Agnes was living in

Sacramento—small stag parties for the most part, given by prominent men in the state. He needed to talk with men of all kinds—engineers, businessmen, ranchers and reporters.

He had seen a good deal of Tom during the session. His brother made no secret about the fact he was lobbying for the power companies, but that was no reason for Edward not to enjoy his brother's company in the evening, even listen to his arguments. Edward prided himself on his willingness to examine all sides of any issue. A senator could not possibly know all the facts about two or three hundred bills to be voted on. Men of various power companies had been extremely helpful in supplying him with information about their own dams and power lines. They had given him a picture of the issues of the Central Valley Project as they saw them.

All this information put together had made him acquiesce in the passage of the act in the form the power companies were willing to go along with. It had seemed to him that it meant better relations all around. Compromise, he had come to believe, was an essential attribute of any statesman. Representing the state and not one district as his colleagues did, he had come to see himself in a succession of mirrors—the flattering interest the power companies took in him, the adoration his wife Agnes had for him, and his mother's pride in him. Even in his father's eyes he was now important. Their measure had come to be his measure of himself.

He paused on the steps of the hotel to speak to one of his colleagues; then, to avoid any further interruption, he cut directly across the street into the park, intending to enter the Capitol by a side entrance. He strolled along the walk bordered by the great deodars, grateful for the shade, loitering a little, giving the corridors outside the Senate chamber a chance to empty. He wanted to encounter no last-minute lobbyist, he told himself. Leave his mind clear for decision.

38

AGNES sat in the gallery of the Senate chamber, looking down on the pit soon to be filled with its members. She had sat here often the first session after Edward's election. What a strange, baffling experience it had been! Government had come to seem to her like a medley of card games all going on at once. Today the game of water was to be played—an intricate, difficult game that would test the players' prowess and also their souls, she was thinking.

By courtesy Edward could have arranged for her to sit on the main floor behind the senators' seats, but she had always preferred the obscurity of the gallery. Even Edward did not know she was here today, for she had driven up from San Francisco on an impulse, intending to make her presence known to her husband later.

She had come early in order to get a seat in the front of the gallery. Now glancing over the empty room she wondered who the architect had been and why she had never thought to ask. He had given the room a dignity fitting to its purposes. The pit was square with high stately windows on either side, curtained with red velvet. Thin white gauze was stretched across the window, imprinted on each pane of cloth a black bear. Behind the speaker's desk was a portrait of Washington, on one side of it the flag of the United States and on the other the state flag, red with a black bear rampant. The seats of the senators were grouped below the speaker's desk in a square, each with its accompanying desk. Off to the side, at the right, was the seat of the senator at large, Edward's place. It seemed to make his responsibility greater than that of the others.

Agnes watched intently as the gallery filled with delegations from all over the state—a great many farmers, representatives of clubs and chambers of commerce, businessmen, even the idly curious, so great was interest in the water bill. Last of all the lobbyists filtered in from the corridors where they had been making final appeals to senators whose votes they hoped to win. Among them she recognized her father-in-law.

Just before eleven, the time set for the bill to come up, the senators began to straggle in, some of them making a show of studying the pile of pamphlets on their desks. A few who had secretaries sitting in chairs in the aisle talked in low tones to them. Reporters were taking their seats at the desks under the windows. There was a general air of activity and expectation.

Whenever a senator turned and faced the gallery, Agnes studied his face. Here and there a face stood out, touched with strength. But mostly they were ordinary faces, perhaps a little more than usually suave in expression. Had they trimmed the corners too much in getting here, she wondered, or was she too skeptical?

At last she saw Edward come down the aisle. He stood out among his colleagues, partly because he was younger than most of them. But it was more than that—some quality which leaders have, she thought. She must give him his opportunity, no matter how much it cost her.

Their growing separation frightened her. When she had thought they were to have a child, the gulf between them had narrowed. I must have a child, desperately she told herself.

The fall of the gavel bringing the House to order brought her back to the scene before her. She bowed her head as the chaplain offered the prayer opening the special session. "Humbly do we beg divine guidance for our legislators. May the blessing of Almighty God remain with our country forever! Amen."

"Assembly Bill 259," droned the clerk—The Central Valley Project. The chamber was immediately a battleground. A half-dozen senators sprang to their feet demanding that the president of the Senate grant them the floor.

"The senator will be recognized for five minutes," said the president, indicating a gray-haired man who, Agnes knew, was a fearless fighter.

"If this bill is to do the people any good, it must safeguard their interests," he began in clear tones that could be heard in the gallery. "We cannot give away their right to the electric power generated by the dams for which they will be taxed. I ask unanimous consent to present four provisions."

As soon as the provisions were read the fight began. Senators opposing them were on their feet. "I'd like to ask about the extravagance if districts all over the state are allowed to get electricity direct from the state," one of them demanded. "The power companies have lines. Why should the state duplicate them?"

"Do not the power companies put in extra lines?" asked the first senator.

"They are supplementary lines," snapped back his opponent.

"But you call them superfluous lines when the state puts them in," retorted the first senator. There was a low murmur of approval. The president pounded his gavel for order.

The struggle went on. Excitement and anxiety spread over the chamber and up to the close-packed gallery. Jeremy Dodd was standing far to the left, close to the rail where he could look down on the Senate floor. At this angle he could see Edward, and if Edward turned his head and glanced up, he would see his father. That should be enough. Patiently Jeremy had worked to bring his son in line.

Edward was sitting with one arm over the back of his chair, turned a little to the side so as to accommodate his long legs between seat and desk, listening to the arguments. He was inclined to give a good deal of credence to an argument now being advanced by a young senator from the southern part of the state. "Why let government do anything we can do for ourselves?" he asked. "Private enterprise was the sacred principle upon which this great democracy was founded."

True, true, thought Edward. Something made him glance toward the gallery. His father raised his hand in salute and smiled, as much as to say, "This is what you and I stand for. We are one in our desires." Suddenly Edward realized what had been happening to him these last months. He was being led quietly but surely by the great power lobby. He had almost surrendered to it, forgetting that private power had had years in which to give The Valley abundant electricity. They had not done it. They had not fully served the people. He saw himself clearly in this moment, not in the flattering position of senator at large who dispensed his favors evenly, but as one about to betray the trust the people of the state had put in him.

He rose. Not for nothing had he been a good prosecuting attorney. A hundred incidents lying dormant in his mind leaped to the surface. A hundred points.

"May I ask the senator who speaks of private enterprise why he considers it so when a corporation is granted the electricity generated by the government-owned dams (incidentally, paid for by our taxes), but not private enterprise when a group of citizens organized into a utility district for the purpose of distributing electric power to themselves asks for the same privilege?"

The senator so eloquently defending the corporations was caught off guard. He opened his mouth like a fish suddenly taken out of water.

Edward seized his advantage to set forth a case for the people, drawing on many a conversation with his father, turning his father's arguments against him. "The private companies have contended it is too expensive to supply electrical power to small, isolated farmers. Are we, then, as representatives of the people, going to give private companies the right to decide who shall and who shall not have electric power to run their farms?"

The fighting, embattled group of senators who had in the regular session fought a losing battle for the small farmers knew now there was hope. It was time to play their trump card. One of them was on his feet demanding the floor, getting it from Edward.

"Do we, or do we not, want Washington to put up money that it is willing to grant us under the Federal Recovery Program? It will not grant funds unless we adopt provisions safeguarding the rights of the people. The farmers of the state are in desperate need of water. Thousands of men are out of employment. Such a project would give employment to twenty-five thousand of them if we start working on canals and dams immediately. Can we afford to risk losing Federal funds to carry on a project of such magnitude? It would be cruel to our people."

The last argument had been given. The vote was to be taken. On the electric board to the right and left of the speaker the lights by the senators' names sprang up—red and green. Three more green lights than red. The Central Valley Project Act with the rights of the people safeguarded had passed!

Down in the rotunda of the Capitol a group gathered around Edward. Farmers and townsmen were coming forward to shake his hand and thank him. As the crowd began to thin out, Edward realized most of his family were there! Agnes, looking proud and happy, his sister Bettie and her husband—she had married the young, hardworking reporter three years ago, a week after Edward's election. They had one child and were expecting another. So they'd been in the gallery, too. Under one of the murals that lined the rotunda, Edward caught a glimpse of Tom, his father—yes, and his mother.

He stooped and kissed Agnes, squeezed Bettie's hand, accepted the congratulations of her husband. Then together they went forward to greet the heads of the family. Edward had a feeling of strength he had never experienced before in the presence of his father. Matters could be as man to man between them from now on.

"Glad you waited to speak to me, Father. Sorry I couldn't see things your way."

Jeremy laughed easily. "You proved yourself the better man. We oldsters will have to step down. Suppose we all go over to the hotel and have a cocktail? Most of the family seem to be here," he added, looking around. "All in your honor, son!" He turned to Agnes. "He's making a great politician. Kiss me, daughter."

Edward listened, astounded. His father appeared to be without rancor toward him! He's really a wonder, he thought. As full of spirit as if he had won. He ought at least to be tired after the way he has been driving himself these last weeks. Marvelous comeback he's made after his sickness years ago!

Jeremy had seemed old then, he remembered—now he didn't. His skin had a ruddy glow. His hair was as thick as ever and no grayer. He was smoking one of his favorite stogies. As he shifted it from one side of his mouth to the other, with an up-and-down motion of his jaw, his long, uneven teeth seemed to clamp down on it with viselike force, his only sign of tension or distress.

"Father's the best sport I know," Edward said, turning to his mother. "Most men wouldn't speak to a son who opposed him as I did today."

"Isn't it wonderful," she answered, "that we can differ so in our opinions and yet be such a united family?"

"You see, Mother," said Jeremy Dodd, overhearing her remark, "Edward and I are not so far apart. Our ultimate aim is the same. Edward is working for himself, and I am working for myself. I get my support from the keen business brains of the state. Edward gets his from the near failures, the little men who come whining to the government to help them because they haven't the brains to go it alone." He looked solemnly around at his family. "As I see it, any one of you is worth more to California than a hundred poor valley farmers. You are good examples of my constituency."

His father wasn't fooling Tom with these fireworks. All Jeremy was doing was going under cover. When he looked as he did now, Tom knew he'd only begun to fight. His father was dangerous in his present mood. He had seen this affability often when Jeremy Dodd was being opposed in business. He guessed his present cold anger was not so much because the bill had passed, as because he hadn't been able to rule his son. He was pretty sure his father had told certain power men he could keep Edward in line, and he hadn't been able to. That put him in a bad position. The fact of the matter was that his father and all the power men had underestimated Edward's strength of character. I did, too, thought Tom.

Edward took the remark about his constituency with good grace. He was willing to let his father get all he could out of the moment. He could afford to. It was he who had triumphed, a triumph greater than any of them guessed. He had today cut himself free of parental domination.

"You'll have to class Herb with the poor valley farmers. Do you mind, Father?" asked Bettie.

"Why, daughter," exclaimed Beatrice Dodd, "your husband is a rising reporter! How fanciful of you to talk as if he were a farmer simply because you and Herb bought a few acres of valley land."

"I heard a rumor—" Edward put in, "anything in it, Bettie?—that one of the big-city papers offered Herb a splendid job as editorial writer?"

"Yes," said Bettie quietly, "but he didn't take it."

"What do you mean, didn't take it?" Jeremy Dodd spoke sharply.

"Just that I didn't feel I could," Herbert interrupted his conversation with Agnes to say.

"Why, if I may ask?"

"Well, they said I must follow the policy of the paper on all water and power questions."

"What's wrong with that?" Jeremy demanded.

"Nothing—only it didn't go with my convictions." Herb was short and stocky, with red cheeks and a turned-up nose. Jeremy, surveying him, thought heroics didn't fit very well with his type.

"You gave up a good income because you couldn't strut your own stuff! And in the midst of a depression! You're a fool, with a family to support." Jeremy couldn't keep his dislike for his son-in-law down any longer. "It isn't going to do you any good to refuse a job like that. A little picayune upstate sheet isn't going to get you far."

"He's not with the picayune paper, as you called it, any more," said Bettie. "They didn't want him after they knew why he didn't take the other offer. Herb and I have seen it coming," she added quietly. "He's with the small farmers, and it isn't popular with a lot of papers. That's why we've been buying a little land from time to time."

"You don't mean you're going to try to *live* off it?" her mother exclaimed.

Bettie smiled. "Herb wants to prove that a small farm can support a family. It's one of the things that's said—that small farms aren't practical."

Edward slipped his arm through Bettie's. "Come, let's go over to Father's rooms." She's whole and not afraid, and so am I now, he thought, feeling a deep affection for his sister.

At home that evening, as Jeremy Dodd put out the lights in the living room preparatory to going upstairs, he opened the front door, looking around at the fine houses across the street and at each side of him. They gave him a feeling of established wealth—something that could not be shaken by Edward's pigheadedness, or today's drop in the stock market.

It angered him that there should be men within the ranks of the class to which by heritage and by personal achievement he belonged who would break down the barriers which separated them from the mass of humanity. And that one of these should be his son and another his son-in-law! His son-in-law was a fool to throw away his opportunity to become both prominent and well-to-do! It was he, Jeremy Dodd, who had suggested Herb to the city newspaper. What was the Dodd family coming to? Bettie with two children on a two-by-four farm with a reporter husband to run it! And Edward, forgetting all about his own interests today, voting to hamper the electric-power companies at the very moment when they had the chance to expand enormously, and he to get the backing of such an influential group! The power men won't forgive him for that unless I can patch things up, Jeremy thought. They'll try to get him out of the Senate.

What would my family do without me? he wondered. After they've let me work myself to death to save them, perhaps they'll know. Standing in the doorway of his handsome house, he gave way to a moment of self-pity. I suppose I'll have to continue to be the brains and the will for the family until I drop.

"I'll be up in a minute," he called to Beatrice, who for the second time had come to the head of the stairs, reminding him that it was late and he ought to be in bed. But for a moment he did not move, thinking out the next step. Ask for a referendum; then flood the state with the arguments supporting the power companies' high office in defending the American spirit of initiative and freedom. The people could be counted on to vote against any proposition that seemed to interfere with their freedom. Once you convinced the people that the state water program was against their rights as individuals, they'd vote for what the power companies wanted. He'd suggest it to the other power men tomorrow. He had failed so ignobly with them today after practically promising them his son's vote, he must do something to regain their esteem. As for the site for the dam he wanted to put in, that was off. His rival had nothing to win and everything to lose in letting him get it. He's a wolf at my throat except when we're fighting the government, he thought.

39

ALREADY there had been a good many foreclosures of farms over the state. Two around Doddstown. One of them Ward, J. T.'s father. He was working for Lesly now. The other was a man who had bought twenty acres of the Dodd estate. Farmers, standing on street corners in Doddstown, bulwarked their failing courage by telling one another these two men were bound to fail. Twenty acres of cotton weren't enough on which to support a family. Twenty acres weren't economi-cal to run. They wouldn't support a tractor. May Roberts hadn't a bit of patience with her husband when he repeated such talk to her. "We could be efficient if we'd get together. We could run our farms as if we were big like Lesly—buy tractors together, and we ought to have a cotton co-operative and the gin we've been talking about."

Jed Roberts was a good farmer, but suspicious of his wife's mania for organization although he had to grant she put her ideas to practical use. Because of her help he had something ahead in the bank to meet this year's payment on his mortgage. May herself was strong and a good worker. With her aid and that of their son, fifteen, and the two girls, ten and twelve, they had taken care of their sixty without hiring extra laborers. Even on the lowest prices Roberts figured they'd squeeze through. He hadn't done too badly on his early potatoes. But he didn't want to try any fancy experiments.

Jed came into the kitchen one morning late in July. May was peeling potatoes for dinner. Her plump fingers sent the knife nimbly around the potatoes, the peelings falling in rings into the pan planted firmly on her ample lap. She landed a peeled potato in a pail of water at her side, rested her wrists on the edge of the pan, paring knife erect in her right hand.

"There's something we've got to do, Mr. Roberts."

"I know," said her husband, "what you're going to say, but what I say is, you keep still about our helping one another out. People like us soon would be holding the bag. You want us to buy a lot of expensive machinery. The weak fellows wouldn't meet their part of the payments. We'd lose it and all the money we'd put in."

"If we'd stick together we'd be as strong as Lesly—stronger because we'd be working for ourselves and there'd be so many of us that with machinery we wouldn't have to have itinerants work for us. Give a few men all-the-year-round work. Treat 'em like human beings."

"Now, now!" said Jed.

"How long do you think we could last if all our neighbors got foreclosed?" May demanded. "Here we'd be sittin' right in the midst of Lesly's land. He'd crush us like fleas."

"You've got Lesly on the brain. It's the banks that foreclose. What's Lesly got to do with it?"

"Mr. Roberts, for a smart man sometimes you don't show the sense of an infant. Lesly's standing ready to gobble up any foreclosed land in these parts. Land gets to be a craze to men that own a lot."

"Guess maybe you're right this time," Jed Roberts conceded.

"Course I'm right. There's no question about it. So what?" She rose, set the pail of potatoes on the sink, sat down again, her knees crossed, her right leg, with its knobby calf, sticking out belligerently.

"So we start a co-operative, I suppose, to take care of our cotton." Her husband's tone was edged with sarcasm.

"No. We get together over our water rights."

Roberts, headed toward the porch, his hand already on the screen door, stopped short, startled by his wife's answer. She'd struck at the very heart of their problem. He knew some of his neighbors were already in arrears on their water payments. Together they were evenly matched against Lesly in the water company to which they all belonged, but let some of them fail to make their payments and their water rights would be put up at auction. Lesly would have his man ready to snap them up.

"But what can we do about it?" he asked helplessly. "We can't pay other people's water bills. At ten dollars an acre, any one farmer's bill is around four hundred dollars."

"Couldn't we get together and maybe get a loan from the bank?"

"Same thing," said Jed dejectedly. "We gotta pay in the end. Suppose they foreclose on a farmer's lands?"

"We could meet and talk it over. We could ask 'em all here."

May Roberts' parlor was full the night they met. Jed stood up before his neighbors, sweating over the ordeal ahead of him. "I guess we're here," he began, "because we either sink or swim, all dependin' on how good we are at getting together. We all got mortgages we got to meet. We all got water bills to meet. You all know the setup of the water company. Some of us are already in arrears. If anybody's water rights get put up at auction, Lesly is sure to buy them in. Then we might lose our voting power."

The Professor—so called by his neighbors because he once taught school—interrupted, "Couldn't we buy them up ourselves?"

"I was coming to that," Jed went on. He was easier now. He'd forgotten what May had told him about how a chairman should act. He was just a hard-pressed farmer talking to other hard-pressed farmers. "We need a fund on hand to do that." Jed swallowed hard. "I'll start the fund. It's money I got saved for my mortgage. I could put up a hundred."

May Roberts sat up straight, her ample bosom to the fore. She was filled with pride. She hadn't believed Jed had it in him.

There was an audible mass drawing in of breath, but Jed did not falter. "We'd have to dig down in our jeans and haul out whatever we've got for a rainy day, and we got to get all the other farmers in the water company to go in with us." He looked around. Not more than two-thirds of the members were here tonight.

A babble of voices rose in the room. "Mighty big risk, I'd say!"

A meek little man turned to a heavy-set Portuguese sitting next to him.

"No lika da talk. Taka da savings," answered Griffanti. Dissent and opposition were gaining.

May, without sound, shaped the words with her lips: "Hold 'em now, Mr. Roberts."

Jed leaned forward, sweat again breaking out on his forehead. "Look! Supposin' we each persuade two other farmers to join us. If each could put up something—maybe only a hundred, mebbe even fifty—I believe we could do it. I believe it enough—" Jed hesitated a moment. May's lips said two hundred—"I believe it enough that I'm willing to put up three hundred. It's my nest egg," he added with a grin, looking at May.

"I will meet him." It was the quiet voice of the Professor.

The other pledges were small and given reluctantly. Griffanti didn't promise. "I talka da mama," he said. "She smart like hell. I aska da old lady."

Outside a car door slammed. Jed's dog lying under the table woke, sniffed, suddenly dashed between the legs of the seated men and women, barking furiously. Jed pulled him back by the collar as a tall, gaunt-looking man pushed open the screen door. None of the occupants of the room knew him very well. He'd been an itinerant laborer coming quietly back to town every year with his son. Somehow he'd saved enough money to buy a piece of the Dodd property. But he'd kept to himself, not certain of his welcome, feeling the stigma that attaches to the itinerant in Central Valley.

"I got your word about the meetin'," he began, not waiting to be introduced. "It ain't going to do you any good to meet. Lesly's got next to some of the farmers who ain't doing so well. He's bought their land and their water rights. Givin' 'em more than they paid for it, I hearn. He figgers any man's got his price. All he has to do is figger out what it is."

"He can outvote us, you mean?" asked Miller from Iowa, the father of Bertha, who had taken Sonya as her best friend.

"Worse—he can block off your water."

"But he wouldn't dare!" exclaimed the Professor. "It's a very serious offense in this state to interfere with anyone's water rights."

"Yeh, if he's caught—but try to catch Lesly." The man pulled a water map out of his pocket. "Where can I lay this here out? I'll show you what's up."

May Roberts, stunned at first, was all action now. She had set the dining-room table, meaning to serve coffee and cake after the meeting.

but with swift movements, Katya helping, she cleared it of cups, spoons, napkins and her best cloth. Everyone gathered around.

"Course you all got water maps, but this one I got marked. And I made it bigger. I've worked all over these-here acres, and I know how every foot lays. Lesly's on one side the main ditch, we-all is on the other. Come time for us to irrigate, Lesly's goin' to give out the weir is low. He's got hold of all the land round the weir, so we can't go there and see if he's telling the truth. And he's got the men who owned land next to the main ditch to sell to him. Those are the folks who ain't here tonight. He's goin' to give us jest a trickle of water. He's blocked the outlets on our side the ditch."

"But he can't," insisted the Professor. "It's against the law."

"My eye!" The man turned on him. "Who's to keep him from it? Didn't I tell ya he bought the land *next* to the main ditch. He's got signs up against trespassing. The pumps are going to be workin'. How'll anybody know he's blocked the outlets on our side?"

"He wouldn't dare! It'll be as plain as the nose on your face. Growing crops on one side of the main ditch, dying ones on the other. We can go to court," Miller protested.

"It takes money to go to court, mister," the man answered.

The men and women crowded round the table were not altogether convinced. How did this ex-laborer find out all this? Maybe he was in Lesly's pay. Maybe his tale was a scheme of Lesly's to frighten them, get them to sell.

The meeting broke up with nothing settled. Katya, driving home, was troubled. As she had no flow-water rights, she was not a member of the water company. She had gone to the meeting simply to help her friend serve the coffee and cakes. The danger that threatened her neighbors did not threaten her directly, but if they were crowded out, it meant Lesly's land would surround hers. She knew he wanted her place, too. After Lesly had tried to get her to sell and Mishka had suggested that Lesly might sometime take their water, she had gone to the Board of Water Resources. They had drawn her a sketch based on what findings they had of the underground basin. It seemed to have a sharp, downward pitch like an inverted mountain peak. Her ranch was on the upper edge of the basin. Lesly, if he ever owned the land directly east of her would own the deepest point and might draw the water out of her part if he used powerful-enough pumps. If he ever did this, her rich acres would turn into desert.

40

By the end of July everyone in the water company, including Lesly's manager, agreed there'd have to be another irrigation. Just as Garroty, the former itinerant, had said, Lesly's manager gave out the news that the weir was low. One morning the pumping began, but almost no water flowed into the side ditches.

Jed Roberts sat on his doorstep that evening, thinking. He'd staked everything on this venture. A year ago he and May had seen their way to send their boy Hal to agricultural college when he finished high school. Now it looked as if, along with the rest, they'd be forced to give up their farm. Jed heard a car coming up the private road that led to his house. It stopped. In the dark he couldn't see clearly, but he would have said the car was full. However, only one man got out and came toward him. As he reached the steps, Jed saw it was Garroty.

"Howdy," said Jed.

"Howdy," answered the man. "We got to do something and do it quick," he began without preamble.

"I thought you said there wasn't anything we could do the last time you was here."

"I said you couldn't do anything in the *courts*. What I come to say is, we do it ourselves. You and me and those fellows out in the car."

So there are others in the car, thought Jed.

"We got to break the padlocks Lesly's put on the water gates. I been reconnoiterin', nights. I know all this country as if it was my own hand. We can open 'em and let in the water."

"Yep, and Lesly'll lock 'em up come morning."

"Not if we break 'em. We get started irrigating tonight. You better be in your own field tonight. Me and them men out there are going to tend to the padlocks. They're laborers once worked for Lesly. They got it in for him. They're helpin' me, see? The big Russian from the Suvorov place he's helpin' too. He's got hands that'll handle anything up to a fallen tree. I jest dropped around to tell ya to get to work on your own cotton. If Lesly don't get things fixed up too soon everybody'll get their irrigatin' done."

"What's going to happen on your ranch," Jed asked, "you bein' away? You ain't doing this for philanthropic reasons, are you?"

"I got some friends helpin' me. It's up to you what you do on your own cotton patch. We're givin' you your chance."

Behind the screen door May stood listening. "We must do it, Jed," she said as soon as the man had gone, "but I don't like the children in on a thing like this. It seems kinda lawless."

"We gotta have 'em, or we won't get all the cotton watered to-night."

"Jed, get inside!" commanded May in a whisper, hearing another car coming up their road. "We can't have visitors tonight."

And then she heard Mrs. Suvorov's voice. "It's us. We've come to help—Peter and I, and Daria and Song."

Peter, Song and the Roberts children, in tense excitement, worked their way through the dark field. No flashlights had been allowed; their flickering might rouse suspicion in Lesly's men. Peter was guiding himself by letting his hands rest lightly on the cotton plants. "The water is coming," he told them as if they were children who needed his assurance and could hear his voice.

Peter was tall and slender, having grown fast in the last three years. With each year his love for the ranch had increased. Freed from conflict with his schoolmates, his imagination stirred by activities in the community, he seemed to be tapping some rich heritage that made him a part of the land.

He took pride in the fact that they owned land—he and his mother. But there was a deeper, more fundamental tie than mere ownership, a sense of identification with the earth, something the older countries have in common, lost usually in the second generation in America. Hal Roberts had helped to interest him in practical matters of farming. The older boy, although silent and diffident among his elders, alone with Peter showed he was May Roberts' son. He and Peter were going to start a Four-H club in the fall. They were going to raise the finest cotton ever grown. Hal's father had promised him a quarter acre on which to experiment next year. Peter was to have the same amount on his mother's ranch.

As the water poured through the side ditch edging the Roberts' cotton, Jed and his helpers skillfully used their shovels to open the channels running between the rows. As he let in the water Peter felt that he and this land in some undefinable way were united. It was right that he should see to the earth's needs. And yet he had an unhappy feeling because of Mishka who was breaking the law. He was trespassing and destroying property. If they caught him, what would they do to him? And, too, Peter felt a slight sense of loss. Mishka until tonight had stood for law and order, and now he was breaking the law.

But after a while Peter was too tired to think. Mechanically he went on, opening up, shutting off the flow of water down the channels between the cotton rows.

Back at home and in bed he could not sleep. Anxiously he listened for Mishka's return. Then he found he must have slept, for the sun was streaming into his room. Hastily he dressed and went outside. Everything about the ranch was as usual. Mishka was talking to his mother about the cotton just coming into bloom. The night's happenings seemed far away and unreal.

As the days went by and Mishka went quietly about his work, Peter forgot his sense of uneasiness. Katya tried to forget, too, forget that in a few weeks another irrigation would be necessary to save her neighbors' harvest. There had been no sign from Lesly. "He don't dare let on what's happened. That's what the men think," May Roberts told her.

41

As THE time for another irrigation drew near, everyone insisted he felt no anxiety. Surely Lesly wouldn't try it again. There'd been a meeting of the water company, to transact routine business and to decide on the date for the next irrigation.

Just as the Professor was starting his car after the meeting, Jed Roberts came along and stopped to chat, a foot on the fender, his elbow on the window frame. "Guess we settled him, Professor."

"I hope so. But I don't like the method we used."

"No more do I," Jed answered soberly, "but I'm going to see it through even if I have to get out next winter. We got to make good this year, or else we lose everything we put into this venture."

They saw Lesly's manager coming toward them. He smiled affably but did not stop.

Garroty went by, too, without stopping. He wasn't going to take them into his confidence this time. Wouldn't many of them go along with him, he had decided, feeling pretty certain most of them would be too law-abiding to help him with what he was planning. He was going to win out over Lesly, no matter if he was jailed for it. He could depend on the men who'd helped him before: they had things to settle with Lesly. Lesly had done something to the Russian over at the Suvorov place, too, it seemed, although he didn't say what it was. They had met at Mishka's house, the safest place because Widow Suvorov wasn't in the water company. Lesly's men wouldn't be looking for a meeting there.

"What we gotta do," Garroty had told them in a whisper, "is blow out the concrete he's put in. It's thin. It won't take much of a blast, but it's ticklish work. We gotta set the fuses and get off his land before they go off. Maybe he'll have men prowling round, but I guess not. He's too sure of his concrete. Two men to each barrier. We gotta figure the farmers is smart enough, when they hear it go, to know it's up to them to get their fields watered; and we gotta make the blowoffs as near together as we can. If we don't, someone'll get caught."

The night after the pumping began, Mishka moved stealthily along by the big ditch. His companion had his hand on the Russian's shoulder. They were nearing the spot where the main ditch and a side one met. They crouched low, stopping to listen. A gopher scudded away ahead of them. They moved on. They were close now. They could feel the rising edge of the dyke under their feet. Mishka lay flat, reached down into the ditch. A certain amount of water was seeping through at the bottom, but not enough even to wet the lateral ditches a couple of yards away.

"Wicked, wicked," he whispered, "to starve the earth. Now I serve the Lord." Carefully he placed the dynamite. In the distance he heard a sound like a giant firecracker.

"Run, for God's sake, run!" whispered his companion. "They'll be after us!"

"You go. I stay a little more." Carefully Mishka lighted the fuse. He had to be certain it was burning. Now it was. He rose to a crouching position, began running making the best time he could.

His companion, far ahead, heard a shot. Bet Lesly's men got him, he thought, running faster, stumbling along over the channeled earth of the field.

One, two, three—at the third blast Katya sat up in bed. The sound was hardly more than the backfiring of a car, but it didn't reach her from the direction of the road. From the fields! Things fell into place now in her mind. Men coming to see Mishka, coming in on foot in the middle of the night. . . . Something he'd said about the water being short for the second irrigation.

Would Lesly succeed in driving her neighbors out? What then would he do to her and the two others who lived along the bench, as they had come to call the higher portion of the Dodd land? There in the dark she shivered, feeling his two fleshy hands on her arms, knowing he would never forgive her rejection of his advances. I don't care what the flow-water people try, I will help them, she promised herself. Some sinister force seemed to be pushing them toward violence. Where would it end? Two years ago they were a hopeful, peaceful community. She remembered the pageant they had put on at the school. It had been May Roberts' idea. "Our Valley" they had called it. Peter had taken the part of the first American from the East to look down from the pass in the mountains into The Valley. How proudly the words "Our Valley" had rung out!

Katya woke with a start. Day was just breaking. Someone was speaking her name just outside her window. It was Daria. "Please, Madame Suvorov, come. I don't want to wake Peter so I speak to your window. Mishka is hurt some."

Stopping only to throw on a bathrobe, Katya hurried across to Mishka's house. Even in her anxiety she noticed the beauty of the early morning. The sun, just risen, was throwing its light across the top of her acres of cotton, making the leaves shine with unwonted brilliance.

She found Mishka sitting by the table unwinding his blood-soaked shirt from his leg. Daria began sobbing and imploring God to testify to their innocence. "Be still, woman!" commanded Mishka. "Get water and clean cloth." In the doorway of her bedroom, unnoticed by her parents, Song stood, clasping and unclasping her hands.

"We should have a doctor!" But even as she spoke, Katya knew they must not call one. She had some small medical knowledge gained in her girlhood when the peasants injured at their work, or sick, used to come to the big house for aid. Kneeling beside Mishka, she examined the wound. A flesh wound only, she was certain, and no blood vessel punctured. It was not bleeding enough for that. But suppose infection should set in? They'd have to chance it. She turned to Daria, taking the clean linen from her hands, bandaging Mishka's leg as best she could. "Now get him into bed and have him rest," she commanded.

Rising, Katya had a sudden startling impression of Daria. With the sun shining full on her, she saw that Mishka's wife was no longer the robust, vital woman upon whose strength they had all rested through the years. It was not only anxiety for Mishka that gave her eyes such a

somber expression but pain silently endured—yes, for a long time—
until it had given her eyes a look of resignation. When Daria saw her
mistress studying her, a smile full of animation concealed both pain
and resignation.

"It is nothing," she said, following Katya to the door. "All night I
wait for Mishka."

When Katya reached her own house, Peter was standing in the
doorway, his eyes wide with excitement. "What's the matter, Mom?"

"Mishka's had a slight accident. He'll be all right after he rests,"
she answered, hating the furtive role that seemed to have been pressed
upon them all. "You'll have to take over today." She wished they
could go and help the Roberts family with their irrigating as they had
done before, but she didn't dare leave. In case anyone came, she must
be here to shield Mishka. Would Lesly invoke the law over last
night's happenings? Would he succeed in crowding her neighbors
out? Her own land eventually would be no more than a pocket amid
Lesly's vast holdings. Mishka understood and was fighting desperately
to save them—of that she was sure. Disaster was closing in upon her.
And Daria—suppose they should lose Daria? Only now did Katya
realize how much she had leaned on her. There were qualities of
greatness in Daria.

The day dragged on. No one called on the telephone, Katya called
no one. It was safer not to talk just now to her neighbors. Outside
heat waves shimmered over the fields. At Mishka's house there was
no sign of life.

Two days and Katya could bear it no longer. She took Peter and
went to see May Roberts. Everything at her place seemed as usual.
How much did Jed and May Roberts know, she wondered, about what
had happened two nights ago? She had meant to ask Jed to come
and see Mishka, but she decided it was better not to. She felt isolated
and very lonely.

Peter found Hal in the quarter acre his father had given him.
"How's Mishka?" asked Hal.

"What do you mean?" Peter countered, and in the next breath,
"What happened night before last, Hal?"

"We're not supposed to know, but I heard Dad telling Ma it had
to be that way. If we didn't blow the barriers out, we'da lost our
cotton. We gotta harvest this year's crops. Then I guess we're going
to clear out. Lesly'll get us in the end." Hal's voice had a lifeless
tone.

"You mean go away?" said Peter. "Can't we keep on doing things like the other night?" All at once he was mad at Hal. Going away, not staying to fight for his quarter acre.

"I guess we're licked," Hal answered.

Peter was proud of Mishka now, proud of him for breaking the law. He wanted to be like Mishka, not like Mr. Roberts and Hal, who were going to take a licking.

A wave of hope swept over the buyers of the Dodd property when, for the most part, the cotton harvest promised well and the price quoted was slightly above what they had expected. If the Central Valley Project was begun soon and the men secured work on it, perhaps they'd be able to hold on.

Then it was they learned the Water Project Act was not yet a law. The big landowners and certain business interests insisted that the people should have the final vote. A petition with the requisite number of signatures was presented, which necessitated a referendum. This meant delay and uncertainty and no immediate help.

The more determined, the more resourceful, skimping on food and clothes, managed to meet their mortgages and water payments. The Robertses held on, and Griffanti the Portuguese, a hard worker and thrifty. Miller, a good mechanic, started a shop on the edge of his property. He was doing a fair business mending cars that broke down on the road, although no one could afford to pay him much. The Professor had an independent income and was heard to say that he was supporting his farm, not the farm supporting him.

The vote of the people, although it meant delay, furnished May Roberts with a new impetus; that slow, paralyzing feeling that they could not win against Lesly which had taken hold even of the energetic Mrs. Roberts changed into a determination to fight. She was on her own ground now, where she could organize committees and go to call on people and arrange for them to be taken to the polls to vote.

How could people fail when they could get together and say things openly? It was doing things you couldn't tell your neighbors that had rendered May Roberts powerless. Gathered around her dining-room table, the small farmers made out lists of people they knew over the state to whom to send letters, telling them about the need for water in the southern part of The Valley.

"We got to prove that what a lot of the newspapers are writing isn't so," May Roberts stopped stamping envelopes to say. "Imagine saying we've money behind us! And that we are fighting the best interests of the people!"

"If they could see us copying our letters longhand because we haven't a typewriter, maybe they'd change their tune," said Miller, who found letter writing an arduous task. A letter once a month to his mother back in Iowa was his usual output.

"Spending our time and money on gas to go and see people," some-one else chimed in.

"Even telegrams," Katya Suvorov put in, thinking how she had sent one to friends in San Francisco.

It was good to talk like this, all of them together again. No secret, violent acts to hold them apart in fear or divide them with expediency.

42

JEREMY DODD shifted his cigar with unusual vigor from one corner of his mouth to the other. His scheme was working well. He had formed a society called the California League of Patriots. The purpose set forth in its folders was to make California the greatest state in the Union. Any society that promoted state pride could count on heavy support, Jeremy knew. Contributions poured in from all quarters. Quietly he deposited the money to the league and kept his own counsel over the fact that he was president, vice-president and what-you-will of the organization. With the league's money he financed persons willing to stump the state in behalf of the "beleaguered people." Leaflets bearing the league's name appeared in hotel dining rooms where businessmen's clubs were meeting, in women's club houses.

As if by magic, other societies sprang up. All of them seemed to have for their main purpose defeat of the valley project. Every mail carried pamphlets opposing it. Farmers stopped on street corners in the towns to discuss the intent of the project. Men's luncheon clubs in Los Angeles and San Francisco debated it. It was the subject of discussion for women's club programs and newspaper editorials. Full-page advertisements claimed the Water and Power Act was Bolshevik in intention. Let the power companies, guardians of private enterprise, serve the people of California. They alone could save the state from ruin. Assemblymen and senators who had supported the bill with the safeguards the Federal Government had asked for found themselves attacked as enemies of the people.

Working night and day, Jeremy would have believed that he had fully reinstated himself with the other power companies except for the fact that a whispering campaign against Edward had started. Tom was the first person to tell him what was going on. "They'll get him before the next election if they can make the things they say stick," said Tom. Jeremy could only guess where the talk came from. He was worried over what might happen to his son's career.

"What do they say?" demanded Jeremy.

"Nothing definite. That's the difficulty," Tom replied. "Hints of inefficiency, lack of understanding of the people, that he's not definitely enough tied to any district. Too impersonal—oh, a lot of vague things! The best I can say, it's a kind of belittling of him. Out-and-out opposition would rouse defenders. This sort of thing affects even his friends."

"Well, we have two years to work," Jeremy answered. "If we can win this referendum—and Edward votes even once or twice the way we want him to on other matters—we can begin to build him up."

Edward at first was puzzled, then frightened. In a tone here, a word there, he felt his prestige going. The sense of strength he had had when he had risen in the Senate chamber and turned the tide of opinion which defeated his father and the power companies began to evaporate. After all, was he the wise public servant he had thought himself? As usual, was his father's judgment not proving to be better than his? A good public servant? At times he thought so; at other times, no. In the eyes of some people he was; in the eyes of others he was not. Depending as he did on approval outside himself and finding it slipping from him he grew anxious and uncertain.

The fight grew more bitter. People who had never thought about the state's water supply began to look on the conservation of water as an unprincipled effort of government to burden them with extra taxes. They saw the power companies as victims of the state along with themselves. Public-spirited men who had worked for years to preserve the limited water supply of a semidesert California found themselves treated as public enemies. Farmers like Katya and her neighbors and small businessmen fighting without funds had their backs against the wall, and yet in some mysterious way they felt their strength growing. The tide seemed to be turning. There were many who began to detect flaws in arguments so vociferously advanced by the power interests.

On December nineteenth Katya rose early. She must get the house in order, put up Peter's luncheon, see him off to school and dress for town. Today the referendum asking for the reconsideration of the Central Valley Water Project was to be voted on. She, Katya Suvorov, was to cast her first vote, and later she was to be one of the helpers at the polling station.

The polling booths had been set up in the hallway of the schoolhouse, a familiar place to Katya now. For in spite of Lesly and in spite of the difficulties facing them all, they continued to do things for the children. She went up the steps and in at the door. Miller sat at the end of a long table. "You registered?" he asked. "I have to look you up, though." He hunted through a great ledger. Then she was in the booth unfolding her ballot. She picked up the rubber stamp, pressed it down where it said "No"—no reconsideration of the Central Valley Water Project. Carefully she folded her ballot, then opened it, fearful she might have placed the cross after the wrong word. What would she do then? But it was all right. The heavy black cross was in the right place. She came out of the booth, handed the valuable folded paper to the man at the table, saw him drop it into a box. She had voted!

May Roberts was just bustling in at the door. "You can take over now, Mrs. Suvorov." As usual Mrs. Roberts seemed to be running things.

Just as Katya took her seat with the list of voters in front of her, the noon bell clanged and the children began pouring out of the doors of their classroom. Katya watched them as they marched past the voting booths and the table where she sat. So many of them were ill clad and evidently ill fed. There was Peter! Long before he reached her, she saw him. He was a head taller than most of the boys. His hair tumbled about his face. He needed a haircut. Now he was passing the table. He gave her a shy, proud grin. It was his mother who was telling the men and women coming in about the voting.

J. T. was just behind Peter. She didn't like the boy. Still a wave of pity swept over her, even as she realized he would much prefer to have her hate him. Since the bank had foreclosed on his father's mortgage and the family had gone to live in one of the poorer houses on the edge of the town, and his father worked as a day laborer, J. T. had refused to take any part in school activities. He did come to the sociables but only to make trouble. Peter staunchly defended him. Ever since school opened this fall the old alliance between the two boys, almost extinct the last three years, had been revived. And at the same time Peter showed no interest any more in Hal. Did all boys' friendships wax and wane like this?

The thought came to her, I'd almost rather have J. T. for Peter's enemy than his friend. His blue eyes held the most vindictive look she had ever seen in a child's eyes. His mouth was set in a sarcastic smile. Katya had a sudden vision of him in the school pageant last year before his father lost his land. Peter had been good in a childlike way, but J. T., leading the Donner party down from their winter vigil in the High Sierras, seemed to take on himself the tragedy of all foot-worn, distressed people seeking a haven. That he was lame, that he was poor, he made serve some histrionic instinct. Katya, who knew something of acting, sensed the artist in him that day. If he had the opportunity, she thought, he might be an actor, even a great one.

"I'd like my ballot, Mrs. Suvorov." Katya's attention came back with a jerk to her duties. Jake Bodkin enjoyed the uneasiness his bold look created in her. Did people like this Suvorov woman and the fat Mrs. Roberts and a lot of these upstarts who had bought up the Dodd acres think they could beat the big fellows? When the fight had started over the referendum, Lesly had come down from San Francisco and given him the sign that the big landowners were standing pat with the power companies. A lot of money was going to be used to tell folks which side their bread was buttered on. Show 'em that canals and dams cost money, and they'd have to reach down into their jeans and pay for them. He'd like to see this Suvorov woman's expression when the referendum showed the big boys had won, and he'd like to see that Professor guy who owned fifty acres and had shot off his face such a lot about water belonging to the people. Jake handed in his ballot, went off counting over in his mind how many votes he had lined up.

The next evening in farmhouses all over The Valley the lights stayed on. Katya had invited Mishka's family to sit with her and Peter and listen to the returns coming in over the radio. Between hope and despair the hours went by. In the hands of the people of California lay the chance for their own and their neighbors' survival.

It grew late, later than Mishka had sat up for years. His head sagged on his chest, his heavy sleep punctuated with snores. Song put her head in her mother's lap and slept. Peter tried valiantly to keep awake, but finally he, too, slept, his head against his mother's shoulder. Silently the two women kept vigil. Daria's hands played with Song's curls; the strands of her hair, soft as silk, clung to her mother's work-roughened hands. Finally Daria spoke. "Please do not be parted," she said.

"We'll none of us be parted," Katya answered, refusing to recognize what Daria was trying to tell her. "Listen:" she cried, turning up the radio, "there is our answer!"

Loud and clear came the final report. The Central Valley Water Project Act had been upheld by the people.

"Now our land is safe, and you safe," cried Daria. Then she said softly to herself, "Soon I go." No one heard her. Mishka was praising God for their delivery, and Katya was waking the children to tell them the news.

43

THE winter crept slowly forward. Hope died again. No funds either Federal or state were voted to carry out the valley project—no dams and canals would be built.

"Iowa Miller," as his neighbors now called him, had not been able to meet his fall payment on his mortgage. As his land was far back from the main irrigation ditch, only a small amount of the water that flowed along the lateral ditch the first time they had broken Lesly's barriers had been left for his acres after the nearer fields had been given their portions. Another twenty-four hours and the water would have reached him in full supply, but by that time Lesly had again reduced the flow to a mere trickle. In consequence Miller's cotton harvest had been small.

Over and over, his mind trod the run-around of his misfortunes— a frail wife, a new baby, doctor's bills, meager returns on his cotton, his wayside repair station bringing in next to nothing now that much of the floating population had gone away.

One night he sat by the kitchen stove reading the evening paper. His wife was ironing a dress for Bertha to wear to school the next morning. "Here's what they're doing in Iowa." He read her of armed farmers preventing an auction of farm property.

"It's terrible to think Iowa is in such a shape," she said. "It's good we came to California. We got a nice place here."

What should he do? He hadn't told her that foreclosure threatened them. But somehow that paragraph in his home paper comforted him. A man still could fight for his own. He carried the clipping with him, showed it to his neighbors when he met them in town, took it to a meeting at Jed Roberts' house called to plan how to combat Lesly in the mutual water company next summer. But nobody showed much interest. Their will to win seemed to have been spent in the summer fight against Lesly.

By Christmas not many of the buyers of the Dodd ranch were left. Farmer after farmer had moved away. They were hard-working, respectable people—American farmers who had been raised on the idea that only lazy people failed. So they slipped away quietly, sometimes in the night, not telling their neighbors they were going.

Lesly was gathering in his harvest. His men were at every auction of foreclosed land. Farm by farm he bought up the Dodd acres. Closer and closer to Katya crept the signs PROPERTY OF A. F. LESLY. NO TRESPASSING. Closer and closer to Garroty. Closer and closer to the Robertses.

One day the news spread through all that part of The Valley that the bank holding the mortgage on Iowa Miller's farm had foreclosed. His ranch would be auctioned off the next week Wednesday at the courthouse. Iowa Miller went into town that afternoon, stopped and bought medicine and a few groceries. "Let them come and drive me out. I've got a sick wife and a baby down with croup," he announced. "Let Lesly try it."

Katya heard the news first when the children came home from school. Bertha had confided in her friend Song that her father said he guessed they'd be moving soon. Song was in tears. Every time Katya tried to use the telephone that evening the party line was busy. Indignant neighbors were talking about Miller's sick baby. Two or three quoted the paragraph from Miller's Iowa paper.

The night before the auction Mishka came in to see Katya. "I go auction tomorrow," he announced. "You come?"

"Mishka, we can't do anything about it. Please stay here."

"I go," he answered with stubborn determination.

"Then I am coming with you," said Katya. "But I don't want Peter there. In that you must obey me."

The next morning she and Mishka drove over to the county seat. When they reached the courthouse, they found a crowd already gathered. All appeared to be prepared for hunting. They wore high boots and carried shotguns and rifles. They talked loudly of ducks and pheasants shot on former expeditions. There was a general drift toward a young man standing off to one side. "That's him— that's Lesly's stooge." The low-spoken words died away and rose again.

"There don't seem to be anyone but him come to bid. Guess everybody knows enough not to buy property Lesly wants," someone said. The crowd was increasing—a great many people Katya had never seen before. She looked at Mishka. His eyes were on Lesly's man.

Down the steps of the courthouse walked the auctioneer dressed in sports clothes he evidently deemed suitable for the occasion. A low but unmistakable hiss greeted him. Memory awoke in Katya—the ominous sound of peasant voices outside her father's house. Now, here in America, her neighbors were in rebellion against a landowner, and she was among them. "Forty acres of good valley land with water rights. Do I hear a bid?" the auctioneer cried.

Lesly's man opened his mouth to speak. No sound came. With one quick movement, man after man around him displayed his shotgun or sporting rifle, but no word was spoken.

"I'm ready for bids," cried the auctioneer. Again the exposed barrels of rifle and shotgun warned Lesly's man to remain silent.

Katya saw Peter and J. T. edging their way through the crowd. She tried to reach them, but she was wedged too tightly into the throng.

"Mister," a voice addressed the autioneer, "you aren't going to sell Miller out to Lesly while we're around, so you better get back inside before you wear our patience out."

The autioneer backed up the steps and in through the door of the courthouse. "Why didn't you call the police?" he demanded angrily of the group gathered inside.

"We did," they answered. "Nothing happened."

Outside, the crowd closed in around Lesly's man. "You better get out of here and not come back," said one of the men nearest him. "We ain't in a healthy mood. We'll see you get out safe, but get going." They made a lane for him, down which he walked. Just as he reached the open street a small but well-aimed stone hit him between the shoulders.

Peter and J. T., standing at the curb, turned and walked quickly away, down the main thoroughfare of the town, out on the highway leading toward Doddstown. They'd thumb their way home, but there was no hurry about that. In a small orchard beside the road they threw themselves on the ground under the trees to rest on the soft mat of green which had sprung up since the rains began. Peter felt the tension going out of him. He'd thrown the stone and hit Lesly's man. He'd been braver than anyone. Nobody else had done anything. He hadn't been afraid. "Did you see how he jumped, J. T.?"

"Yeh, he jumped all right. But why didn't you hit him again? Were you afraid you'd get caught?"

Had he really been afraid? Peter asked himself. That's why he couldn't stand Hal any more for a friend. Hal didn't have any fight in him. Ever since the older boy had told him what his father meant to do, Peter had been mad at him. Why didn't Hal stand up to his father, tell him he wasn't going to give up his quarter acre? All the fall and winter Peter had kept away from his friend, but he was lonely without him. Lately he had taken up with J. T. again. He told him self that he liked J. T. because he was a fighter. Now Peter rolled over on his stomach, hiding his head in his arms.

"Come on. Own up. You got cold feet."

Peter looked up, saw the insolent grin on the lips of his tormenter. With a quick movement he was on his feet. "Shut up," he cried. "I'm tired of your everlasting complaining about everything I do." He started for the road.

"Aw, I didn't mean to make you mad. Come on back," J. T. coaxed. "Can't you take a joke?"

Peter hesitated. Could it be he wasn't being a good sport?

J. T. took a crumpled package out of his pocket. "Here, I got somethin' to eat." There was meat in the sandwich he broke into two pieces. He didn't get meat often these days.

Peter's anger cooled, sitting by his friend sharing his sandwich. "Gee," he said, wanting now to make up, "I just never would have thought you could work Miss Saunders!" He doubled up with laughter, remembering how easy it had been to get their teacher to excuse them. "My, you were good pretending you had a stomach-ache. I laughed so hard inside I really did have a headache."

The day seemed unbelievably short. It was sweet to loiter along the road, catching a ride for a few miles, resting when they were tired, things you did sometimes on Saturdays, but much more thrilling on a Wednesday with all the other kids in school. There had been a tulle fog earlier, but now the sun was shining. They opened their shirts to feel the warmth on their skins. They lay down on the earth, indolent with their adolescent growth. It was a beautiful day.

Peter came into the kitchen just as his mother was setting the table for dinner. He could see by the way she looked at him that she had seen him at the courthouse. He hadn't counted on that. "Honest, I didn't play hooky," he told her. "J. T. and me, we got excused."

"It's all wrong," Katya burst out. "We're *all* wrong. We shouldn't be fighting Lesly, and yet what will happen if we don't? It's not lawful, what we did today, and yet we have to live."

As with Mishka in the summer, Peter felt he had lost something that was very precious to him. His mother had done something she shouldn't, going to the courthouse today.

Standing face to face with her son, his eyes almost level with hers now, Katya realized he was judging her by some standard of his own and that she could not know what that judgment was. All at once in the tall, lanky boy she saw resemblance to his father. And Edward had judged her harshly. It was too much. Confronted with the necessity of saving Peter's heritage for him, knowing the odds were against her, realizing she'd soon have no neighbors to help in the fight, she laid her head on her son's shoulder and broke into sobs, her distress partially for herself, partially for those in worse plight than she. When she and Mishka had been driving home, under a railway culvert she saw a family had built a rude shelter. Something about the woman washing clothes in a tub at the side of the shanty looked familiar—one of her former neighbors! Katya had looked quickly away so that the woman should not know she had been recognized.

Not for many years had Peter seen his mother cry. Awkwardly he smoothed her hair, his impulse of tenderness gradually giving way to a feeling of importance. He was stronger than his mother. Their roles were reversed. A secret elation possessed him. I'll do as I please from now on, he thought.

Katya's neighbors knew that their defiance over the foreclosure of Iowa Miller's ranch was only a gesture. They could not hold back the hand of the law.

But Lesly could. Last summer when he had shut off the water from his neighbors he had said to his manager, "I'll say to you, as Commodore Vanderbilt said to his lawyer, 'What do I care about law? Hain't I got the power?'" Lesly prided himself on his knowledge of American history.

"Let's see," his manager had answered. "Vanderbilt was one of the first of the so-called robber barons of our country, wasn't he?" It was the only protest he allowed himself.

Lesly jutted out his prominent chin from his fleshy face in a way he had when he felt he was being opposed. Perhaps this manager had served his day. Lesly was sensitive to the slightest disapproval in his hirelings. Wholehearted co-operation was what he expected; loyalty was the ideal of laborer to executive.

By spring most of those who had bought the Dodd land had left, many of them at night, losing themselves among the itinerants on the road, ashamed of their failure. Iowa Miller left as soon as his wife and baby were able to travel. But he drove away in broad daylight, his head held high. Bertha sat on the seat beside him. Mrs. Miller and the baby were wedged in among their household goods in the back seat. As they reached the edge of the town, leaving it forever, the man cursed it and the state, but in a low voice meant only to be heard by himself.

Jed Roberts, without consulting May, sold his land to Lesly in order to salvage a little of what they had put into it. He argued he must think first of his family.

Lesly was not the only one who saw a great opportunity in the plight of his neighbors. Eleven new millionaires were created in The Valley during that winter.

There were other casualties in other parts of The Valley. The following spring Bettie and her husband Herb had to admit they were unable to make farming pay. Jeremy Dodd could have told them, if they had asked for his advice, that the beginning of a depression was no time to expect to break even on grapes. Herb had banked on the wineries buying every grape they could get hold of now prohibition had been repealed. Many vineyards had been pulled up during prohibition years. Herb had figured grapes would be scarce and the price high, but it hadn't worked out that way. He had lost money on last year's crop, gone heavily into debt.

"I was too goldarned anxious to be my own boss," he confessed ruefully to Bettie. "I knew I was taking big chances." He looked out the window at his beautifully cared-for vineyards, the branches tipped with soft, fuzzy, opening leaves.

"It's a lovely place to live," Bettie answered with a sigh. Then she caught herself up. This was no time to mourn. "I'll always remember how nice it's been." She too looked out the window at their well-pruned vineyards. "Now where do we go from here?"

"I've been thinking," he answered, "that I could start an independent paper in one of the valley towns that hasn't a sheet of its own, if I could get someone to back me. That way we could stay in The Valley. And we'll try farming again when we're better fixed," he assured her.

"Father might help. He's not half so hard-boiled as he sounds," Bettie answered.

"I hate to ask him. He'd want me to run the paper his way. That isn't quite fair, though. I guess it's because I hate to acknowledge I showed bad judgment."

Bettie said no more, but a week later Herb came home from San Francisco obviously excited. "Well, I did it," he said. "I went to see your father. He didn't say I told you so, or anything of the sort. Simply said he thought he could arrange for a backer for the paper I'd like to start. He just stipulated one thing. I could say anything I liked in it except when it came to power. He said, 'Naturally if I'm going to back you, I don't want you to undercut me. But I don't insist you take my side. Simply keep still—not make it an issue in the paper.' That seemed fair enough.

"And, Bettie, he knew a group of towns near where your grandmother used to live where he thought a local paper would pay. He proposed that, as Edward wasn't using it, we see if he wouldn't let us live in the old house. He called Edward, and Edward said, 'Go ahead.' "

"What a lovely place for the children!" exclaimed Bettie.

If there was any doubt in Herb's mind about keeping still over issues concerning power, the relief in Bettie's face helped him forget it. They were expecting another child. A man with a wife and three children had to provide for them even if he cut the corners a bit.

The paper was well received, and by midwinter the Dodds' old mansion was filled again with the voices of children.

44

FOR many years the Doddstown school had been in the habit of holding two sessions during the busy seasons when itinerants' children thronged the school. This gave all the children a half day of schooling and six hours in the fields. When May Roberts had lived in The Valley, she and Katya had worked side by side to secure a full school day even if the rooms were overcrowded. The spring of 1935 Katya found herself going along with men like Lesly, who wanted the shorter school day. She must have both Peter and Song to help with the first potato planting and later cotton chopping, if she didn't go under. Depression had meant a smaller profit on her crops—one year no profit. Dry years with the attendant lowered underground water table had made it necessary to deepen her wells, an expense which she met by putting a small mortgage on the ranch. Her margin of survival was now so narrow that hiring laborers to take the children's places might swing the balance against her. She herself was now in the fields eight hours each day. Only rigid self-denial and hard work could carry them through. And there was hope of higher prices this season.

Water had become an obsession with her, as food becomes to starving people. Mishka told her the downdraft in the well was increasing, and the water delivery per minute was dropping. She let the rose-bushes die for lack of water. The oleander hedge, drought-resistant though it was, she began to begrudge the small amount of water it drew from the ground. Like Mishka she looked on each bush as one fewer cotton plant. Finally one day she had Peter dig up the hedge. The water they bathed in she saved to wash the floors. Mishka built each family an outhouse to save the water that would otherwise have been used in flushing the toilets. Over and over Katya cautioned Peter not to let the tap in the kitchen drip. And one day when he forgot to turn off the faucet in the sink she was angry with him. "Can't I ever trust you?" she cried.

"Aw, quit," he told her. "If you didn't nag so much, maybe I'd do better."

When Peter asked if he might hire out to pick fruit during the slack season between the two potato crops, Katya was stricken with remorse. "Is it because I nag you that you want to go?"

Only then had he given her the real reason. "J. T.'s going," he had answered.

"But that's no reason for you to go. You certainly can be separated from J. T. for a few weeks." Had she brought about the very thing she most feared, association with J. T.?

"I have to help him on the ladders. I have to boost him on account of his leg." He had flung the words out in a kind of shame. She had seen then that she couldn't force him farther. In fact, she had forced him too far already. Evidently even to speak of his friend's affliction was to him a form of disloyalty.

"I'll need you to dig the second crop of potatoes. You may go until then," she said, "if you can really get work. Aren't there too many fruit pickers already?"

"They're advertising for workers this year," Peter assured her. Tree fruit was selling again at a better than break-even price.

Peter and J. T. took to the road with the alacrity of confirmed vagrants, wandering from camp to camp. The government camps were good and clean, but the boys didn't care for the supervision. They wanted to be free. Finally they found a place to stay in a road camp, living in a shed set aside for men without families. These derelicts, worn out by toil, poverty and disease, fascinated and disgusted Peter. They told wonderful tales of adventure, many of them filled with obscene details.

One evening, as the two boys started back to the shed, they passed a broken-down trailer with a fruit pie standing temptingly in the window. The pink juice of the peaches was oozing out over the crust. Peter stopped, sniffing hungrily. He'd eaten cold baked beans out of a can for breakfast and more beans for luncheon. "Hi, boys!" a wom-

an's voice from inside called out. "Wanta keep a lady company?"
She had stuffed them, made them take second pieces. When they
left, she told them they'd be welcome any evening. "I don't like
eatin' alone. I'm used to a big family. Got boys of my own back in
Missouri."

A few days later, when they climbed down from the ladders for the
final time, J. T. said, "I got a date with a dame. See you later."

At loose ends, Peter wandered down to the trailer. Suppose the
woman was a crazy old hag with buck teeth and a syrupy voice, as
J. T. claimed. She made awfully good pie. His own efforts at preparing food he had to grant weren't very satisfactory. Sure enough,
there was a pie cooling in the window. "Come on in," she called. He
ate two plates of stew and three pieces of pie and promptly fell asleep
in his chair. That was all he remembered until the next morning
when the smell of bacon woke him. "Guess you was worn out. I
tumbled you into bed, and you never so much as opened an eye."

Hurriedly he swallowed the breakfast she gave him, then ran all
the way back to the shack to find J. T. He wasn't there. Out in the
orchard Peter found him standing helplessly by a ladder propped
against a tree. "Here, I'll give you a hist," Peter cried.

"Don't touch me, a guy like you," cried J. T.

"Oh, come on, hurry up," Peter answered testily, looking over his
shoulder. "The overseer will be around and bawl us out. I didn't mean
to let you down."

"I know where you been spendin' the night." On J. T.'s face was
a leer such as Peter had seen on the faces of the men in the shed.

"I don't know what you're talkin' about. I guess there's nothing in
spending the night in a good bed when you get a chance."

"Nice company in it? Used to such things at home?"

Peter had never thought he could strike his friend, but he felt his
hands clench. He'd sure like to thrash him. He hated him. "You
take that back!" he shouted.

"Aw, can't you take a joke?" All day J. T. worried. Maybe he'd
lost Pete. Pete was his. What'd he mean gettin' mad? Months ago
he had found out how to rule his independent friend. They'd been
walking along the road after school. J. T. had stepped on a round
stone, and it had thrown him. It had nothing to do with his lameness,
and he wasn't hurt. He was about to get up when, seeing the expression of concern on Peter's face, he had groaned and fallen back against
the ground. "It's my bad leg. Gives me a good deal o' trouble. Course
I don't say nothin'." It was after that he found Peter almost his slave,
trying to make up to him for his handicap.

Peter didn't speak to J. T. all day, although he continued to help him up and down the ladders. He couldn't forgive him for what he had said, but it was more than that. Why was his home different from others? Was there something wrong about it? Was that the reason his mother wouldn't talk about his father? Or had he gone away from his mother because he didn't want a son who was part Russian? Anyway, J. T. had no business to say what he'd said.

When evening came and Pete helped J. T. down the ladder for the final time that day, he swayed a little, leaning against his friend. "I guess I ain't no good, can't take it."

"What you mean, you ain't any good?"

"Guess I'm givin' out."

Peter's sympathies were instantly roused. He'd meant to save all the money he could to take back to his mother, but J. T. needed a little of it. "How's for gettin' a ride into town? Get some decent grub. That's all that's the matter with you."

They found an old streetcar which had been turned into a hamburg stand, drawn up on a side lot on the edge of the near-by town. They had two hamburgers apiece and hashed-brown potatoes. The girl at the counter looked at them good-naturedly, bumped a piece of pie before them, picked up a knife, expertly halved it. "It's on the house," she said dryly when Peter began counting out money in payment. "I got a boy with hollow legs. You got 'em, too."

J. T. stopped to look at the pictures displayed before a theater. "It's a hell-raiser," he said longingly, turning away with a sigh. Peter bought two tickets. "Gee!" was the only comment either of them made throughout two performances, both held to a tension that brought perspiration out all over them. At the end they sat back relaxed and happy. There was something in being a tough guy, they confided to each other as they stood on the corner afterward trying to thumb their way back to camp.

The next day Peter whistled as he worked. It makes me sick, J. T. said to himself. I ain't a-goin' to have him cocky just because his ma has got a ranch. But sometimes I guess I gotta let him be happy, like last night.

Peter was glad to get home and have his own room where he could be alone. He was silent and preoccupied. He couldn't tell his mother what the men in the shed were like, nor what he had learned. But when autumn came things were all right again because of Song. He didn't want to tease her any more about the name Song. "Sloppy," he'd called it before. Now he liked it. His lightness of heart had come one Saturday as he and his mother and Mishka's family started for a day's work in the cotton. Mishka headed the procession. Peter was at the other end, Song just ahead of him. Everything about her seemed to be dancing this morning: her feet now on the path, now off it, her hands fluttering about when she raised them to pull forward the kerchief which she had tied over her hair. Her eyes danced when she turned around, walking backward, crying, "It's like a picnic, Peter, don't you think?"

"You won't feel gay like a bird tonight. Better not give strength you have not," Song's mother admonished, more aware than the girl of the toll the exhausting work in the field would take of her daughter's beginning womanhood.

Song patted her mother on the shoulder, swinging out of the line, trailing her bag, swinging her body and hands, stylizing the movements of cotton picking.

Peter, walking behind, watched her light, quick motions. All summer he had seen girls through J. T.'s eyes and the jokes of the men with whom he had lived in the shed. Now, watching Song, he felt as if he had been brushed by something mysterious and disturbingly beautiful. Song seemed set apart, different from any girl in the world. He placed himself in the row next her. As the day advanced and he saw the spent motion of her hand as she threw the cotton back into the bag, he hurried his own work, hoping to fill his bag in time to give her help with hers. But Song's deft picking of the five sections of cotton from the five receptacles of each cotton boll was quicker than his. Always she finished first. But he insisted on carrying the heavy bag to the scales for her.

That evening while Katya was getting the dinner she heard Peter singing. He had not sung since he had come back. She felt her throat growing tight with tears. It was such a funny, quavering voice, cracking now and then, warning her that he was growing up. He was in his fifteenth year and unusually tall. Perhaps the hardest years were past. Peter could soon take over the burden if she could hold on until he was through high school.

She had had to put a mortgage on the ranch. But everything would be all right if the water project was ever started. How much she had learned this last year! She had thought that once the people had voted for the water project, the state would start work immediately. She and Peter together had made a map of The Valley, intending to put in the dams and canals as they were built. She glanced at it now, pinned to the wall of the kitchen. It had grown dingy. Probably they had lost the red and blue pencils so hopefully bought but never needed.

This winter Doddstown took on its old pattern. A number of stores, opened when the hundred-odd Dodd farmers came to The Valley, had closed for lack of business. Without May Roberts and the other women to help her, hard as Katya tried, she was unable to keep the parent-teacher association alive. There was no formal disbanding, but interest flagged, and no entertainments were planned for the winter. At first the Professor attempted to keep the baseball teams together, but what with the loss of bigger boys like Hal Roberts and the opposition encountered in J. T., the Professor, like Katya, finally gave up.

Then J. T. took over the teams' remnants and welded them into a gang. During the months that followed he became a model boy at school, all his sabotage carried on through other boys whom he controlled. He taught them first how to steal the erasers from the pencils of the Mexican children, small articles from the cloakroom. There was little or nothing to steal from the children of laborers who stayed on in the camp. Later he started a campaign of window breaking in Mexican town.

When Peter did not acquiesce in his schemes, he questioned his loyalty. Peter was glad that Pedro's family had gone to Los Angeles this winter to find work or, if no work was available, go on relief.

At the beginning of December one of the new teachers at the school, a young woman all the pupils liked, suggested to bring up the attendance they offer a prize to the child in each grade having the best record of attendance and deportment during December. December and January Mexican and other laborers' children were out a great deal due reportedly to sickness and lack of adequate clothing. Encouraged by the new teacher, the all-but-defunct parent-teacher association took up the scheme and provided the prizes, displayed them in Mr. Miliken's office. There were shoes and sweaters, but best of all a small radio donated by the chain grocery store. Not since the days of May Roberts had there been so much enthusiasm over school. The first week there was scarcely an absence.

"We gotta do something about these Mexicans coming back to school," J. T. grumbled to Peter.

"They won't keep it up," Peter answered.

"Sure they'll keep it up. Mexicans are like that, always taking things away from Americans."

"What you going to do about it? You can't keep 'em away." Peter was growing fast, and there were times when any effort was distasteful to him.

"I hate 'em around me," said J. T. "But it doesn't make any difference to you that I'm lame on account of them."

"Well, what do you think we can do?" asked Peter, never proof against such an appeal.

"You know that shack on the edge of the town. Fine place to lock up two or three of 'em. That'll stop 'em."

"We don't need to lock 'em up," Peter answered. "Just tell 'em we're going to."

"All right if you're so chickenhearted. I'da gone along with you if you'd lock 'em up, but if it's only going to be talk, you gotta do it yourself," said J. T. "If it doesn't work——"

"It'll work." Peter intended it should. He didn't like the idea of locking the Mexican children up. After school that evening he went over to the Sunshine Café and talked to Pedro's friend Manuel. Next morning the Mexican children started to town with scared faces. A few of them loitered along the way and were late. The day after several were out. The new teacher reluctantly agreed that the Mexicans were shiftless, as she had been told, and that the prizes would go to the American children.

Peter won the radio but somehow he didn't want it. He offered it to Song, but she wouldn't take it. He guessed she knew why the Mexican children had stayed away. The day school closed for the holidays Peter was walking along the main street of Doddstown. Someone knocked into him, nearly toppling him over into the gutter.

"What you trying to do?" he demanded, swinging around. To his astonishment he found himself facing Pedro.

"I'm telling you I'm back and that I learned a thing or two in Los Angeles. We don't let ourselves get pushed around there. Just remember——" Pedro walked away. He'd hitchhiked all the way from Los Angeles when his friend Manuel had written him of Peter's threat. He'd always been meek when he lived in Doddstown, but down in Los Angeles he'd seen what Mexicans could do when they banded together. There was a girl who had three hundred in her crowd. They prided themselves that in a half hour after she telephoned the first one, they were ready for any violence she felt necessary.

Peter reflected he'd lost out all around. Tried to do something for the Mexican kids and instead of being grateful here was Pedro acting smart. Next time he'd go along with J. T.

A few days later Peter and J. T., loitering along a back street in the late afternoon, saw a group of Mexican boys and girls walking toward Mexican Town. "I tell you what let's do," said J. T. "Let's take their girls away from 'em."

"Let's," cried Peter, carried along on the impulse of the moment. In the failing light of the short winter afternoon, he thought he saw Pedro in the group, and he wanted to get even with him. "Let's cut across the lot back of Ike's place and head 'em off."

Just as they reached the end of the lot, they saw the group stop, evidently hearing their stealthy approach.

"Give us your girls!" shouted J. T., charging in among them, grabbing one by the arm. The rest of the girls screamed and started to run, but Peter headed off one and gathered her into his arms. His body felt suddenly aflame as he drew her closer.

Just then he heard J. T. shouting for help. He turned, ran toward him. He grabbed for Pedro's arm which was raised above J. T., knife in hand.

"Kill the bastard!" shouted J. T. Slowly Peter drew Pedro's arm down, made him point the knife in upon himself, wanting to hurt Pedro, filled for the moment with the lust for violence. Suddenly he felt himself jerked back. Pedro, suddenly released, sprawled on the ground, his knife flying out of his hand.

"What you boys trying to do?" demanded a man's voice.

"It's the dirty Mexican!" cried J. T. "He drew a knife on us."

"Yeh," said the man looking down on J. T. "I guess you aren't lily-white yourself. I've a notion to turn all three of you in. There's been too much deviltry going on around the town lately. It's lucky for you I'm not the officer. I don't know about you," he said, looking at Pedro. "This business of fighting with a knife." But finally, after he felt he had scared them sufficiently—no knife being visible now— he let all three of them go.

Peter slunk off into the gathering darkness not once looking back.

45

THERE were few people this December Sunday evening at the services being held in the white-frame church which stood in the middle of the block where Doddstown's well-to-do citizens lived. Its members did not constitute a large group: the manager of the local office of the electric-power company and the gas station, the school principal, sev-

eral retired farmers and the managers of near-by large estates. Most
of the women were doing their Christmas shopping in Bakersfield or
Fresno. One or two had gone to San Francisco. There were almost
no young people, for these families sent their children away to school.
It was a considerable drain on their finances, but they made the sacrifice gladly, not wishing to have their sons and daughters thrown with
the itinerant workers or the Mexican and Japanese children. A greater
number than usual had been bundled off to private schools this year
because of an outbreak of petty crimes in the town ascribed to a gang
of boys.

The box-shaped building with tar-paper roof, standing at the north
end of the town, no one passing would have taken for a church had it
not been for the sign above the door announcing that it was a house
of worship. To it May Roberts and most of the farmers who had
bought the Dodd land had gravitated, feeling more comfortable here
than they would have felt in the church which Lesly's manager attended. "They're just folks here" was May Roberts' comment. "We
don't look out-of-place in our everyday clothes." May was sorely
missed. She had put new life and spirit into both congregation and
pastor. Here Mishka and his family worshiped. The bare interior
with no altar other than a plain deal table on which a large Bible was
placed suited Mishka, who had left Russia so that he might worship
without pomp or ritual.

Tonight the service was to be given over to prayer for rain. Mishka
for the first time during all the years he had served Katya Suvorov had
asked a favor of her—to come and pray with him for rain. She had
consented because she realized it meant much to him.

In accordance with the rules of Russia's Greek Orthodox Church,
she wore a black, three-cornered bit of lace covering her head, although Daria and Song and all the other women went with uncovered
heads. Neither did they stand in reverence to the all-powerful Deity.
Even Mishka was sitting. The pastor, dressed in a plain, ill-fitting
suit, offered neither candles nor incense and bowed before no sacred
image. He talked with Deity with less ceremony than Mishka's voice
held for her! Katya was at first startled by the informality and then
suddenly this democratic approach to God seemed to fit America and
bring her into harmony with those around her.

"O Lord, remember Thy servants now in the day of our trouble
and send us rain," begged the pastor, whom she knew on weekdays
as one of her farmer neighbors. "Amen, amen," spoke those around
her.

Now Katya heard Mishka's voice raised in supplication. "Father," he cried, "do not abandon thy children! The earth that is not filled with water cries out even as the womb that is barren. The earth cannot bear if it is dry and beaten to dust. The earth is the Lord's and the fullness thereof."

For a little after he had finished speaking a deep hush fell over the room. Then others spoke, asking the Almighty for rain, voicing the tight fear in Katya's heart.

They stood to sing now. She was swept up into the triumphant song of the people, " 'Praise God from whom all blessings flow. Praise Him, all creatures here below.' " If only Peter were here with her! But he had refused to come.

Where the main street of the town lost itself in rows of shacks stood a small, unpainted building. A large sign over the door read: THE LORD IS COMING. PERHAPS TODAY. ARE YOU READY? At the farther end of the unfinished interior a couple of two-by-fours some three feet high had been nailed to a low platform. On top of the uprights a wooden box had been fastened, making a crude lectern. A portable organ stood near. Suspended from the rafters was an old-fashioned hanging lamp, half revealing men and women sitting on benches around the sides of the room, children in their arms or on the floor at their feet.

The minister, as poorly dressed as his parishioners, advanced to the front of the platform and announced the first hymn. Like the slow movements of receding waves the singing ebbed away at the end of the stanza, then mounted like incoming waves on the refrain, "*Washed in the blood of the Lamb.*"

The minister knelt. "Is there not one who will come to the Mercy Throne?" he called out.

"*Washed in the blood of the Lamb*" came the refrain.

"Not one? O Lord, give us one!"

"*Washed in the blood of the Lamb.*"

"There is one. I see her rising. Come, Sister."

"*Washed in the blood of the Lamb.*"

A woman in a gingham dress and shoes worn at the heels moved slowly forward. Her tired face with its creased downward lines began to change as wonder, surprise and then ecstasy gripped her. She moved forward, drawn by the hypnotic voice of the minister: "Come, come to the Mercy Seat!"

"*Washed in the blood of the Lamb.*"

She was kneeling now, clinging to one of the rough uprights of the lectern. Men and women closed around her, singing, clapping their hands. *"Washed in the blood of the Lamb."*

Above her stood the minister, his head bowed in reverence, his shoulders bowed, too, but by toil. For six days he labored in the field. For this one he was transformed into the messenger of God. He looked down at the now prostrate woman. "Praise the Lord," he called in a loud voice, "she is coming through."

"Washed in the blood of the Lamb."

Suddenly out of the mesmeric chant a woman cried out, "Praise the Lord! She has come through!"

The congregation moved forward, the curious, the eager, the devout.

Peter and J. T. were sitting at the back, drawn into the room like moths by the light and the chanting voices. "It's Ma," whispered J. T. He seemed half pleased, half ashamed.

Peter, hearing the words of the minister, "He'll take away all your sins," and the mounting chant, *"Washed in the blood of the Lamb,"* felt a desire to join her rising within him. Only to be clean. To kneel and receive absolution from the thoughts haunting him since he had returned from camp last summer. And the memory of Song, for it was she whom he had captured the night of the fight. He hadn't known it until he had turned her toward him and seen her white, frightened face. He half rose from the bench. Someone pulled at his sleeve. He looked around. J. T. had his handkerchief stuffed into his mouth, and he was shaking with laughter. Ashamed and humiliated, Peter followed his friend to the door and out into the street.

They loitered along the alleyway on which most of the saloons backed. Peter stood head and shoulders above J. T., but he walked bent over to accommodate himself to the small, limping figure at his side. He had thought for a moment in the church he could rid himself of the remorse which had possessed him constantly of late. Feeling himself J. T.'s protector and at the same time unequal to what his friend expected of him he had forced himself to wilder and wilder acts, culminating in the fight on Friday and what he'd nearly done to Pedro.

Walking down the alley now toward a saloon, J. T. began, "Aw, Pete, you gotta take things like not winning. Pedro was just stronger than you was, that's all. I know you'da killed him for me if ya could."

Suddenly Peter straightened up. He wanted to be rid of J. T. forever. Then glancing down and seeing his friend limping along beside him, Peter wasn't through with J. T. nor was J. T. through with him. That Peter knew. If he offended him, J. T. might raise against him again the cry of foreigner, Ruski. Besides, what would he do without his friend to help him raise hell? There wasn't anything else to do in this damned town. He tipped over a garbage can standing on the curb and felt better. "Crazy old town! I'd like to see it burn," he railed.

"Took you a long time to see what a dirty old place Doddstown is."

"Nobody gets a break around here," Peter answered. He'd never copied J. T.'s sour outlook, loyal to the town because it was in The Valley. He felt a deep, emotional attachment to The Valley. All his great moments had come to him here—the time Mishka had told him to lay his hand flat on the ground and placed his own over it. "The earth," Mishka had said, "it speak to you." For a moment Peter had had tactile intuition of the life that existed in the earth. He felt again the exaltation when he had come to The Valley with his mother and seen for the first time rain-soaked earth. But now that he had spoken against the town, he guessed he hated The Valley, too.

Katya was increasingly troubled over Peter. One moment he had so much energy he didn't know what to do with it. He'd stand in the kitchen while she was getting dinner and tree himself on the low rafters and, like a playful monkey, catch at her as she passed. The next moment he'd be like a huge rag doll, limp and lifeless, sprawled in a chair, his long legs stretched out in front of him, his eyes glazed over, the spirit seeming almost to have left his body. Sometimes he was gentle and anxious to make her happy and worked hard on the ranch. Sometimes he was rough and sullen and went out every evening, refusing to tell her where he went or what he did.

One day she came home from town to find many of the things in her dresser drawers out of place, and the lock on a box in which she kept a few treasures had been sprung. Peter was nowhere about, but when he came in he began immediately to talk of the work he and Mishka had been doing in a distant part of the ranch. Suddenly he fell silent and went into his own room, shutting the door.

What had he been looking for? Katya asked herself. Money? No, he knew there was none in the house. Before leaving for town she had counted out the little she had on hand—scarcely enough for the weekly marketing. With a sense of pain she guessed he had been searching for some knowledge of his father. Several times lately he had approached her on the subject, but always in a roundabout way. Once he had talked about J. T.'s name—Ward. Nice and short, very American-sounding. The kind of name a boy could go far on. "I guess you don't like American names," he had ended.

46

ON COMING in from his work at the school one March afternoon, John Dodd found a note from Mrs. Suvorov in his mail. It read: "You said once to me that if ever I needed help with my son to let you know. Because he is your brother's son as well as mine, I am writing you. Things are not right with Peter, and I do not know what to do. Could you come to see me some day during the hours he is in school?"

John felt now he'd neglected the boy, taking it for granted he was getting along all right. Peter had written him at the beginning of the summer proudly stating that he was going to earn money picking fruit so his mother might take things easier. And then in the winter Peter had written him again, saying he didn't feel he could take the time this year to go skiing. John had supposed the boy meant he was working.

John had been unusually busy these last months, but that was no excuse for neglecting his nephew. Ever since his wife's death John had been pretty hard on himself. The aching need of her presence had gradually changed, as the years went by, into a feeling of strain which he attributed to inadequacy in his work, not conscious that this sense of inadequacy was the frustration both of his physical and spiritual selves which had been so fully realized in the perceptive and receptive nature of his wife. Drained daily as he was of all the creative forces of his nature to meet the problems of the delinquent boys in his care, he suffered from a growing exhaustion. But sternly he took himself to task for allowing weariness to conquer him.

He arranged to be away from his work the next day, which was Friday, intending to leave early in the morning and get to Doddstown while Peter was at school. If the boy's mother wished it, he would try again to get Edward to accept his son. Recognition of him wouldn't have the same hazards for Edward it had had for him at the time of his first election. That he had been divorced and had a son would pass without comment now that there was no political occasion to distort the facts. He was somewhat disturbed that there was so little need to go to Edward's defense. He seemed to be in favor with everyone. John knew from experience that a man who fights for what he believes is never without opposition or enemies.

The old personal relationship between them when Edward was a boy, resumed that night Edward had spent with him just before his first election, had lapsed. Could he influence Edward now? He doubted it, but he would try if Mrs. Suvorov wanted him to. His tired mind could not hold any of these problems long. His thoughts drifted back and forth—thoughts of Edward as a boy, thoughts of Peter standing in the snow looking up at the tall pines on his first sight of them, Peter and Pedro, Peter and J. T. There was a protectiveness in Peter toward the lame boy. He had put his strength at the other's disposal in such a way as to minimize his friend's handicap. Was J. T. exploiting that quality in Peter? It well might be.

Then his thoughts veered to the boys at the school. It seemed to him he never had had so many difficult problems to solve with them. There were any number of itinerant laborers' sons in his classes, bewildered, sullen boys, soured on society. They'd taken to the road during the depression, crowded out of the small shacks by their parents' inability to feed them. Putting them behind bars wasn't the way—he was convinced of that.

Following the Grapevine Grade he reached the top of the pass. As he drove down into The Valley, gradually the problems fell away. The Valley always did something to him. Men were pruning vineyards and orchards. Smoke rose from the burning piles of cuttings. The Sierras were blue in the distance.

He had passed Bakersfield and turned west, and then north on Route 33. In the early afternoon he reached the lane leading to the Suvorov place. His quick eye told him times were hard here. The garden was gone. The house needed painting, and what little machinery he saw was out of date.

Mishka came toward him as he got out of the car. "You wish something?"

"I came to see Mrs. Suvorov. Is she at home?" John asked as he shook the man's hand.

"She has gone to the town. I help you for her?" he asked. There was a note in the Russian's voice which gave John the feeling that he considered Peter and his mother his special care. It might be a good thing to talk to Mishka.

"Well, perhaps you could," he said. "It's about Peter I came."

There was a stubborn silence. John sensed that the peasant's suspicion against the outsider had been roused. "What is Petya to you?" Mishka said at last.

John knew that tone too well. Too often he had encountered it when he had gone to see the parents or friends of a boy in trouble.

He hastened to add, "It's about a camping trip for the spring, as we did not get off in the winter."

Mishka's red lips showed in a smile startlingly vivid against his coal-black beard. "Petya like the mountains. You take him soon?" There was an urgent tone in the Russian's voice now, as if there was some need beyond pleasure that the trip should be made. Or did he imagine it, because of what Mrs. Suvorov had written him?

With a bang and a hiss an old truck drew up almost at their feet. As Mishka helped Mrs. Suvorov from the high seat John noticed she was older-looking than when he had seen her last and thin. Her cheeks were slightly hollowed, accentuating the high cheekbones, the wide forehead. The eyes were deeper-set, it seemed to him. An odd thought crossed his mind: There's a kind of starvation of the senses going on in her.

She came eagerly forward, holding out her hand. "Come, we'll go in. I'll start the tea. You have been riding a long way."

While they drank their tea, Katya spoke of the lack of rain, of next year's crops, of everything except her son. Then at last, seemingly with some reluctance, she said, "We talk now of Peter."

"What is wrong?" he asked.

"I do not know. I can only guess. Much is not right among the children. Bad things have happened, stealing and fights over in Mexican Town. Nobody can find out just who's at the bottom of the trouble. I suspect it's the Ward boy. You remember him? If he's in it, so is Peter. From the outside Peter is not in trouble. But I think J. T. wishes to destroy him here." Katya put her hand over her heart.

"What power has he over Peter so to control him?" John asked.

"Partly his lameness. He's made Peter believe he needs his protection. But that's only part of it. . . . I think, Peter fears him. It's his Russian name. That's what makes him feel J. T. has the whip hand over him. Would Edward accept him now? If he'd see him, he'd be proud of him. He's really a nice boy," Katya ended.

"I can try," John answered. "If I fail——"

"Then couldn't I tell him what his name is?" Katya interrupted eagerly. Then with doubt in her voice she added, "Yet, if Edward wouldn't have anything to do with him, it might make things worse to tell Peter who his father is. I've gone over it and over it, and I don't know what to do."

"Would you be willing to have him sent away to school?" John asked.

"It would do him harm. He'd feel he was deserting. J. T. would see to it he felt that way." After a moment's pause she said, "He

would destroy Peter by long distance." Her speech, touched as it was
with a foreign accent, seemed to give her last very American remark
an ominous force.

"His love for you. Couldn't I make him see that he is hurting you?"
Katya shook her head. "I am his mother and he cares for me, but
it's only the girl a boy loves who can exert that much influence over
him."

"Peter's too young for love," said John.

"Nobody is too young for love!" cried Katya.

"Or too old." His remark startled him. He had not meant to make
it. Katya had raised her head. Their eyes met. Then John knew that
he loved her. The knowledge brought him to life with a suddenness
that was pain, like blood coursing through numbed muscles. For a
moment he could not think clearly of Peter. He rose. "I'll write Edward and let you know what he says as soon as I hear."

He had taken his seat in his car, had his foot on the starter, when a
girl came out of Mishka's house. She looked like a small, indignant
bird as she alighted on his running board. Her black eyes snapped,
she tossed her head, setting her black hair flying. It was Mishka's
girl, of course. He had not seen her since the evening they had all
trooped together into the Suvorov kitchen, the evening Peter had
returned from his first skiing trip. She was a child then, a pretty girl
now.

"You've come to see Peter. You mustn't go away."

"You're Song," he said.

"Yes. Make Peter just once do something big and grand, all by
himself."

"I can't *make* Peter do anything. I wouldn't if I could."

She seemed to be considering that for a moment. "Anyway, please
wait and talk to him," she begged.

"Why do you want me to," he asked. "Has Peter done anything
wrong?"

She gave him a look full of suspicion not unlike that her father's
face had held earlier in the afternoon. Were the two trying to protect
the boy from the consequences of acts already committed? Was he
in time? He was convinced he should act immediately.

"I'll try to catch him along the road. He ought to be on his way
home by now," he said.

"I'm afraid he'll be late," said Song, jumping down from the running board. Her tiny, vivacious face looked pinched with anxiety.

I must do something, but what? he thought, getting out of his car
and going back to speak to Katya once more. "I think I'll try to find

Peter. If I can get him to go home with me, will it be all right with you? I believe I'd better talk to him—not wait until we hear from Edward."

47

THE two boys were slouching along toward the center of the town. At the sound of a motor horn almost at their elbows, "Nursey-nurse," scoffed J. T. Peter looked over his shoulder, expecting to see Mishka. It was not Mishka but his friend John Dodd parking his car at the curb. He felt an impulse to jump into the car, ride away, never come back—but close on its heels came the impulse to dodge John Dodd, go off with J. T.

And then he *was* sitting in the car beside John. He didn't look up to see J. T., his eyes full of amused tolerance. But John had seen. I guess Song is right, he thought. I've got to make Peter do something big all on his own, and there is no time to lose. "Look here," he said, as they drove along the main road: "you didn't come with me for Christmas vacation. How about coming along with me now? I'd like to take you home with me. You've never seen where I hold out."

There was only a feeble protest from Peter as he stretched his long legs out in the space under the dashboard. He seemed too tired to set up any opposition when John said, "We'll just drive in and get your mother's consent and pick up your toothbrush and something to sleep in."

The first hour of the long drive south Peter was uncommunicative, even sullen, but gradually he became more friendly. Finally he was talking naturally of skiing trips they'd made, of fruit picking the sum-mer before, of the neighbors who had lost their ranches and moved away, even about Hal and what they had planned and had had to give up.

As they drove over the pass and out of The Valley, John talked about his own work, told Peter the stories of two or three of the boys. He didn't want his nephew to come unprepared to the school. He could see, though, it was a shock to Peter when later the high iron gates of the institution clanged shut behind them and then were locked. He even seemed frightened. It was obvious he was afraid of anything connected with the law.

But when they entered the living room of John's house, there was a marked change in the boy's mood. "Gee, it's nice here!" he exclaimed, impressed by the soft rug under his feet, the easy chair he sat down in. "Do the boys live here, too?"

"No, this is my house." Evidently he has not fully grasped what it means for a boy to be sent here, thought John.

"Gee!" Peter said again, looking at the well-filled bookcases lining the room. "Mother'd like to see such a lot of books. She likes books." He thought of the eight they owned—especially of the history of Russia. He'd grown up on that history. He knew the Emperors' names by heart. There was a bulky volume the Mohkovs had sent his mother last Christmas about the old Russian ballet—pictures he sometimes looked at, but which his mother pored over evening after evening. And one with the score of operas she knew. Sometimes she would prop the book up on the table and move her fingers as if she were playing. He looked at John's piano, then back to the crowded bookcases. "Gee!" he said for the third time. "That's a lot of books."

I wonder if he has never before seen a library, thought John. Why, even the boys in the reformatory had access to a richer environment than boys brought up in a place like Doddstown. And this boy was the grandson of Jeremy Dodd, great-grandson of the rich pioneer! There was a wry twist to John's mouth, as he thought how superior most people feel toward poor boys who get into trouble. "Bad stock, naturally mean and vicious!" How often he heard it! Here was his own nephew close to trouble. He'd reached him once, but how was he to reach him this time? Boredom and insecurity, not only his own but J. T.'s, had eaten away like termites at the foundations of his personality.

Perhaps it had been a mistake to bring him here where he was less certain of himself than in his home surroundings. How would he take having a servant wait on him at the table? But when they sat down to a late dinner, John saw he need not worry on that score. Something of the ancient and beautiful culture which was Katya's inheritance had been passed on to her boy. He had the manners of a gentleman, and furthermore he knew how—once his training as a gentleman had asserted itself—to place a barrier between them. He was far less accessible than in his first burst of astonishment on entering the house. John tried several approaches—school, winter sports, the ranch. Were the wells holding out? Last year Peter had been deeply interested in engineering, especially water engineering. Now he evinced only polite interest.

They had risen and were entering the living room when John ventured, "I thought you might like to go to a technical school instead of to high school next year. If it interests you, it might be arranged. There are scholarships, you know."

All at once Peter seemed to break to pieces. "What is it to you what I do?" His voice, heavy and sullen as he started the sentence, broke almost into a cry at the end. "Why don't you let me alone?" He twisted his hands until the knuckles cracked. "What did you bring me into a place like this for? I can take care of myself. I'm not going to get into trouble. J. T. and I——"

"I brought you here to talk about yourself," quietly John answered, "and J. T. You wouldn't want him to get into trouble, would you?"

"Who says he's going to?" Peter demanded.

"Boys like J. T. do," John replied.

"Boys like J. T.! What do you mean, 'boys like J. T.'? Crippled, I suppose, and his dad losing his farm. Why do you pick on him?"

John stirred the fire, pushed a stool before Peter. "Might as well stretch your legs out and be comfortable." His tone was casual, with a kind of man-to-man note in it. "I know J. T. is up against it in a lot of ways," he said, seating himself, "but not entirely. He's smart, isn't he?"

"Smart as hell."

"Well, then, what are you breaking him down for, pitying him?"

"Me! Breaking him down. Me!"

"You are pitying him, aren't you, when you stay home from skiing on his account? You wouldn't let a boy with two good legs keep you from going, would you? You stayed home primarily because you felt sorry for J. T., didn't you? You're helping him to believe he can't do things. Isn't that breaking him down?"

"He'll——" Peter stopped. "I gotta do what he wants me to do," he ended miserably. "But I don't know. I'm all mixed up."

"We've been friends for some time," said John. "If you're mixed up in any trouble, I might be the one to straighten things out for you."

"Nothing happened," Peter answered, sullen again. "If Pedro hadn't drawn a knife on J. T., I wouldn't'ta gone for him. Anyway, nothing happened. It's . . . It's . . ." No, he couldn't tell about Pedro and how he'd tried to hurt him—and yet it hadn't been enough to satisfy J. T. He couldn't tell about Song. "I'm just no good," he said.

"I doubt if you can help your friend by being no good," John answered quietly.

Peter gave him a searching glance.

"I'm going to ask something of you I believe will make J. T. think he's able to do things. It's simple. Decide tonight that the two of you will take a camping trip with me this spring."

"No, I can't do that." Peter's voice rose again. "J. T. is lame. I can't leave him out."

"You don't need to. Lots of lame people do things. Show him he can."

"But J. T. said last winter it kinda got him down, sitting around while the rest of us boys——"

"J. T. didn't sit around," John interrupted. "Remember? We went tobogganing. He steered."

Peter's eyes were full of hostility. "What are you trying to do? Say J. T. is putting it on? You needn't think you can work me that way. I ain't going with you."

"All right, Peter. I'd like to have you boys go along, but of course I'm not trying to force you. It wouldn't be any fun for me either if you didn't want to go." He took out his watch. "It's very late. I guess we'd better get to bed." He led the way upstairs. If I could only get him to take one step toward freeing himself from the web J. T. has woven about him, John thought.

Peter stretched himself out in the unfamiliar bed, feeling all around him the strangeness of his surroundings. A light outside threw the pattern of the reformatory's iron fence on the ceiling. Peter, looking up, saw it and shivered. Ever since the afternoon he'd told J. T. he hated Doddstown and would like to see it burn, J. T. had been talking to him about setting fire to some empty shacks on the edge of Mexican Town. "They'd burn like tinder," J. T. had said. Peter had almost consented to attempt it this very night. Then Mr. Dodd had come along. The man who had separated Pedro and him had said next time he caught him doing anything wrong he'd turn him in. The law was on one side—J. T. on the other, J. T. who might again class him with the foreigners. He felt caught—any way he turned he was caught.

Suddenly the man downstairs seemed to offer security. Why had he told Mr. Dodd he couldn't do what he asked him to do? "High Sierras"—the phrase repeated itself in his mind. He liked the words. He'd only seen the low Sierras. They were beautiful. But the High Sierras, the trees taller than he had ever seen. He'd feel safe there with Mr. Dodd. For the moment J. T. seemed far off and unimportant. Gee, perhaps Mr. Dodd really thought he wouldn't go! Perhaps before he went to bed he'd written to another boy to take Peter's place. He said he was going to write some letters. Peter had better tell him now. Tomorrow morning might be too late.

John, sitting at his desk downstairs, heard his name called. He went to the foot of the stairs, switching on the hall light as he went. In the light flooding upward he saw Peter, his feet bare, his pajama top rumpled around his middle, his hair on end, as he peered anxiously down. "I just knew all of a sudden that I'd like to go. I mean if I can get J. T. to go. Could I reconsider?"

"If you want to," John answered, thinking how Peter's language changed. It was interesting how it seemed to accord with his state of mind—cheap and ungrammatical when his friend swayed his mind, correct and even grown-up at other moments. "I'll put your name down, and J. T.'s."

Seated once more at his desk, John started a letter to his brother Edward. Perhaps if he'd see the problems of The Valley in a more personal way and fight harder, he would stop dodging the fact that Peter was his son. Perhaps I'm doing him an injustice, thinking he isn't fighting. But surely if he were close to the people he'd have realized their discouragement when the money had not been appropriated for the water project.

John wrote swiftly. He decided to begin with The Valley but not say anything about how the underground water level was dropping, or how many small farmers had been pushed to the wall in the last three years. Those issues had been gone over until they were threadbare. He wrote about the boys and girls of Doddstown, the drabness of their lives and what it led to. Only at the end did he write directly of Peter.

After he had finished his letter, released for the time from Peter's problems, he found his new feeling for Katya surging to the fore. He drew back. Did he wish to open his heart to another woman, run again the chance of loss, perhaps the pain of her refusal? Then he knew he was helpless before his love for her.

48

EDWARD found the letter in a pile of mail at his office in Sacramento. Just another plea for his influence, he had thought, or a request for money, before he noticed the name of the state institution in the corner, recognized his brother's handwriting. He opened the letter, read the first page. Well, if John wouldn't think up something like that! Wanting him to see that the Central Valley Project went through so as to give better recreational facilities to the children of California! As if they didn't have all the Sierra mountains to play in, an ocean on their western border and a climate that let them live outdoors the year around. At least he had the sense left to say recreation is only a by-product of the water project, he thought.

He read on. "Doddstown has less to offer than ever." Now he was interested in spite of himself. But why did John have to use the old satirical name for the town? The Dodds had nothing to do with the place any longer. "Maybe you can't imagine it," the letter continued, "but the town, a couple of years ago, was beginning to be something like the one we were brought up in, a community of middle-class families. There aren't more than ten or a dozen of the families who bought Father's land left today. Lesly has managed to get most of them out. He's put up a private cotton gin near the Mexican settlement, a cotton camp just beyond.

"Lesly seems to have persuaded a group of big landowners over in that part of The Valley to join him in a swanky subdivision, where he has built himself an extravagantly beautiful house. They bring their wives down during the ginning season and have a pretty lively time while they're there. That's the community: the very rich and the very poor, with a dwindling number of small farmers squeezed between. This is what's happening to their children: Take two boys I know. The father of one of them lost his land last year. He's one of Lesly's laborers now. The family of the other boy is pretty hard-pressed, but they are getting by. The first one is lame, an infantile-paralysis case, contracted, I believe, during an epidemic in one of the camps; the other is tall and strong, but dominated by loyalties to the lame fellow. They're pals—you know what that means.

"Lately they have come near to disaster; they are still very near to it—just the thin thread of a boy's resolution holding them from toppling over into crime. From what I've been able to learn, they had a fight with some Mexican boys recently and nearly killed one of them. Suppose they had? They wouldn't even have been put behind the fence we have here but might have been sent up for life to a penal institution. And yet they are not essentially bad. In fact, they're both I'd say above the average in intelligence. But there isn't a place to go fishing within miles, as you know; there isn't a swimming pool; there isn't a damn thing for a boy to do, Edward—so they turn to crime to amuse themselves and to get rid of their sense of frustration."

Edward had come to the bottom of the page. Just another appeal, he was thinking, another effort to win his sympathy. Six years in the Senate had had its effect on him. How many thousands of letters he had received in that time designed to stir up his sympathy! A man had to protect himself. He couldn't go chasing every fly-by-night scheme to aid the people. He had to be objective.

Too, he had to be careful not to appear a kind of crackpot on social questions. He'd almost wrecked his career over advocating those amendments to the Central Valley Project Act. For some time afterward his stock had gone very low. The rumor got around that he was too idealistic, too visionary, to be trusted with the responsibility his position in the Senate entailed. If it had not been for his father's help during that hard period, he might have lost out entirely. "You need to balance up your stand on the valley project with some definite stand for private business," Jeremy had told him. "Compromise is essential in a public officer." He couldn't put on a campaign to hurry the Central Valley Project in order to keep boys out of mischief! It was preposterous. Imagine what his opponents would say to that!

Edward turned over the page to see how much more there was of this kind of stuff. "The tall, strong boy beyond a doubt is your own son. Why don't you face it? Half the boy's trouble is the insecurity he experiences in knowing he is an American but not being able to prove it plus the feeling that he is unacceptable to his father. Even if you don't feel you can take him into your home even for a visit, if you'd acknowledge him I could do a good deal more for him. As things stand now, I have no authority over the boy. I can only try to persuade him to do things. I don't know but what I am reaching the end of my rope with him."

Edward rose, walked across the room to the cooler, got himself a drink. He had some difficulty swallowing. Then he sat down at his desk and answered the letter.

"Are you trying to compromise me, John?" he wrote. "Get me to sponsor a state-wide recreation program for the sake of someone you are trying to fasten on me as a member of my family? I guess that's what it comes down to. In all the years I've been in the Senate I've never had a letter to beat it. What kind of a skunk are you, anyway?

"Why didn't you just come right out and tell me that the boy is in trouble, or you're afraid he will be? It's obvious he should be sent away from his evil companions. Undoubtedly the best thing would be to send him to a private industrial school for problem boys. If you'll let me know the cost, I'll send you a check to cover his first six months. By that time you'll probably know whether anything can be done for him or not. Like mother, like son, I'm inclined to believe."

Edward's letter fell from John's hand. A skunk—but good enough to do his dirty work for him. Damned sanctimonious attitude on the part of brother Edward! So he thinks I was trying to demoralize him and that he is keeping to some high level of integrity! John laughed a hard, dry laugh. Just take Peter right up out of The Valley, make him feel he's failed and that I can't trust him. Insist he accept charity because he's failed. How else would he interpret money given to him by a stranger? Put him with problem boys! Kill any self-respect the kid has left in him. I can't forget Peter's words: "What is it to you?" Indeed, What is it to me? I well may ask.

It was one of John's darkest hours. The authorities had recently refused to let him take any more honor boys out camping because on the last expedition one had run away. It was idle to point out to them that many boys had kept their word; idle to point out that there had been breaks even from behind the high wire fences. The only answer was "There's been a complaint from camps near yours. Decent people don't want boys like that near where they go to rest and relax." Well, he'd have to inform Katya of Edward's answer.

When he told her she received the news in silence—a silence barring him out.

49

MONDAY morning Peter hurried out of the bus and into the school-yard, looking for J. T., wanting to get the matter of the camping trip over before he lost his courage. But J. T. wasn't there; nor was he inside the school building. All morning Peter worried over what might have happened to his friend.

At noon he raced over to J. T.'s house, a two-room affair the family had moved into when they'd lost their land. It barely escaped being in Mexican Town. He circled the house, hoping to catch a glimpse of his friend if he were at home sick. In case he was off somewhere doing something he didn't intend should be known, Peter didn't want to give him away.

But Mrs. Ward saw him and called out, "You looking for J. T.? He's clerking downtown. I guess he'd like to see you."

She was a trifle uneasy about her son this morning, try as she would to leave him in the hands of the Lord. God had sent all their tribulations to bring them to Christ—J. T.'s lameness, the loss of the ranch. She even praised the Lord for her husband's bitterness over working for Lesly. At the church she danced and sang and prayed that the new affliction sent upon them would bring her husband and her son into the loving arms of the Saviour. And once, as she was washing dishes in the lean-to, light shone all around her. Mrs. Ward was happy. Only it frightened her when her son and husband quarreled as they had last evening.

"I ain't a-goin' to work my fingers to the bone for you any more," Mr. Ward had told his son. "You got to take that job clerkin' at the drugstore I got lined up for you."

"I'm going to finish the year out at school even if you won't see me through high school," the boy had retorted.

"I tell you," shouted his father, "you're going to hide your legs behind a counter right now. Tomorrow! I say it and mean it. Tomorrow or get out."

"Where'll I find him?" Peter's question broke across Mrs. Ward's thoughts.

"I guess at the drugstore. Come tell me if he's there." She was fearful that when J. T. left this morning he might be intending to leave home for good.

Peter raced back to town, not caring if he were late for the afternoon session at school. Surely J. T.'s mother was lying. But when he reached the drugstore, there was J. T. behind the counter, handing out Coca-Colas and milkshakes to the school kids. "What's yours?" J. T. asked, looking coldly at Peter.

Peter was back again at the end of the afternoon session. Still J. T. paid no attention to him. He hung around the door until his friend was off duty at six. He had to see him, had to talk to him.

At last J. T. came out, started down the street. Peter followed him. "Get out!" cried J. T., turning around. "What'd I ever have anything to do with a skunk like you for? Going off and leaving me! Too stuck-up, you was, to ask me to get into the car with your fine friend. If you'd taken me with you, Pa wouldn't have had a chance at me."

He went on pouring out his bitterness, accusing his friend of every breach of faith he could think of, hating Peter with burning envy. He could not forgive him his sound body, his possession of land, his friend who drove a good motorcar and put in Peter's hands benefits to bestow on others like him who could only accept and never bestow. And now Peter would go to high school and get a chance to be somebody, and he—— "I tell you, get out!" he shouted in final rage. "If I hadn't played around with you, I mighta got somewhere."

"Aw, J. T., I didn't mean to leave you in the lurch," Peter began, ready to propitiate his friend, sorry for him. And then all at once he remembered what Mr. Dodd had said about pitying J. T. "What have I got to do with your bein' where you are? Haven't you any guts of your own? What do you want me to do, nurse you?"

Panic took hold of J. T. "Hey, Pete!" But it was too late. Peter was far down the road, running as hard as he could.

Next day Peter hunted out his friend, but again J. T. would not speak to him. He wished now he'd gone back last evening when J. T. had called him.

The rest of the school year passed slowly for Peter. Things hadn't come out the way John Dodd said they would. He had lost his friend. And there had been too much work on the ranch, so he hadn't been able to go on the camping trip. And yet except for missing J. T. nothing terrible had happened. J. T. just stayed mad, but he didn't say anything about Peter's being a foreigner. Next year Peter would be going to high school in a town miles away. He'd be out of J. T.'s reach then. Peter began to gain more confidence in himself. The need to find out about his father grew less urgent.

Then summer came and the small human unit to which he belonged was shaken to its core and he with it. Daria, on whom they all unconsciously leaned, was dying. First, only Daria herself knew it. Then Katya and Mishka. And when Daria could no longer rise in the morning, Song understood and was frightened.

And then at last Peter, but only in the final week before she died. Nobody wanted to tell him, and he did not see it for himself until the day when all work stopped on the ranch. His mother hadn't called him as usual, and he slept late, wakened at last by the day's crescendo of heat. A valley child, he could tell approximately the time of day by how hot the air was. In the early morning it touched his skin lightly. Eleven, twelve, one, two, a kind of tension grew within one at the mounting weight of the heated air. Then at three its peak was reached. Slowly, imperceptibly, it receded until, as the sun went down, the air had a velvety touch. It must be noon, he thought, starting up from bed. Hurriedly he slipped into his trousers, stepped out the kitchen door. Mishka was sitting on the bench in the thin shadow his house cast. Peter ran across, feeling the sandy loam burning hot against the soles of his feet.

"Where's Mother?" he asked.

Mishka did not answer. Then Peter saw Katya standing in the doorway of the house, motioning to him. "It's not going to be much longer, son. Come in now and see Daria. She has been asking for you." He didn't want to go in, but obediently he followed his mother to where Daria lay propped against pillows. For a moment her face broke into the old friendly smile. "Petya, you are good boy," she said in a hoarse, unnatural voice, and after a pause, "Help my Sonya."

He heard a stifled sob close at his side, and then Song slipped out of the shadows to wipe the perspiration gently from her mother's forehead with a soft white towel.

He turned and ran out the door and into the cotton; and then, ashamed, he came slowly back. Mishka had gone inside. Peter entered and stood between his mother and Song. He took Song's hand, but she broke from him, threw herself on the bed. Peter shivered and looked away. It was so still except for Song's sobbing. And then a great cry broke from Mishka.

It was terrible for them without Daria. For a few days Mishka sat all day outside his house in stricken silence. When Song called him to eat, he would not come. It was then that his black hair and beard became streaked with white. At least Song said it was then. It was only when Mishka went back to his work in the fields that Peter felt that mysterious, frightening encounter with death retreating.

In August two more families moved away from the neighborhood, and one was their next-door neighbor to the north, the Professor. He and his wife came in one evening to say good-by. "We dare not risk staying any longer. We must conserve enough for our old age. In fact, we've cut deeply into our security already," he said.

"But when the reclamation program goes through, you'll be assured of water," protested Katya.

"Possibly," the man answered. "I've been keeping in touch with Washington. The Federal Government has started Friant Dam as a part of their Recovery Program. No contracts have been demanded before work began. The controls under the Reclamation Act don't apply at present . . . may never be enforced."

"We had hoped to finish out our lives here in The Valley," said his wife with a tired smile, "but I guess there isn't such a thing as security even in your old age."

"Now as for you," the Professor hastened to add, seeing the frightened look in Mrs. Suvorov's eyes, "you can afford to gamble a little with this young man—" he turned to Peter—"to take care of you."

Katya did not answer, busy reviewing in her mind her own possibility of survival. Although she would get no benefit from that particular dam, it gave her hope that in time the Highline Canal on the west side of The Valley would be put in. That would entitle her to supplementary water. The dry cycle ought to be nearly over. If the underground-water level began to rise—— If only the farmer to the east of her did not sell to Lesly, thus giving him control of the underground basin——

To give up now would, she felt certain, mean the end of Peter's schooling. Ever since J. T. had gone into the drugstore, Peter had played with the idea of getting a job. Something would break in him if they gave up the land. Something would break in her, too. They'd be rootless. She'd seen too many rootless people drifting through The Valley of late years not to know what it did to the children. "I'm going to try to carry on," she said finally.

Hardly were the Professor and his wife out of the house when Peter broke out in bitter denunciation of them as quitters. "They're leaving us holding the bag!" he cried.

"They can't help it, they're old," his mother answered.

"You won't sell, tell me you won't sell!" Peter was truly frightened. In his eyes his mother was old, too. Was she fixing a build-up to sell out herself? And she'd said only she was going to try to carry on.

"No, I'm not selling if you'll help me," she answered. "But we'll have to work hard, both of us."

That summer Peter worked harder than he ever had before, and he made Song work hard, too, although he spared her the heaviest labor. But he teased her about how tanned she was from the summer sun. One day he called her a Mexican, and she cried. He was ashamed. "Aw, I didn't mean to make you cry," he said. "I guess I didn't know what else to do with my voice."

"It's all right," she had answered. "I'd rather have you make me mad than be the way you were last winter when you were always with J. T. You didn't even *see* me then. Don't ever have anything more to do with J. T., Peter," she begged. "He'll get you into trouble."

"Look," he had answered roughly: "you stay off J. T. and me. He's my friend even if he's mad at me. See!"

"I'm not going to stay off J. T., and he isn't going to let you go that easy." And then, abruptly changing the subject, she added, "I wish we had something nice to do. There isn't any fun for kids in Doddstown. It makes us all kind of bad."

What did she mean? The things J. T. had said about her last winter when they had found her with the Mexican boys came back to him. He took her roughly by the arm. "What do you mean? Don't you dare hold out on me! You been fooling round with Mexicans?"

Song wrenched herself free, a bit of fury incarnate. "You're a nasty, horrid boy!" With a quick movement, before Peter realized what she meant to do, she had slapped him full in the face, then turned and fled, sobbing.

50

LESLY was enjoying his cat-and-mouse game with the Widow Suvorov. Of course he'd have her land in the end, just as he had secured most of the other Dodd acres. He was negotiating even now for the land east of her. She'd come to him one of these days, begging him to buy. Then he could set his own price. But in the meantime, now that he had the Professor's land to the north of her on the bench, he could work a nice little trick. He'd use the land for one of his big labor camps and put it close to the edge of the widow's property. He had never forgiven her for her dignified resistance to his advances the first day he had met her. He had sensed her distaste for him physically in her quick withdrawal.

A few days later Katya, looking out her window, saw that the Professor's house, which stood near her border, was being torn down. Another day a crew of carpenters arrived, erecting row after row of one-room cabins, and closest to her line the dozen privies that were to do duty for the camp.

When it came time for the cotton harvest, and the cabins were occupied, no longer did the quiet night so loved by Katya settle over the fields. There were the cry of babies, fretful in the heat of the shacks on which the sun had been beating down all day, the angry, sullen voices of men deprived of their sleep after hours of backbreaking work picking the low-growing cotton, the petulant voices of women who had toiled in the fields all day and now at night tried to sleep crowded into one room with their children. Shouts of revelry and fighting.

At first Katya could not sleep either, but after a little she grew accustomed to the noises and slept, tired with her own day of toil, for she was taking her place beside Mishka picking cotton. She was holding to her promise to Daria that Song should go to high school, though it meant hiring laborers to take both Song's and Peter's places. But it's only for four seasons, then Peter will be eighteen and able to take over, and I will have saved his heritage for him—so she said to herself as she worked down the rows, deftly pulling the cotton from the bolls, thrusting it into the maw of the long white bag trailing behind her, harnessed to her by the band over her shoulder, the pressure of which grew greater as the bag grew heavier. At last, when it was full, she pulled the drawstring, closing the opening, hoisted the tubular bag over her shoulder, carried it to the scales, then climbed into the cart and emptied it. One more link in the chain she was forging against the rootless life she feared for herself and her son. If only Lesly made no move against her—— She tried to make herself believe he was satisfied with all the land he had gobbled up.

It was toward the end of the cotton harvest when only the late-maturing bolls scattered over the fields remained to be picked that Katya received a note from John Dodd asking if he might take her to a concert in Fresno to be given by a band of Cossacks. Despite her determination to shut John out, she found herself accepting. But when the evening came, she was nervous at the prospect of going out with him. Her clothes were so cheap and old. Everything had gone into the ranch. Her hands were rough from work in the fields, and she was deeply tanned. Still, when she put on her only black dress, placed the brooch Grandmother Dodd had given her at her throat and fastened in her ears her mother's gold filigree earrings, she knew that she was not without distinction.

When she greeted John at the door, she saw admiration in his eyes. Suddenly all that was woman in her awakened in a mysterious rushing out of her spirit to meet his. As they drove through the twilight a kind of splendid excitement took hold of her. It was years since she had experienced a man's companionship. In response to his questions, she described the Russian ballet as she had seen it in Moscow years before. She talked, too, a little of Russian books she and her father had read together. How wonderful to tell him of her past and have him accept it! No need with him to give proof of her identity. Ever since Edward had ceased to recognize her as the person she told him she was, she had been haunted by a sense of lost identity. She felt reinstated in the world to which she rightfully belonged.

How lovely she is, thought John, with the color coming and going in her cheeks, her eyes filled with light, not dulled with fatigue as I have so often seen them when I went to the ranch.

When they entered the concert hall, impulsively Katya put her hand on his arm, exclaiming, "I feel as if I'd found myself this evening! It's because you believe in me." He laid his hand over hers where it rested on his arm. Their eyes met in understanding.

But later as the deep, rich voices of her countrymen aroused in her the memory of how romantic she had been as a girl in her father's house, the Katya Suvorov of Doddstown, surveying the dreamer she had once been, saw semblances of that dreamer coming to life this evening, and suddenly it was distasteful to her to be with John Dodd. Where was her dignity, her self-respect? she asked herself bitterly, accepting the attention Edward Dodd offered her through his brother?

John sensed her change of mood and that the understanding between them which had increased during the evening was suddenly gone.

For days afterward Katya rebelled at the barrenness of her life, her bitterness against Edward again an active, living emotion. Then once more anxiety closed in upon her. All the Dodd land except her hundred acres had at last come into Lesly's hands.

Lesly was growing impatient again. "It is senseless of her to hold out," he told his manager. "Her land is like a sore thumb to me. If the water level hadn't risen, I'd have had her in a tight fix this summer."

His manager did not reply. He was remembering that day when Katya had sat in this very room. He knew even then that she was fighting a losing battle—that the boss would never be satisfied until he had her land. It was a fire in Lesly's veins to devour the little fellow. Butterfield worked for Lesly, but he hated him. He kept his job by always agreeing with him. At the hearings held recently in Sacramento, he had testified that cotton could not be raised profitably on a hundred and sixty acres. Yet here Widow Suvorov, with her canny Russian peasant, had been getting by on a hundred acres, even with the handicaps Lesly put in her way.

In September the week after school opened Peter made occasion to go into the drugstore. J. T. acted as if there had been no quarrel between them. "If you'd like to, I could bring you books from school. You're so smart, it would be easy for you to keep up," Peter volunteered.

J. T. gave an indignant snort. "That's kid stuff. Wasting time at school. I'd be ashamed if I was you. Who do you think you are, anyway—son of a senator or a big landowner? You could do a man's work on your ranch. Take it from me, your folks will be the next to lose out if you don't turn in and work."

The words haunted Peter. Often the shadow of disaster would descend on him unheralded—in the bus riding over to high school, in the midst of a ball game. At such times he would lose interest in his studies, hunt J. T. out, follow the old pattern, hanging around with the men in the saloons, worrying his mother by his sullenness and unmanageableness at home.

But in the spring something momentous happened to Peter. Rain, unusual for this time of the year, was falling, and the athletic field was wet. Having an hour to be filled in before the school bus left for Doddstown, he sauntered into the school library. Despite his interest in John Dodd's library, he had displayed no special interest in the one at the Union High School. It did not give him the same sense of an unlimited number of books which had so aroused his admiration the evening he had first entered John Dodd's house. With many of the shelves only half filled, he experienced no sense of the plenitude that had so stirred his imagination in the smaller library. To John's disappointment, he had not proved to be much of a reader so far. He scarcely looked at the books John brought when he came to see them.

Today he took down a volume of the encyclopedia, thinking he might as well look up some material he had to have for his history class the next morning. The volume fell open to an article on vine-yards. Forgetting what he had come for, he read eagerly, for there set before him was the story of the vineyards of California and how they were started from stock sent from Europe.

He began to feel a lively curiosity in what was inside other books on the library shelves. There were so many things he didn't know. He believed he'd see what the encyclopedia said about cotton. What about soil? He believed he'd look up soil. And then, what was there to know about valleys? Vaguely he remembered some things he'd learned in his geography class—the Nile Valley the most fertile in the world. Perhaps they didn't know about the Central Valley of California. With growing excitement he searched in the index. Yes, there was The Central Valley of California listed as "the most fertile valley of the world with the exception of the Nile Valley." So his mother's ranch was a part of one of the most productive regions of the whole earth! It gave him a sense of pride deeper than he ever had had before. All at once he wanted to read everything he could find about farming. He went to the desk, asked the girl in charge if she had any-thing on farming. No, she didn't believe so.

That night Peter wrote John Dodd asking him if he had any such books. John sent him, among others, one called *Forty Centuries of Farming in China*—farming in another valley, the far-off Yangtze Valley. Suddenly out of his childhood came the memory of his friend Mr. Ching and what he had said about the place of the farmer—how had he put it?—something about the honored place the farmer held at one of the four corners of the universe. And there was the picture of the boy on the buffalo. Vaguely he remembered Mr. Ching saying, "I think water buffalo nice to go with truck." For forty centuries men had farmed on the same land in China. It made Peter angry when he thought how, in the Central Valley, men used up land and drained off its underground waters. He began to dream of going to an agricultural college after high school.

The evening he finished a book John sent him on soil conservation, he was so excited he raced into town to see J. T. "I tell you, you must get into this," he told his friend. "Let's go in together. We're both smart. We could have a model farm."

J. T. was clearing up the counter preparatory to closing. He was tired and bored. It was more than he could bear to look into Peter's shining eyes. "Be your age, Pete! By the time you get ready you won't have any land to be so smart with."

He waited to see the light go out of his friend's face as so often he had seen it go, but instead Peter grinned. "You old sourpuss! Climb out of it." Peter laughed, throwing his hands up over his head, stretching himself.

The strength and pride J. T. had gained in exerting power over Peter was gone. Some way Peter had escaped him! Imagine a boy named Suvorov trying to lord it over a Ward, thought J. T. angrily. He'd show him. He'd be somebody in Doddstown. He'd make everybody fear him. He'd find a way. Aloud he said, "Ward and Suvorov—I guess I don't like the combination." But Peter thinking of the marvelous things to be done with soil did not notice the implications in J. T.'s last remark.

"So long," said Peter. On his way home he got to thinking of J. T.'s talk about his mother losing her land. It was the bunk, he decided. They were ahead of farmers like the Robertses. His mother hadn't gone into debt to buy the ranch. It had been left to her by his father's grandmother. Hey! If his father had been alive, wouldn't it have gone to him? Hadn't he learned in school that property is left to the next of kin in America—or something of that sort? He believed he'd look it up tomorrow in the school library. Aw heck, why bother? he asked himself. He'd bothered long enough about this father business. He was going to forget it.

51

Rain this year—the year of Peter's graduation—lasted well into the spring. The earth was unable to hold more water; it stood in every hollowed spot, seeped away slowly. It even delayed the plowing. And then one morning from all over The Valley came that *tick-tack*ing sound of the tractors. Almost before Katya could realize it, the potatoes were showing their green leaves in long, even lines across the fields. It would be a good crop, and with the upsurge of prosperity over the country, this season's potatoes and cotton would bring a fair price, pay something on the mortgage which she had had to put on the place when she had deepened her wells. After such heavy rainfall she would not need to irrigate her cotton until later than usual in the season. The pump log showed as yet only a very slight rise in the underground-water level, but given two years of heavy rains and a good snow pack in the mountains it was bound to rise. And at last Shasta Dam at the head of The Valley was to be built, a great water bank to be established behind it. In time that meant the High-line Canal down the west side of The Valley would be constructed. Another step bringing security nearer to them. Their worst years were passed.

She had saved Peter's inheritance for him, land which for generations had belonged to the family. Peter was eighteen now, six feet and one inch tall, and very strong. When he graduated from high school in June, he and Mishka together would run the ranch.

Today was for Peter. Today he would graduate, the only one from Doddstown this year. Pedro, J. T., Song, all of them once planning to go through high school, had had to drop out. It had been arranged between Song and her father that she would help with the work this spring. He had explained to her that they could ill afford to hire an extra hand. If she didn't help, he'd have to have Peter. She had dropped out at Christmas so Peter would not guess why and had clerked for a few weeks in the five-and-ten in a near-by town to make it appear that she was tired of school.

Song was happy this June morning. "Hurry, Pa, Mrs. Suvorov is waiting," she called to her father, who was getting into his Sunday clothes. As Mishka came from his room, he shook his head. "You have not learned sobriety, Sonya. The Lord asks sobriety of a grown woman."

"But I'm not a grown woman!"

Crushed in with other mothers and fathers and sweethearts, Katya and Mishka and Song listened to the congressman from the district who had come to speak to the graduates.

"You who are standing on the threshold of opportunity——" he began.

Song clasped and unclasped her hands, her eyes traveling along the line of boys on the platform. She could not find Peter. At a distance all the boys looked alike in their blue coats and white trousers. And the girls—for a moment her eyes rested upon them in their white dresses. It was for Peter she had done it.

Katya, too, was searching for Peter. She had knelt long before the icon this morning, very early before Peter was awake, asking that the Blessed Virgin intercede for her son, the fruit of her womb. Let him prosper in this new land! Let him be a power for good in The Valley! Today she would turn over his portion to him. In this lofty hour the mortgage she had had to put on his heritage did not trouble her.

Now the speaking was over and the graduates were filing by for their diplomas. There was Peter, taking his, then moving forward, a part of the long line marching down the central aisle. Song, sitting at the end of a row, put out her hand and touched his sleeve, but so lightly he did not feel it, and he passed on out of the auditorium into the sunshine.

Family groups gathered, excited and happy, showering presents on their children. Peter was standing by his mother, his gifts in his hands. Katya had managed to get him a wrist watch. Song had used the money she had earned clerking to get him the class ring.

Then everybody all at once seemed to be saying good-by, hurrying off to cars. Song had seen to it that Katya's truck was parked a couple of blocks away. She didn't want Peter to be humiliated, today of all days, by the old truck. If only they'd been able to have a party for Peter! she was thinking. Then she saw a familiar figure moving through the crowd. "Mr. Dodd! Mr. Dodd!" she called.

"Oh, here you are," he said. "I've been trying everywhere to find you. My car is here, and I've a table reserved at the hotel. How about it, Peter?"

So they'd be just like the others. Song gave a sigh of happiness.

Only Mishka could not respond. "You bring them back, Mr. Dodd. You not need me." Such unwonted festivity made him uneasy. He must walk the earth, regain sobriety. And he was troubled. The downdraft in the well was increasing. This morning, when he had filled the tank which supplied the two houses with water, he had found the amount he could pump in the hour he usually allowed for filling the tank had only half filled it. That meant the flow was decreasing rapidly. He had a well-founded suspicion that Lesly, knowing the water level was bound to rise in the next year or the year after, was up to something. Just what Mishka did not know.

When he reached the ranch, he changed to his farm clothes, and walked across their acres to where Lesly's land joined theirs, on the east. He hadn't paid much attention to what Lesly was planting this year. But he had observed that instead of plowing his land for the irrigation water to run down between the rows, he had divided the field up into oblongs, dyking them on four sides. Mishka, scornful of the many newfangled things Lesly tried, had dismissed it as a foolish irrigation scheme. Thoroughly conservative in his ways, he was beginning to fear that Peter might want to try out new ideas, too. But Peter was a good boy and a hard worker, he thought, noticing with saisfaction how healthy the cotton plants looked.

He had come to the edge of his land and Mrs. Suvorov's. Lesly's dyked fields were completely covered with water, tiny green spears standing an inch or two above the lakelike surfaces. And he saw that two new pumps had been installed, higher-powered, of course. Now he understood—Lesly was using water for a crop that took many times the amount needed to grow cotton. He did not know what the crop was, but he was in no doubt why it had been planted—to draw off their water.

The summer evening was coming down over the ranch. Peter and his mother were sitting by the table in the kitchen. John Dodd had left immediately after driving them home, pleading he was busy. He felt that Katya wanted this evening alone with her son. He knew she had planned to turn the land over to him on his graduation day. The samovar was between them, boiling and gurgling. Katya made tea and filled their glasses with the hot liquid. Peter, twisting the glass about in his strong fingers, looked into the tea's amber depths, dreaming a secret dream of his own about agricultural college.

"Petya," said his mother, using the old name in this moment of deep emotion, "tomorrow let us go together to the courthouse to register the deed to this land in your name. It is right you should have it——" Now, Katya thought, now is the time to tell him it is indeed his heritage, he a Dodd owning Dodd land.

A shadow fell across the room as Mishka's great bulk filled the doorway. He was standing just outside the screen door, his hand on the knob. Katya wished he hadn't come just now, but he never came to the house except on important business. At her bidding, he entered. Katya noticed with alarm that tears were running down his cheeks into his gray-streaked beard.

"The water is gone. The Lord giveth and the Lord taketh away."

"Certainly nothing could happen so suddenly," Katya said firmly, silencing her own apprehension.

"This morning I pump little water. This afternoon I look at Lesly's fields. Water deep on them. Something like grass stick up."

"It is rice," cried Peter. "I have seen pictures of it in my book on Chinese farming. I know they grow it in the bottom land along the Sacramento River in the northern part of The Valley. But it is no crop for land where water is scarce!"

One moment hope and faith in the good life—and next this! If they went on through the summer and the cotton died, which it would without water, they would not be able to meet the interest on the mortgage. Lesly had won. Katya had exhausted every resource at her disposal. She stared across at Peter sitting opposite her. She stared up at Mishka standing by the table.

"We could take it to court," said Peter. "Certainly we have a right to our share of the water. I'm going to call Mr. Dodd. He'd tell us what to do."

"We oughtn't to bother Mr. Dodd," Katya answered. "There must be a lawyer we could find at the county seat."

The next day Katya and Peter set out for the courthouse just as she had dreamed of for so long, but not on the errand for which she had worked and sacrificed. She was still hoping a little. But the return journey was without hope. "There is no law in California regulating the amount of water a man may take out of the underground basins. We are still in some ways robber barons," the lawyer had said.

52

BOTH Katya's many acres and Mishka's few went for a song to Lesly, the only bidder. It was now land without water and next to useless. Today the Suvorovs were leaving the ranch. This morning there had been the auction of their household furniture. With grim-set mouth Peter helped Mishka carry everything out of the house. "I'll not have you going through this," he told his mother. So Katya sat inside waiting for the cars to drive away.

But now at last all was over, and the four—Katya, Peter, Song and Mishka—stood awkwardly, waiting to leave. How close they had been to one another only an hour ago, sharing the mutually bitter experience! But now the bonds of intimacy seemed suddenly loosened.

Mishka and Song were waiting for the Russian landowner whom Mishka had visited when he first came to The Valley to take them to his great holding, for Mishka was to serve again. Never more, he thought, would a bit of the earth be his. He felt an old man. After sixty-five a man never could accumulate enough to buy land.

Katya and Peter were waiting for John Dodd, who was driving them to San Francisco. Katya was going to join her own people until Peter found work. There was room for her with the Mohkovs, for the countess had died. Peter was determined to care for his mother, but just now he felt too numb even to make any effort. A sense of failure stalking him all his life but never quite claiming him before had taken hold of him the night of his graduation, when Mishka, the heretofore invincible, had come to the house and told them what Lesly was doing, that there soon would be no water in their part of the underground basin, that the crops would wither and die, that there was no use trying to carry on. They were ruined.

As they drove north through The Valley, John glanced often at Peter sitting by his side, his lips compressed into a hard line. He wanted to propose something that would, he thought, give Peter an incentive to work, make him feel that what he had struggled for had not been in vain. If the boy had no purpose, he might turn to the destructive ways of a few years before, once he had awakened from his present indifference. John wasn't certain there was not already some new understanding between Peter and J. T. Peter had insisted, short as the time was, that he had to stop in Doddstown to see J. T. on their way to San Francisco. John hadn't liked the expression on his nephew's face as he leaned over to catch an aside made by his friend.

The sun, so brilliant in this semidesert country, was sending its last hot rays across the land. In a moment it sank behind the mountains, and there was a sudden release from its heat and light. Some mystery of the earth always seemed near being explained to Peter in this hour after sunset. Now unconsciously responding to the memory of countless such summer evenings when, tired with the work of the day, he had looked out over the growing cotton, his numbness gave way to pain. Evening had been settling down when Mishka had come to tell them that all their work was in vain.

"They're going to begin excavation for the Shasta Dam in another month, I hear. It's a big step toward security for the small farmer," John remarked.

Peter shifted uneasily. "I wouldn't kid myself if I were you, Mr. Dodd. The small farmer's got as much chance as a snowball in hell."

"Oh, I don't know," John answered. "Anyway, the dam is going to be something to see. One of the biggest in the world. As a straight engineering problem it's some feat."

Peter did not answer.

"I've been wondering," John went on, "whether you'd like to get a job up there. I've a friend I think could get you in."

"Me!" Peter pointed his forefinger at his chest, half turned toward his mother on the back seat. "Head engineer, I suppose." It was said in J. T.'s most sarcastic vein.

John, ignoring the remark, asked, "How about taking the job of timekeeper first?"

"You mean it?" In spite of himself, Peter was interested.

"Yes. I think I can get it for you if you say the word."

As soon as he had learned about the loss of the ranch John had written to Edward, asking if there was any job on the dam for an untrained boy, telling him frankly for whom he wanted it and why the boy needed it. Unexpectedly Edward had promised to see what he could do.

So that was the kind of slippery business Lesly was engaged in! thought Edward when he read John's letter. It came pretty close home when an upstart like Lesly could do a member of an old valley family out of his heritage. A member of his own family . . . He drew back from such a commitment. Lesly's tactics simply had roused in him a desire to see fair play. It was time something was done to control men like Lesly. They had altogether too much power.

Edward had an uncomfortable feeling he had been playing into the hands of Lesly, taking, as he had of late, a middle position on valley affairs. If political life were only as simple as some of his confreres seemed to think it was—black or white. Either you were for a measure or you were against it, they said. The men in the California Senate who sided out-and-out with the power companies and the big landowners always knew just how to vote. The men who upheld the small farmers stood firm for the enforcement of the Reclamation Act. But Edward was finding his position more and more complicated as he tried to take a middle course. Construction of Friant and Shasta dams under the Recovery Program did not require the enforcement of the Reclamation Act's provision that one man could buy water for no more than one hundred and sixty acres. Although he knew this played into the hands of the big owners, Edward had let pass the opportunity he had had to explain to the Secretary of the Interior just what it would mean to the small valley farmer if Federal money were granted without safeguarding the original reclamation plan. Thinking now of the growing number and therefore strength of the big owners he wondered if such regulations would ever be enforced.

His chance of getting elected at the next election to the Congress of the United States as representative at large, he was convinced, lay in keeping the precarious footing he had preserved of late between the two factions. He could not afford just now to get himself mixed up in anything which could be interpreted as favoring one side or the other.

But that was no reason why he shouldn't get this protégé of John's a small job. The head engineer at the dam was a friend of his. All he needed to say was that the boy and his mother had recently lost their holdings in The Valley. Their plight had been brought to his attention. He didn't need even to mention what part of The Valley they came from—maybe not even that they were from The Valley.

John had received his brother's letter that morning stating somewhat curtly he could arrange for the job. "How about it, Peter?" John asked.

"Well, I don't know—I guess it's as good as anything," said Peter, drifting back into indifference, indifference that was necessary. Necessary to be wary. His world had just been shattered; it was safer not to trust in any hope for its rebuilding. But to work on the Shasta Dam, the biggest unit of the Central Valley Water Project! Peter's life, almost ever since he could remember, had been predicated on the project. But it, too, had failed them. It was all too late. The ranch was gone. And his plans to go to agricultural college—they, too, had to be given up. Still, to have a hand in the building of the dam, the fountainhead of water for The Valley. "I guess I'd like it," he ended.

Peter was not due for work on the dam until September. August he spent with his mother at the Mohkov's. Under the warm friendliness of Madame Mohkov and Maria he began to see his Russian background in a new light. In Doddstown, with her name and her way of speaking, Peter had considered his mother's foreignness a stigma. The black-bearded Mishka had added to their foreignness, and foreignness, Peter had come to believe, made them inferior. Although he had a deep respect for his mother he had always felt slightly apologetic for her. Now here in San Francisco she took on stature and he with her.

The group of Russians whom Madame Mohkov and her daughter Maria had gathered around them were men and women of education and breeding, a number of them trained musicians. Sometimes in the evening they came to play and sing. His mother took no active part, but Peter, sitting a little outside the circle, noticed they seemed to be playing *for* his mother. Once a man jumped up, grasped her hands, crying, "You have artistic taste. You shall be our mentor." Peter felt pride rising in him. He had not known before that his mother was gifted musically. He had heard her sing at her work in the early years when she had not been worried, though of late she had sung not at all. The sense of failure so strong in him those last weeks in The Valley began to leave him.

Speaking to some hidden stratum of emotion in him was the service at the Greek Orthodox Church. It was the expression of a people steeped in centuries of ritualistic religion. Within that framework these Russians forced out of their own country channeled the homesick longing of the refugee, a cry first voiced thousands of years before when the people of Israel had cried, "By the rivers of Babylon, there we sat down, yea, we wept, when we remembered Zion. . . . How shall we sing the Lord's song in a strange land?"

Peter, standing beside his mother, felt the lifting of a burden carried as long as he could remember, the burden of the necessity to assert his claim to his American birthright. Out on the river of nostalgic longing flowing all around him the frail craft of his American spirit drifted. Russia was his home! It was to Russian aristocrats he belonged.

On the second day in San Francisco he hunted out his friend Mr. Ching, now a very old man. In the curio shop which his Chinese friend now owned, Peter stood idly by, watching him wait on a group of tourists. Mr. Ching did not recognize Peter, and Peter hardly recognized Mr. Ching in the suave, obsequious salesman.

"This good tea?" the tourists seeing Chinatown asked him. "No fool us now."

"Alla good tea. Sell only good thing from China. Maybe you likee this." He showed them a cheap, vulgar figure of the God of Plenty. "This you like?"

The tourists passed out into the sunshine. And Mr. Ching turned to Peter with the same half-suave, half-insulting manner. Peter put out his hand. "You remember me—Petya? You gave me a picture of a little boy on the back of a big gray cow."

"Your honorable self I take for tourist." Mr. Ching's obsequious manner slipped from him. With dignity he now spoke. "Come." He motioned Peter to go before him into his private rooms. "Here is good tea. I sell them what they deserve." There was scorn in his voice.

Now Peter understood. His Chinese friend, too, felt himself an alien. After Peter had told his story of how he had lost his land, Mr. Ching told how he had been forced out of The Valley during the anti-Chinese disturbances years before. Sitting in the dim, sheltered room Peter withdrew still farther from the life of conflict it meant to be an American.

Part Three

LAND AND WATER

53

Septemer came and Peter prepared to go to work at the dam, not from any eagerness he now felt participating in the undertaking but because the job was offered him, thus freeing him from the necessity to put forth any initiative of his own. He must support himself and his mother, but he cared little how it was done.

As the train moved north through the northern half of Central Valley, he sat by the window at first indifferent to the scene, all his defenses raised against the country of his birth. But gradually The Valley exerted its old spell over him. When the train stopped and he went out to the platform, drawing in the familiar summer scent of sun-baked ground, the need to retreat into the life of the exile he had felt the last month left him.

By the time the train reached Redding and he saw Mount Shasta in the distance, its snow-white surface aloof and pure against a deep-blue sky, he was eager to be at work. Early the next morning he stood by the side of the road looking for a lift out to the dam site.

A man in a broken-down Ford pulled up beside him. "Working on the dam, son?" he asked.

"Timekeeper," said Peter in his most businesslike tone.

"You'll do a lot of leg work if that's your job. A cussed big hunk of earth we're going to take out. I guess there won't be nothin' bigger 'n this dam anywhere in the world when we get it built." There was a note of pride in the old fellow's voice.

Talks as if he owned the dam, kind of like he'd hatched an egg, thought Peter as he climbed into the Ford, trying to imitate the superiority J. T. would display in like circumstances—an instinctive effort on Peter's part to guard against the growing excitement to which he feared to give himself over.

The road was crowded with vehicles. Off to the right, as they drove along, Peter caught glimpses of white-capped Shasta. "Is that where we're going?" he asked, pointing.

"Hell, no! You don't build dams on mountains, kid. We got the Sacramento running through a tunnel. While we got her cornered, we aim to get this-here dam built in her river bed."

The cars were moving slower now, inching along, finally coming to a halt. "This is it. Better get along over to that shack and report, or you'll get your tail in a sling."

Peter walked over to the building the man pointed out, entering it with some diffidence. A broad-shouldered, muscularly well-developed man was just locking his desk. "Is this where I come to report for work, sir? I'm Peter Suvorov, one of the timekeepers."

"Come back after the ceremony." As he spoke the man rose and put his keys in his pocket. "We're going to break ground in a few minutes. Better come along and see the show."

Peter followed him out and around the shack. Then he lost him in the crowd of men making their way down the sloping wall of the canyon, slipping, sliding over rocks and sand, to the dry river bed at the bottom.

"Something, to turn the Sacramento River out of her channel," the man next him said, staring up at the walls of the canyon. "It's some job we got ahead of us to dig down to solid rock, now we got the river running through that tunnel. See where we put the Southern Pacific Railroad?" He pointed toward a long trestle bridge, a train rumbling across it. "Water will reach to within fifty feet of her when we get the dam built."

"How long you figure it's going to take to build it?"

"Well, they figure on two years to do the digging. Say four before they pour the last bucket of concrete. That is if——" The man's voice was drowned out in the noise of the bulldozers and draglines maneuvering into position. Just over Peter's head the boom of a power shovel loomed, a clamshell bucket swinging at its end.

As the last machine took its place, Peter felt a wave of excitement running through the waiting men. Then a profound silence settled over the canyon. It was so still the crunching of sand and gravel under a man's boot was startlingly clear. A little way up the canyon wall a group of men were standing on a platform which had been erected for the occasion. One stepped from the group, facing the crowd.

"That's Senator Dodd," someone said.

Peter wished he were nearer. He had long known that Edward Dodd, senator at large, was John Dodd's brother. He was curious to see if the senator was anything like John. He was interested, too, that both brothers should be out of sympathy with large farms such as Lesly's, for the family had once been the chief owners in that part of The Valley. Ironic too, that their name should stick to the town near the old estate. All he could see at this distance was a tall, thin man with a long, thin face. His voice, coming through the loud-speaker, boomed out over the listening men. "I am proud to be here for this occasion," the senator was saying. "Since I first heard my grandfather talk of the water problem, I have known that some day there would be a dam here. I am proud to be at this historic occasion in the development of California's resources."

The governor stepped forward, began speaking. His voice seemed low even through the loud-speaker. His words drifted slowly down to the silent men. "The people of the state have waited long and patiently for this great project to begin. It has taken men of vision, men of skill to bring it to pass. There have been bitterness and strife— there still are. There have been frustration and discouragement. There have been daring and courage and now achievement. This is democracy. Slow, perhaps, but strength is gained through struggle. It means people moving forward, not by a decree of a mighty few but by the will of the many. Today we break new ground. Gentlemen, the Shasta Dam!"

Cheers broke from the waiting men. Booms swung out; the clamshell buckets dipped, opened, picked up chunks of the river bed, carried them to the river's bank and deposited them there. Bulldozers moved forward, their huge front blades scooping up the earth. The draglines dropped their buckets from their long booms, shoving the earth before them.

Suddenly Peter grasped the magnificence of the reclamation project, its imagination, its daring—rivers turned from their courses, railroads rerouted, vast sections of earth moved, lakes such as it had taken centuries for nature to create built in a few years, thousands of miles of canals, transporting water from one end of The Valley to the other. An imaginative, daring plan to press back forever the shadow of drought from the millions of acres of this semiarid valley. It was a greater project than the Boulder Dam development, greater perhaps than anything of its sort yet tried in the world. He remembered something John Dodd had said, "Democracy is only as strong as the individuals in it." He was ashamed of his bitterness, ashamed of the denial of the American side of him he had indulged in of late. He'd never forget that he had been squeezed out of his land—but men always have had to fight for what they wanted, and get up and fight again when they were thrown down.

He went back to the office to get his orders.

At first the "leg work," as the man who brought him to the site had put it, consumed his energy. An entirely different set of muscles were brought into play tramping the dry river bed from those he had used walking his mother's irrigated acres leveled to floor smoothness. Over rough ground, jumping into the scooped-out holes the power shovels and bulldozers made, slipping and sliding on the soft, newly scraped earth behind a dragline, hunting the men out, locating them morning and afternoon, day in and day out, that was his job. Dead-tired at night, he went to bed early, fell asleep quickly, his mind free of any desire to evaluate his experiences.

Then his mind seemed to wake again. The men he had known well were the mystically silent Mishka and the sensitively attuned John Dodd. Now he was thrown with men who lived with machines which did exact, special jobs, men who found their satisfaction in the objective world of tools. One morning, as he finished his first checkup and was on his way to the office, he passed a group of them surveying the excavations already made.

"They've struck quicksand," one said, waving his hand toward the opposite river bank where the clamshell scoops of the power shovels, depositing their load on the slope to the side, were throwing out a liquid substance.

"Just as we expected," a young-looking man replied, as he turned to the third man, evidently a visitor. "The dam will fit neat as a pin into that cut." The pride in his voice was not lost on Peter. With almost the force of a revelation he realized what pride of craftsmanship could mean.

He turned in his report and then, instead of joining the men making for the cookhouse, he walked along the embankment to a place where he could be alone and think. Sitting on the ground of a pine-clad slope, sheltered by the trees, he let his eyes wander over the scene before him. Some day Lake Shasta would be at his feet, a deep reservoir of water, every trickle down the mountainside conserved and put to use. A vision of what it meant to be an engineer rose before him. To construct, to create could bring a man tremendous satisfaction. If he could become an engineer! But what use was it for him to think of a profession? He had no money except the small sum he was earning, and he must help his mother.

Suddenly he straightened his shoulders, stood up. He could do it if he wanted to. Lots of boys worked their way through college. There was that other timekeeper, a fellow older than he. He was working his way—halfway through right now. He had left college this year in order to get enough money to go back next year. He'd ask him about books, begin studying. "I'm going to do it." As he said the words, Peter had a new sense of well-being.

54

Long ago the news had gone out over the country that in California a man's savings went far. You didn't need a cellar under your house. You didn't need an expensive roof with beams heavy enough to carry snow. You didn't need thick walls to keep out the cold. Why, you could build the house yourself! It had brought to California men like the Professor and Iowa Miller. It had brought people from the Dust Bowl, and it had brought people from all the countries of Europe.

It was almost inevitable that news of the construction of Shasta Dam should cause the upspringing of a town near by, a town populated mainly by older people who had saved all their lives with the intention of some day owning homes of their own—a type of settlement that seems to spring up spontaneously in California. First one house appeared, then two, then three, a dozen clustered around an eating place built to get trade from the men going back and forth to the dam.

One noon Peter went over to the new town with some of the other men to try out the restaurant. Sitting at the counter munching a hamburger, he noticed across the way a sign reading: For Rent. I wonder if it would be a good idea to bring Mother here, he thought. It ought to be cheaper for both of us and nicer than living apart. As soon as he had finished his luncheon, he crossed the street to inspect the house, which proved to be a one-floor duplex. The wing to which the sign was fastened had a separate entrance.

On entering Peter found the wing had only one bedroom, but the living room was large enough for a couch on which he could sleep. Both rooms were sealed with plasterboard, the seams covered with metal strips. The bathroom and kitchen were tiny cubicles, but each shone with new paint. A gas stove had been installed and a hot-water heater.

"Pretty neat, isn't it? Want to rent it? I'm the owner," he heard a voice behind him say.

"Will you hold it for me until I can wire my mother?" Peter asked, turning to face an elderly man with shrewd blue eyes.

"Not a mite past six this evening," the man answered. "Can you stand the rent?" Seeing Peter's eagerness, he raised it a couple of dollars over his original intention.

"That's O.K.," said Peter and hurried off to send his mother a telegram. Would she want to start out again on a new undertaking? he kept asking himself during the afternoon. Her wire, received sooner than he had expected, assured him not only that she was willing but eager to come.

"It's like the inside of a shell," exclaimed Katya when Peter, with considerable pride, unlocked the door and ushered her into the home he had provided for her. He had asked for the day off, and after they'd inspected the house, they went shopping in Redding. Of necessity they bought sparingly, but even so they felt almost wealthy and were as excited as two children when the salesman promised to see the things were delivered before five o'clock.

With aluminum pots and pans suspended on hooks in the kitchen, a white shower curtain in the bathroom and filmy white curtains at the living and bedroom windows, the place did resemble the glistening inner surface of a shell. A bed for Katya, a cot for Peter, two comfortable chairs upholstered in terra cotta, a dinette set with four chairs which Katya meant to paint to harmonize with the upholstered chairs constituted their furnishings. The table could be used as a desk for Peter in the evenings. The house, still smelling of paint and new lumber, gave them both the feeling of a fresh start.

From the beginning Katya was welcomed in the shallowly rooted town. Everybody was a stranger to everyone else. No one was an outsider. Most of the women made extra money helping out at the hamburger stand, which in a few weeks became a thriving restaurant and finally a night club. Katya worked in the afternoon at the candy and soft-drink counter.

At first she would wake in the morning with a sharp sense of anxiety. As the day advanced, it faded slowly into a vague apprehension which she could trace to nothing tangible. I must in my dreams go back to the ranch, she thought. But I'm not there. I'm here, and I haven't a thing to worry about. We're not in debt, we've a little money saved. I can be proud of Peter. Night after night, sitting quietly sewing or reading while Peter studied his engineering books, she drew around her again illusions of permanence—her reliance upon her son growing as he became more and more responsible.

At the end of six months, Peter told her one evening that an engineer at the dam, observing his interest in the work, had taken him on as assistant. "There's no reason you can't become a practical engineer if you stick around here until the dam is finished," he had said.

"You'll be learning firsthand. If you want to go to the university later, you'll have the best groundwork possible."

When the cut was finished, he taught Peter how the forms were built, how the steel reinforcing bars were laid inside them, how to compute the needed strengths. Now for weeks at a time Peter forgot the purpose for which the dam was being built, forgot how he and his mother and Mishka through the years had based their chances for survival on the completion of the dam and the canals which would syphon the reservoir of water down The Valley. The engineers didn't talk about such things. Their interest was in building the dam. They were specialists, and they taught Peter to be a specialist. The first time he laid a steel reinforcing bar entirely to his own satisfaction, he felt the craftsman's pride in his job.

That night when he returned from work two letters lay on the table in the kitchen where he and his mother ate their meals. One was a letter from J. T., the other from Song. He read Song's first. She hadn't written him often. When she did she had been self-conscious and reticent, but in this one she was too troubled to be inhibited.

"We've been here almost a year," she wrote, "and my father has never ceased to long for the ranch. It is pitiful to see him. And now his health isn't good. But if I get work in town and take him away from the land, he'll die. It isn't that Mr. Kudynov isn't good to us. He isn't like Mr. Lesly. He comes out every day and works on the land. He loves it the way Pa does. That's the trouble. He says it's like fire in his veins. He can't get enough. But it bothers him. He's not sure he has a right to so much. But he keeps on getting more. He could let Pa have a few acres, let him pay for it in crops little by little. If he would, Pa would get well, but I know he never will."

Peter handed the letter to his mother. He was troubled over the plight of his friends, but he was so absorbed in his own work that the need to own land seemed unreal. And Katya, reading the letter and remembering the constant anxiety over making the ranch pay, felt only thankfulness that they were free of it.

J. T.'s letter was short. "When you get this, I'll be on my way north. All this applesauce about the dam has got me worried. Do you think you're the head engineer? It's about time somebody put a little sense into you."

Not long after Peter left Doddstown, J. T. had taken the first step in fulfilling his ambition to show the town what he could do. Clerking at the fountain in the drugstore, he had come to know well the man who serviced the juke box.

"What you stickin' around on a job like this for?" the man asked
J. T. one day when the two were alone at the counter. "I could get
you into this game. I'm going to be a supervisor for the pinball-
machines company, come the first of the month."

"Where would collecting nickels get me?" J. T. answered with his
usual skepticism.

"Collecting nickels! Were you born yesterday? Begin with that
and work up!" The man leaned closer. "In the end I'll see you play it
big."

J. T. had taken the man's advice. He proved to be smarter than his
adviser. He was placing pinball machines now in places others had
never thought possible. He knew kids, how those who sneaked into
the town's poolrooms at noon used the nickels with which they were
supposed to buy milk to try their luck at the pinball machines. He
went after the other places which they frequented.

Peter grinned. Just wait until J. T. sees the cut. "Look, Mother. Do
you think we could put him up for a night or two?" he asked, laying
down his letter. "He wants to see the dam."

Katya didn't like the idea. But surely Peter could not be influenced
by J. T. any longer. "If you could get hold of a cot, we could put it
in here, I think. Move the table out," she replied.

The next morning as they sat at breakfast Peter, glancing up, saw
his friend standing outside the screen door. In his haste to get his
long legs out from under the table, Peter tipped over his chair. "Well,
you old son of a gun!" he cried. "Another five minutes and I'd have
been gone. Look, you sit down here with Mom and fill up, and come
out when you're ready."

"You can't be five minutes late?" J. T. asked. "I've my car out
here. I'll drive you over when we're ready."

"Pretty classy, aren't you! My jalopy just holds together with wire."

"Mine might be better." J. T. tried to sound nonchalant, but owning a good car was really something.

Peter glanced at his watch. "You can't miss the road. I'll be looking for you."

"If you won't wait, I'll drive over with you now. I've had breakfast."
J. T. hadn't, and he was hungry and tired. But he didn't want to be
left alone with Peter's mother. He knew she didn't like him.

"How come the grand car?" Peter asked as he took his seat.

"It's all a part of what I came up here for. I'm pretty much in on
the make. It's good going. How about joining me?"

"What's the game?" Peter asked.

"Concession for juke boxes and pinball machines. It's easy money."

"Suppose we talk it over at noon. There's the works!" Peter pointed out the raw cut just ahead of them. I give up engineering for a proposition like that? he thought. Well, hardly! But he didn't want to hurt J. T.'s feelings. He'd at least pretend to be thinking it over. At noon, as they drove back for luncheon, Peter told his friend, "I'm afraid I can't do it. You see I'm pretty well committed here. It was something to take me on, green as I was in the beginning. Now I'm just getting useful, I guess I couldn't let them down."

J. T. wandered about most of the afternoon, bored and angry, his sense of injury against his friend growing. At least Peter could have stayed away from work for one afternoon. He actually seemed to like the discipline and responsibility that his work entailed. My friend, you'll be sorry when you find out that I'm leaving tonight, he said to himself. It had just come into his head to say this to Peter. That would bring him around.

About four he saw Peter coming toward him. "Say, I got off an hour early, so as to show you around."

"I'm afraid there's not time," J. T. answered with elaborate coolness. "I've got to start back as soon as I can."

"You kidding?" Peter stopped dead in his tracks. "What did you come here for, just to turn around? Anyway, we've got to look at the blueprints."

Silently J. T. followed him into the office.

The relief Katya felt when J. T. was gone told her how much she had feared his visit. Looking across at Peter bent over his books, she forgot J. T. and Doddstown.

55

THAT autumn Edward Dodd was up for election as California's representative at large in the United States Congress. Even his father believed his son's chances were good. Of recent years Edward had supported many issues of which Jeremy Dodd and his friends were in favor. He believed the original government restrictions on the Central Valley Project were safely buried, now that both Friant Dam and Shasta had been started without their enforcement. And he had reason to think that Edward's one outstanding deflection had been forgotten, at least by some of the more influential men of the state. In reality that was wishful thinking on Jeremy's part.

There were many men who believed that as long as the restrictions on the Central Valley Project were not definitely changed, the Federal Government menaced both their state rights and their rights as free citizens. These men, contrary to Jeremy's hopes, were not entirely satisfied with Edward Dodd. They remembered the day he had changed the thinking in the Senate against them and in favor of the amendments desired by the Federal Government. They wanted a man in Washington who would be out-and-out for them. Quietly they put their influence behind Edward's opponent. He was a man they knew would support any measure they proposed, a man they could depend on. However, Edward Dodd's popularity throughout the state might well defeat their candidate.

Lesly, a man Jeremy had not thought of as dangerous to Edward's chances, was leading a group violently opposed to his election. With Lesly the issue was personal. It would be too humiliating to have gained all the Dodd acres only to have Dodd's son uphold the Reclamation Act as it now stood, which would mean that he could buy water from the government for only a pint-sized ranch. A hundred and sixty acres, three hundred and twenty seeing he was a married man! But what was that against the five thousand he now held? Of course he could make a fortune selling his excess acres, but he didn't want the money—he wanted the land and with government-supplied water on it. The issue of water limitation was not being pressed at the moment, but the more he thought of it, the more he saw Edward Dodd as deliberately planning to ruin him by forcing the issue. Probably Jeremy Dodd, too, is sore because I own all the land he once owned, he reflected.

The only chance, as Lesly saw it, to defeat the Dodds was to find something in Edward Dodd's personal life that would turn the people against him. Try as he would, he could find nothing. "Too god-damned pure," Lesly grumbled. "Good husband, faithful to an invalid wife."

Lesly had tried every angle he could think of and turned up nothing. Worrying about it one night, thrashing around in his bed unable to sleep, he suddenly thought of Jake down at Doddstown. He might have an idea! Early the following morning he started out in his high-powered Packard. He knew the Widow Suvorov was Edward's divorced wife. He had found that out from the will, when he looked up the title preparatory to buying her land. Or was she? Maybe it was something else. Maybe they could turn it into something else. He'd wire Jake to meet him at the ranch.

As the gates swung open, he saw Jake lounging in the doorway of the Administration Building. He was growing old. His florid complexion gave warning he might drop off any time; his once full cheeks hung down in seamy folds. He'd given up his janitor's job at the school, but he was still the political boss of the region.

"What's on your mind?" Jake asked as Lesly motioned him into his office, closed the door behind them.

"I dunno as you can make much out of it, if the Suvorov woman really is his divorced wife," Jake said when Lesly told him of old lady Dodd's will and Katya's former status in the family. "It seems to be all straight enough—unless we can screw it around a bit. One of them Dodds used to come down every winter and take the Suvorov kid skiing. Toward the end he hung around the missus a good bit."

"It wasn't Edward Dodd, was it?" Lesly asked eagerly.

"Well, now, it just mighta been." Jake winked. "You kinda want it to be?" Jake enjoyed hunting out scandal. He'd done it before for Lesly.

"Suppose I leave it to you to do a little investigating. See what you can make out of it," Lesly answered, then turned the talk to other business, local matters, the re-election of school-board members. There was one man they must get rid of—he was far too extravagant in his ideas.

Jake looked off through the open window. Shimmering heat waves hung above the swimming pool. Over the neat lawns surrounding the main building water sprinklers were throwing their fine sprays, cooling the air a bit. He felt less languid than when he came in. An idea began to take shape in his mind. He might look up the Ward boy, see what he could get out of him. He was a great pal of Peter Suvorov. Understood he'd been up to Shasta Dam to see him. "Eh, wait a minute. I guess I got it, Lesly. If I can make the little devil of a J. T. Ward fellow talk——"

That evening Jake strolled over to a new gambling joint recently set up in an old building on the edge of town. He'd understood Ward played poker there every evening for an hour, then left if he had good luck, and had dinner at a restaurant in town. J. T. was just leaving as Jake arrived. "Mind if I walk along with you, Ward?" he asked.

Grudgingly J. T. complied, immediately suspicious. He knew Jake's game. Get something on a fellow, then he had to vote his way.

"Heard you been up to Shasta Dam. Kinda curious about that new dam. I thought maybe I'd take a run up and see what was doing, and

I wondered if you could give me some points about the trip," said Jake walking along beside the short limping figure.

There's something he wants of me, thought J. T. I'm important enough so he thinks it worth while to be friendly. He had a moment's real satisfaction.

"Understand Peter Suvorov is learnin' to be an engineer up there. Making pretty good, ain't he?" Jake asked when J. T. had finished telling him about the dam.

"Well, what if he is?"

"Kinda young for that, ain't he? Didn't have a drag of any kind, did he?"

"What do you ask that for? Pete is smart as you make 'em," J. T. retorted, wondering again what Jake was after.

"Sure, sure, I know. He's smart at hell raising. You and him. But being an engineer is something else. Let's see. It was Edward Dodd, wasn't it, that used to take you boys skiing? Mighta helped him out. It'd be natural, wouldn't it?"

"Well, what if he did? Anything against that?"

"No, just pretty soft for a Doddstown boy, I was thinkin'—gettin' a job like that."

All J. T.'s old bitterness toward Peter, all his new bitterness over Peter's success at the dam and his lack of interest in the pinball business made him answer, "Of course he's got it soft, with Dodd getting him a chance like that!"

"That the Dodd who's running as our representative? He the one that used to hang around the mother?"

"Yes, I guess that's about it," said J. T. Why should Peter get the credit for being so smart? His head is getting too big for his hat, he said to himself in justification.

They were at the restaurant now. "How about my having dinner with you? I'd like to talk more about the dam." Jake led the way in, thinking this Ward fellow might make him a pretty good successor in the county when he dropped out.

For some reason J. T. found he wasn't hungry, but he pretended to enjoy the lavish dinner Jake set before him. Afterward, as he limped away into the darkness, he felt utterly lost. Peter was his second self, his larger self.

Jake drove off, planning the details of the scandal. Start the story easy-like around Doddstown. "Mighty queer, Widow Suvorov owning Dodd property." Then mention one of the Dodd boys coming to see her, off and on. Could just mention Edward Dodd's name in connection with the visits. Her moving away. Might be because the senator wanted to cover his tracks now he was getting ready to run for U. S. representative. Mention her son going to work on Shasta Dam. What'd he know about a dam? Just a high-school kid; used to raise the devil when he was in school here. Not the stuff that makes good.

Trust the story to grow if he made it dirty enough. Jake was pleased with his evening's work.

Lesly sent one of his henchmen to the dam with a detailed description of Peter with which Jake had furnished him. "Pretty young, isn't that boy," the man asked, pointing Peter out, "to be working with the engineers? Didn't know you hired 'em that young to do expert work."

"I believe we were asked to take him on," answered the man in charge. "But he's made his own way since."

"Some high-up wanted his own kid to get in on the ground floor, I suppose."

"No, nothing like that. Senator Dodd's above such things. Said he didn't know Suvorov, but he was one of his constituents, a poor boy who wanted to get a start."

The two stories fitted together like clasped hands. With a little judicious help, the stories whispered around would run through the state.

56

ONE hot July morning a few weeks later Edward's manager, Jim Bricket, sat in his office in one of the larger towns in the southern part of The Valley. He had called a meeting to plan Edward Dodd's campaign in the near-by towns. The men and women who had promised their help were beginning to straggle in. Several of them had worked in other Dodd elections, including two women, personal admirers of the senator.

Bricket noticed there was none of the enthusiasm he expected from these women. They were talking earnestly as they came in, but when Bricket walked over to them, they stopped. It made him uneasy, tuned as he was to all the undertones of a campaign. He was more uneasy as the meeting progressed, for it lacked the zest the campaign demanded if Edward was to win.

After they'd gone, he sat trying to figure out what was wrong. Had he started the campaign too early? Should he have insisted that Ed

Dodd be there? Perhaps that's what the women wanted. And yet they had worked for Dodd in state elections, and in all justice to them he had to admit that, much as they liked Dodd, their fundamental interest had been in the measures Dodd advocated. Why then with the same issues at stake and Dodd's sphere of influence increased as a national figure were they so lukewarm over his campaign?

The postman entered. "Hello! Going to make your bag pretty heavy from now on, I guess," Bricket greeted him.

This was the salutation with which he always addressed the postman at the beginning of a campaign. But the usual reply, "I'd carry two bags for Dodd," was not forthcoming. Instead a polite reference to the weather.

After the postman had gone, Bricket picked up the first letter on the pile. "Better check up on your candidate," it read. "We're not standing for any loose living in our representatives." The letter was unsigned.

Fitting the happenings of the morning together, Bricket came to the conclusion that some slanderous story about Edward was going around. What on earth had they hung on him? Quickly he ran through the rest of the mail. There was no other threat to Edward Dodd's fitness. He picked up his hat. He'd hunt out an old friend of his in the town, a certified public accountant who audited a number of irrigation districts. If anyone could give him the story, this somewhat gossipy middle-aged man, close to the farmers of the region, could.

In the front office were a half-dozen girls standing at high desks, working on the monthly operating statements. Accountant Appleton was moving up and down the room, looking over this shoulder and that, as if he didn't trust one of them. In reality they knew as much about the irrigation districts as he, but he liked to have his finger in everything.

"Hello, Bricket," he called out. "Hear you're running Senator Dodd's campaign again."

"Got a few minutes to spare?" asked Bricket.

"Sure," said Appleton and led him to a cubicle at the back of the building. Motioning Bricket to a high stool, he climbed up on another much as a child would, rung by rung, then sat down facing his caller. "So you got word of it, did you? I meant to step over to your office later in the morning to find out how much you knew."

"I only know something slanderous is being peddled. Can you give me the low-down?"

"Don't imagine there's any truth in it," said Appleton, "though you never can tell what shenanigans a man's up to. I believe there was an old divorce, but what's being whispered is just a sordid tale about a kept woman. I guess what's at the bottom of it is that some pretty important people would rather not see him elected."

"There's opposition to Dodd, I know, because of his previous stand on the water project, but this sort of thing sounds as if someone had a personal grudge against him," Bricket answered.

"If he's to win, you'll have to stop the whispering campaign," Appleton replied.

Late that afternoon Bricket arrived in Sacramento. Edward had been making a few campaign speeches in the region preparatory to a swing over the state. "Your wire reached me just in time this morning. I was just leaving," said Edward, shaking hands with his old friend. "I knew there must be something urgent or you wouldn't ask me to meet you tonight, so I canceled my evening's engagement. Come and have dinner with me, and we'll talk things over."

"Let's have dinner first," Bricket answered. "I'm tired. I need to relax."

All through the dinner he dreaded what was ahead. It wasn't easy to pry into a man's private life. Personally he had a great deal of sympathy for Edward. An invalid wife didn't make a man's life too easy. To the very human Bricket a little moral frailty in Ed Dodd was not to be entered in the debit column. But a man in public life ought to be more discreet. Ought to have more sense than to hang around a woman in a small town. Only a damn fool would do that, and Ed Dodd wasn't a fool. If the story was true, he guessed Dodd was finished politically. The rank and file of people were strangely hard on such things in a public man.

After dinner Bricket suggested they go over to the park opposite the hotel. Under cover of darkness he began. "There's no use keeping anything back, Ed. There's a tale being spread about you that we've got to scotch."

"Well, let's hear it," Edward answered.

When Bricket had finished speaking, Edward dropped his cigarette on the path, crushed it out with his foot. He had a queer feeling that he had always expected fate would deal him this blow.

"Mrs. Suvorov was my first wife," he said. "I married her when I was in China. There was a divorce soon after I came back, but my grandmother was against the divorce and left her a bit of the Dodd ranch. I've never seen her since. My brother John has occasionally gone to her house on business over her son—who, she claims, is mine.

What do you want—a statement from me to refute what's being said?"

"What do you think a denial from you would do against malicious whisperings?" his friend asked. "A person is always at a disadvantage when he has to take the defensive. We've got to go into action immediately. You must be *seen* with the boy, have him fully recognized by the family as your son. In fact, we'll have to make quite a display of him if we're to kill this tale."

"But I can't do that," exclaimed Edward. "Agnes doesn't know about him."

"Suppose she hears the gossip? Wouldn't that be worse than for you to tell her the necessity of claiming him as your son? Easy enough to do, as you say your former wife has always insisted he *is* your son."

"I don't know that the boy would accept me as his father. It's a pretty late date for me to declare myself."

"Either he and you accept each other, and publicly, or you're finished politically. Whoever started this story did it to get you out," Bricket answered. "And they'll use it where it will do you the most harm—with church people for instance. You've had considerable backing from them in the past."

For a moment Edward thought of giving up public life. He had a good law practice. He could make himself a rich man. But no, he didn't want to give up his political career. Besides, it would only confirm the story to drop out now. He certainly wasn't going to let his opponents get away with a thing like that.

"There's just one person who is in a position to talk to the boy," he said. "It's my brother. It was he who persuaded me to ask for the job for him at the dam. I knew it wasn't wise then. I guess it's up to him to straighten things out now." After a pause he added, "I guess I can manage to set things right with Agnes."

"O.K.," said Bricket. "We'll get busy. Where does your brother live?"

"About a five-hour ride from here. He's a teacher in the state school for boys down south."

"You call him while I get my car from the garage," said Bricket, getting up from the bench. "I'll meet you in front of the hotel."

Their road led straight down Route 99. Through towns, through the silent countryside, they drove, half of The Valley to their right, half to the left. It was years since Edward had driven the length of The Valley. Memories filled his mind. Doddstown—here it was rising up again to hurt him. The road leading straight on, and then at last the car was climbing the low hills at the southern end of The Valley.

57

JOHN had spent the evening trying to prepare himself for his brother's visit. Over the telephone Edward had told him nothing except that he was facing an emergency and needed his help. As communication between them for years had been limited to matters concerning Peter, John felt pretty certain the emergency involved him. He hoped nothing had happened that would upset Peter and his mother, but he could not rid his mind of an uneasy sense of disaster ahead for them. He tried to read a book on juvenile delinquency, but found he could not apply his mind to it. He picked up a detective story, but that too failed to interest him. The evening seemed interminable. He looked at the clock on the mantel. It was only eleven; they could not possibly arrive before one.

He must have dozed in his chair, for all at once he heard their car, and the clock said three. Wearily he got to his feet. As he opened the door, he saw two men get out of the car. So he was not to see his brother alone.

Once the first greetings were over and they were seated in John's living room, there was an awkward pause. Bricket, whom Edward had introduced as his campaign manager, seemed to be waiting for Edward to speak, and Edward for Bricket to tell why they had come.

John waited, too, feeling no inclination to make it easier for his brother. He could not entirely forget Edward's accusations when he had tried to enlist his aid for the children of Doddstown and for Peter in particular.

"Of course you know I'm running for United States congressman," Edward said at last, when he saw neither of the others intended to speak. "I've come to ask you to help me. I think I have a right to do so, as it's you who have placed me in the difficult position I find myself. I told you long ago I didn't want anything to do with Peter Suvorov, but you've never let up on me. Finally, against my better judgment, I gave in to you about getting a position for the boy at the dam. Now my opponents have made capital of it. They've coupled this bit of patronage on my part with your trips to see Katya—it seems a good many times through the years—saying it was I who went to see her. I don't need to give you the sordid implication. If this story isn't killed, it will ruin me politically."

"Why don't you drop out of the campaign? I have an idea that would mean the least hurt to everyone involved," John asked.

"So you're no longer interested in the issues involved in my election?" Edward countered.

"More interested, rather than less," said John. "But to state it frankly, I've not observed your accomplishing much of late."

"That's not fair," Bricket cut in. "Nobody's been accomplishing much on water matters recently. You can't expect your brother to do it all. He's had a lot to fight against."

"Why do you suppose this smear campaign has been started if I'm as ineffective as you seem to think me?" Edward demanded.

"Forgive me," said John, his long-standing affection for his brother coming to the fore, "but I've waited a lifetime to see any real change in valley conditions."

"Trust me, John. I'll show you I'm worthy of it," pleaded Edward.

"Just what is it you want me to do?" asked John, moved in spite of himself.

"Bricket here—" Edward turned to his manager—"believes the only way to kill this story is for Peter Suvorov to appear in public with me."

"In what capacity?" asked John.

"Why, as his son, of course," put in Bricket.

John for the moment, was too astonished to answer. What kind of a man was his brother, asking him to enlist the help of the son he had persistently refused to acknowledge?

"You mean you want him to accept you as his father after all these years?" John asked.

"Only for the time being."

"Suppose he does," said John trying to keep down his anger, "has it not occurred to you that his doing so might involve you in a worse predicament?"

"How's that?" asked Bricket.

"They might say that Edward had neglected his son, allowed him to grow up without the advantages a man in Edward's position could give him. That might do Edward more harm than any amount of scandal."

"Smart on your part to think of that angle," Bricket replied. "Perhaps the boy would be willing to help out on that too for the sake of the cause," he ended somewhat lamely.

"I can scarcely ask that of him," replied Edward, feeling a growing distaste for the whole affair.

"It seems to me," John said turning to his brother, "that it is you who should talk to Mrs. Suvorov. I've been your messenger long enough."

Bricket protested: "It would be very awkward, almost impossible. Nothing Ed could do would feed the scandal faster than going to see the woman around whom the story is built."

"Then Edward had better get out of politics." John found himself going back to his original opinion. "Too many people are going to be hurt."

"I'm not going to get out," Edward answered with unexpected stubbornness. "We either kill the story in the way Bricket has proposed or I'll ignore it and trust to my standing in the state to pull me through. I'll leave it to you, John, to decide which it shall be."

John again was about to refuse to have anything to do with the affair when his mind veered to Peter's and Katya's side of it. For their sakes something would have to be done. The story, as it now was going about, would bring Katya the most unpleasant kind of publicity. As for Peter, if he suddenly found himself played up in tabloid newspapers as Edward Dodd's illegitimate son—he inevitably would be— he might even turn against his mother. John had known the anguished disappointment of too many boys in their mothers not to realize what danger lay in that. But how would Peter stand up under the knowledge that his father, who through all the years had not acknowledged him wanted to now when it served his own interests to do so, and furthermore asked Peter to pretend that his father would have helped him had he been allowed the opportunity!

I can't ask this of him, he thought, especially now just as he's making good. In this moment John realized that he loved the boy as he would have loved a son of his own. And he loved Katya.

Bricket rose and went out to the porch, feeling he was getting too involved in the brothers' personal affairs. They'd better settle it without him.

Once they were alone, John began to plead with his brother. "Katya has gone through a great deal at your hands, Edward. Don't you owe her something? After years of struggle she's come now to the first security she's ever had. She lives for her son. Whichever way you plan to play this, he's going to suffer, and she with him. You can have a good life without going to Washington. Father gave up politics for a private life. Maybe the time has come for you to do the same."

"You seem very much interested in Katya's happiness. By any chance, is there something behind what is being said? Am I by any chance suffering from your indiscretions?"

John stared at his brother for a moment, too angry to speak. "I love her," he said finally, "although she does not know it, probably never will. But for your information let me say, a man does not make it more difficult for the woman he loves."

"Forgive me." Edward spoke with such sincerity that John had nothing to do but accept. Then both were silent, each facing his own dilemma.

At last John said, "If you won't give up your political career, Ed, I guess there's nothing for me to do but to talk to Peter and his mother."

"I'll never forget this," said Edward rising. For one moment in passing his hand rested on John's shoulder. He wanted to say, "Don't be taken in by Katya," but he knew it was useless. He had had to learn by bitter experience. He supposed John would have to.

58

ON THIS July morning the Shasta Dam site stood for all to see, a great cut crossing the river bed. The bulldozers, the power shovels, which for two years had scraped and pushed great quantities of earth out of the way, were stilled. The forms were ready for the pouring, the reinforcing steel was in place. The cement mixers were ranged on the riverbank. From high steel towers on each bank a cable swung in a catenary curve, buckets hanging from it.

Peter was standing a short distance from the side of a huge concrete mixer bearing on its side a white billboard with the inscription in bold, black letters:

FIRST BUCKET OF CONCRETE
SHASTA DAM
U. S. BUREAU OF RECLAMATION
JULY 8, 1940

Below the billboard stood the head engineer and contractor, the brims of their straw hats snapped down to shade their eyes from the fierce sun, their white shirts open at the throat. These were the men Peter worked with, men he understood and who understood him, men who knew their job and did it.

"Drop it," the head engineer called out. The mix poured forth from the mixer into the dump bucket. It rolled along the cable out over the cut, moved slowly downward and dropped its load into place. A camera clicked, recording the momentous event. Then one of the engineers came forward, slapped Peter on the shoulder. "Guess we'd better be getting to our job."

All morning with deep satisfaction Peter worked, climbing over the site, taking samples of cement for testing. At noon, with the rest of the force, he sat in the shade of the high embankment, eating the sandwiches his mother had put in his lunch pail, then stretched himself out with his hat over his eyes, only half listening to the talk going on around him. Today was the culmination of two years' hard work. The thought of the great dam, the first bit laid this morning, stirred his imagination, bringing to life in him the poetry of his mother's people, the creative instinct of his father's.

He was nineteen this past spring, tall, well-built, quiet almost to taciturnity, a tense drive about him which made his engineer friend predict he would go far as a practical engineer.

When the five o'clock whistle blew, he trudged up the embankment, weary and content. As he reached the top he saw standing by the building where the men checked out a familiar figure. John Dodd! Warm affection for the older man rose in him, as suddenly he realized what John Dodd had meant to him through the years. Always before he had taken his kindness for granted. Guess I would have been a pretty bad kid if it hadn't been for Mr. Dodd, he was thinking. Pretty nice of him to come today to see the laying of the first concrete, knowing what it means to me.

He paused for a moment before declaring himself, taking stock of John Dodd in a way he had never thought to do before, contrasting him with the men he had been so closely associated with of late. John Dodd's deep-set eyes had a penetrating gaze, not at all like the penetrating gaze of the engineers who detected flaws in concrete. The expression in John's eyes was gentler, yet in a way far more searching. Studying the heavy lines which led down from the nose on each side of the mouth, Peter's conclusion was, He looks as if he'd suffered.

He went forward now, eager for the meeting. He's tired, he thought as he came nearer. Maybe he could persuade Mr. Dodd to stay a few days and take it easy.

John Dodd felt the warmth in Peter's greeting. He felt, too, what amounted to a father's pride in the boy. Peter's gaze was steady. He gave the impression of one who has himself well in control. There was a time when I hardly dared hope for this, John thought. Then his mind went back to the afternoon's talk with Katya. She had said,

"Why does Edward, after all these years when he wouldn't help, have to spoil things for us now? I'm not sure Peter is strong enough yet to meet such a situation. There was a time when he was terribly conscious of his father's rejection of him. You remember. And then afterward he seemed to grow out of it. Given a few more years to mature, gain confidence in his own ability to make his way in the world, he'd be proof against the shock of such a thing as you want him to do. You're always asking a boy to defend a man," she had added bitterly.

"Have you seen Mother?" Peter asked.

"Yes, I stopped on my way here. She invited me to stay for dinner."

"Well, you didn't have to be asked, did you?" Peter took his friend's arm, elbowing his way through the crowd of men.

During dinner Peter talked of his work, explaining to John some of the technical difficulties of dam building. He noticed how preoccupied his mother seemed. This man's talk was a little hard on her, he thought, but, after all, it might be his only chance to explain a lot of things to Mr. Dodd.

As he finished, John said, "I hope when the dam is completed, it will mean what it is intended to for the farmers of California, especially in the San Joaquin Valley."

"I haven't thought much about that side of it lately," Peter answered. "I've been so absorbed in my work."

"You are still interested in the purpose of the dam, aren't you?" John asked.

"Of course I am," said Peter. "But I'm not in a position to do much about it, am I?" he added smiling.

Now that the opportunity had come to which John had been leading up, he hesitated to make use of it. Peter's answer was such a good opening that he felt like the boy's betrayer, gaining advantage over him by arousing his latent interest in The Valley to further Edward's political ambitions. But putting aside such thoughts, he played his next card. "You know, of course, that my brother Edward Dodd is running as representative at large for Congress, I suppose."

"I hadn't paid much attention to it," said Peter. "I've been so busy. How are things going?"

"There's a great effort on the part of the big landowners to defeat him. The old issues are to the fore again and they want a man who'll play their game."

"If Lesly's in it—and I'd bet a dollar to a doughnut he is—there'll be dirty work."

Katya, listening to this agonizingly slow approach to the revealing of so much that was painful to her and which now promised to shatter the obscure but safe pattern of their lives, burst forth, "I wish you to listen, Petya, to what I have to say. I suppose I should have realized that sooner or later you would have to know who your father is. I made a promise before you were born not to make use of his name. Only today have I been freed from that promise."

Peter looked from his mother to John Dodd, then back to his mother, defense growing up in him. There was a time, he remembered, when it would have mattered to him. It didn't now. "I'm happy. I'm working. Why do you bring it up at this late date?" he asked her.

"You've got to listen," answered his mother in a kind of desperation. "I was married to Edward Dodd in China. You were born a few months after we separated."

Peter felt as if a bomb had burst in his brain. Edward Dodd, John's brother, his father! Many things he had not understood before began to be clear to him. At the time of his difficulty at school because of his Russian name his mother had all but guaranteed she'd produce his American name, which she said he had a right to. That was when Mr. Dodd had taken him on his first trip to the mountains and persuaded him to stick to the Suvorov name! Now he understood why. It wasn't because John Dodd was interested in him personally. He was covering for his brother who was shirking the responsibility he owed his son. His father must have been ashamed of him and of his mother! All the difficulties of his childhood, pent up in Peter for years, surged to the surface, all his mother's struggles and his own.

"It's too late to interest me in my father," he said. "As Edward Dodd's stooge, tell him that for me, *Uncle* John." There was both bitterness and contempt in his voice.

"For you, Petya, is a duty to perform," cried Katya, "and I expect you to perform it. A man honors his father." Why was she talking like this to Peter, whom she loved above everyone else in the world? Why should he honor his father? Why should she defend the man who had not defended her? But in spite of herself she added, "I want you to listen to what Mr. Dodd has to tell you."

Peter stared at his mother. Her stern tones, her manner, put her on his father's side. But he obeyed her. With head bowed in his hands so they could not see his face, he sat without speaking while John told him the story that was going about The Valley.

When he ended, Peter's only remark was "I can take care of myself."

"And your mother?"

"Let Edward Dodd clear my mother."

"If you do not wish to do anything to straighten things out personally, couldn't you do it to help families placed as you were once?" John urged. "If you take the stand you are taking, you will wreck your father's chances to become California's representative in Congress. The reason certain interests don't want your father elected might be a sufficient reason for you to help him at this time."

"As I see it, my father, after all these years when he has done nothing for me, is asking that I come to his rescue to save his skin. I should think he'd hesitate to ask it, just as a matter of taste!"

"You realize how ruthless a political campaign can become," urged John.

"Why should I concern myself with my father's career? He certainly has never concerned himself with mine."

"Well, then, if you'll do it neither for your own sake nor your father's, nor for the things he represents, do think again of your mother. From what she tells me, she is beginning to find a place here. As Edward's divorced wife she will be respected. As a woman he has lived with through the years—and that is what is being whispered— her situation in a town like this will be impossible. If you could bring yourself to appear with your father a couple of times, be introduced as his son, I think nothing more would be asked of you."

"Of course I don't want to hurt Mother. I've got to think." Peter's voice sounded strained. "I'll write you."

"It will be too late then. It's almost too late now. They need your answer immediately, so they can act to refute the story before it goes any farther."

"I've got to have time," Peter insisted, rising and going toward the door. "Give me an hour." Without turning he went out.

For a little after Peter left them, John and Katya did not speak. Across the way at the café the juke box blared out its raucous voice. John did not know how she had taken his presentation of the situation to Peter. What was she thinking? At last she broke the silence.

"I should have told Petya long ago. I thought he'd never have to know and so he would not be tempted to hate his father."

"And you wanted him not to feel any bitterness toward Edward?" John asked wonderingly.

"Not for Edward's sake, but for his own. It is bad to live with bitterness," she answered simply. "I must tell you, until tonight I have had bitterness toward Edward and . . . and toward you. I have refused to care for you, always saying to myself, He's acting for Ed-

ward. I've tried to shut you out. It's very strange, but tonight I do
not shut you out."

"I've loved you so long—and tonight when I feared I'd lose you
completely——" John leaned forward about to take her hand, then
did not. "But I forgot. Of course nothing can come of it with Peter's
bitterness toward me."

Katya laid her hand over his where it rested on the arm of his
chair. "I don't understand myself what has happened. Until tonight
in some way I was tied to Edward. Could you wait? Let Petya find
his way out . . . and me find my way, too? I have asked a great deal of
you through the years. But we are not young, John. There is nothing
urgent."

They heard Peter's step on the porch outside. As he came into the
lighted room, John saw his lips were set in a stiff line. Indeed he
would have to wait.

Peter spoke directly to his mother. "I'll do what Mr. Dodd wants
of me, but it must be understood that I do it for your sake. I wish
nothing from my father, and I want it understood that he is conferring
no honor on me by this late recognition.

"I'll meet him twice," he said, now turning to John. "Make it as
public as you wish. But that's all. None of this father stuff afterwards.
I have taken care of myself so far, and I'll continue to."

"Good!" said John. "And now before I leave I must ask one other
thing of you, although I find it the most distasteful part of this whole
business. What you have consented to do will not clear your father
unless you can bring yourself to say you and your mother have never
allowed your father to help you."

"He asks that?"

"Your appearance with your father will knock out the slander. But
the story of your childhood will not redound to your father's glory
when it's told as I feel sure it will be. Does that answer you?"

"Not exactly. But I suppose once I start in I'll have to go the whole
hog. One thing more I want understood," Peter added. "I'll go
through it all only on one condition, and that is that you must be at
both meetings. I think you should see me through. It's your family."

John looked at him for a moment without speaking. How explain
his own position? "If it would be any help to you," he said at last,
"I'd be glad to be there. Only I don't think they'll ask me."

There was a sarcastic twist to Peter's lips, all his bitterness concentrated on John. "You'll see to it they don't, is that it?"

"Petya, you shall not speak this way in my presence to a friend who
has done nothing but good to you. I will explain to you what I can

only guess and Mr. Dodd is too chivalrous to say. He is never called on in his family except to help them out of difficulties."

"So they don't accept you, either?"

"Something like that." A look of pain crossed John's face that was not lost on Peter.

"I am sorry, sir. I guess I've got you all wrong."

"Oh, Peter," cried Katya, "don't feel Mr. Dodd is against you! Think of all the things he's done for us."

Peter looked from one to the other, suspicion growing within him. He wasn't ready for that. Not yet. "The thing stands," he said. "If they don't invite you, we both stay away."

59

IT WAS evening when Edward arrived at his home in San Francisco. The apartment was dark except for a light in his wife's room. She must be less well than usual, for he had wired her to expect him some time before nine. As he let himself in, the silent dark rooms seemed ghost-ridden. Agnes had ardently wanted children. If they had had them, they'd be all over the place now. The house would be full of their chatter and gaiety. Slowly he went through the living room into the bedroom.

"Hello, darling!"

Agnes' face went warm with welcome, but not before he had caught her former look of loneliness.

"You should have let me know that you weren't able to be up," he chided her gently, sitting down on the bed beside her.

"I didn't want to interfere. I know how important your work is just now." Lying across the bed, she put her head in his lap. "It's wonderful, though, to have you come all of your own accord. You did want to come, didn't you?"

"Yes, I wanted to come," he answered, smoothing her hair back from her forehead.

"You have something to tell me?"

"You're not well, darling. Let's wait until morning."

"Tell me now, Edward. It will take my mind off myself."

"Does it need to be?"

She smiled, and in the quietness of the room Edward felt tension going out of him. For a moment he seemed suspended in peace.

Gently he laid her back on her pillows, got up, walked about the room, then once more sat down on the bed beside her. He reached over, taking her hand in his. "Darling, we've never talked of my former marriage."

"And you want to talk about it now?"

"I must. There was a boy born several months after we separated. I didn't know about him for years. Now a whispering campaign has started. My opponents are trying to make out that I'm his father, and that I've been living with his mother all these years."

"But you haven't!" Her words were steady without the slightest doubt of him.

He was humbled before such love and trust. He put his head down on her breast. He could feel her light, fluttering breath. For a long time he lay there.

"Do you think you could come to Sacramento and meet him, appear publicly with me? Are you well enough?"

"You mean you need me?"

"Yes."

A kind of incredulous joy illumined her thin face, which he did not see, lying against her.

The more difficult task—the securing of Jeremy Dodd's consent to meet the boy was still to be accomplished. After weighing the matter from every angle, Edward decided the best method of approach was through his mother. *If I can persuade her to meet the boy, thus acknowledging him openly as my son, Father will have to fall in line.*

The next morning, using the latchkey his mother insisted he carry, he entered his old home giving the whistle he reserved for her alone.

Immediately Beatrice Dodd appeared at the head of the stairs. "So you've really come to see your old mother," she called down archly. "I'll be with you in a moment."

"May I come up instead? I've something important I want to talk over with you," he called back.

"You're not in trouble, are you, son?" she asked anxiously, as he entered the little room she called her morning room.

"Yes and no," he answered, beating about for a way to break the silence of years over his first marriage. "That is, I've done nothing bad, if that's what you mean." In spite of himself, he was assuming the role of a small boy reporting to his mother. Trying to extricate himself from such a position, he hurried on, "It's about my campaign. Things aren't going quite as I'd like them to."

"Can I help?" she asked, all sympathy now.

"Yes. Perhaps more than anyone else if you can bring yourself to do something pretty hard. At least, I imagine you'll think it's pretty hard."

"Edward, why don't you come to the point and tell me what you've done?" she demanded.

"You know, of course, that anybody in politics has enemies. Well, mine have started a story that involves my first marriage."

"I don't wish to hear anything about your first marriage. It's something past and done with," she answered stiffly.

"But it isn't, Mother."

"You mean——"

"No, I don't mean what you think. You must hear me through, Mother." He leaned over her, taking her hands in his. "I've never seen her since the day I came home. This you must believe. She wrote me once about a boy born several months after we separated."

"Don't tell me you let her hoodwink you into accepting him as your son!"

"No, but——"

"But you answered her letter, and you did it without telling your mother and father." She wrenched her hands from his clasp.

"You were the first to hide things, Mother. You didn't tell me Granny had left Katya land in The Valley. It was this made her think she could get recognition for the boy out of me. I've never said anything, but I've always resented it that you and father kept from me what Grandmother had done. You see what it's led to."

"I don't see it's led to anything. Women like that can be put in their place. If nothing else we can pay her to keep still."

Edward was desperate. He wished he'd gone to his father, who would instantly have grasped the danger of scandal in an election year.

"Mother, you must listen. Someone around the old ranch looked up the will. I imagine it was Lesly. He bought the acres Granny left Katya. Somebody's peddling a story that the land was given her because I was the father of her illegitimate son. If I can't stop the whispering, I'll be defeated. You know how hard many people are on a man in a public position doing anything irregular."

"But . . . but——" She didn't finish her sentence, seeing at last the corner into which Edward was driven, into which they all were driven—either accept the boy as Edward's son, or have him accepted by the public as illegitimate, but still Edward's son.

"It's a cowardly plot!" she cried. "I wish I could get hold of that woman."

"That's futile. You can't save my reputation that way. My man-

ager says the only way is for us, as a family, to meet the boy openly.
The press will grab at the news that I have a son by a former marriage."

"And then ever afterward have that woman flaunting herself in our
faces, calling herself a Dodd—and her no-good son using our name
to put himself over!"

"Mother," he pleaded, "you must do this for me, or I'll have to step
out of politics. Surely you don't wish me to? Anyway, that wouldn't
end the story," he added quickly, fearing she might advocate such a
withdrawal.

"I don't know, Edward. I'll have to talk to your father."

"Listen, Mother," he begged: "John has seen the boy. He says he's
good-looking. He's been well brought up, really a boy to be proud
of." He found himself putting on a defense of Peter in order to win
her support.

It was only after another hour of recriminations on his mother's
part and pleadings on his own that Beatrice Dodd promised to win
Jeremy over. How she managed it Edward never knew. But she arranged that the first meeting would be a family affair in Sacramento
at the Senator Hotel and Jeremy Dodd would be present. They were
all to gather first in a room upstairs, rented for the occasion so that
the introductions could take place privately. Then they would go
down to the coffee shop, stopping long enough in the lobby for the
newsmen to photograph the party. That would give Edward a chance
to introduce Peter as his son by a former marriage.

Despite the divergence of political views in the family, their solidarity made them all consent to come to the support of Edward, now
that he was threatened with attack. Tom and his wife agreed reluctantly. But it was hardest for Jeremy, who had sworn that he would
never recognize Edward's first marriage. Openly to accept a son of
that union was very much to recognize it. Ironically enough, he found
that his insistence on Katya's taking her maiden name at the time of
the divorce placed him in the predicament now of acknowledging the
infiltration of Russian blood into the family. However, he consented
to recognition of Peter only after he had been assured that Peter's
appearance would not disgrace them and that the boy did not wish to
be associated with the Dodds in any intimate way afterward.

A little before twelve on the appointed day all the family except
Margot, who was still in Washington, had arrived in Sacramento and
now were grouped about the hotel room trying to appear natural.
Tom was giving his mother a detailed account of the last letter he had

from his eldest son who was spending the summer in Europe. His two younger sons, who had come down from Lake Tahoe for the reunion, were talking with their grandfather, who was giving them only the most cursory attention. Tom's wife and Bettie were standing by the window, Agnes between them. Edward was urging Agnes to sit down and save her strength.

At a knock on the door all eyes centered on Edward. "Come in," he called in the heartiest tone he could muster. At sight of the young man who entered with John, he experienced a conflict of emotions. Here was the son who might have been working shoulder to shoulder with him. Except for his clothes, which were not of the quality the Dodds wore, his appearance was all Edward could ask. The boy was good-looking, evidently intelligent. It crossed his mind that here was the one person who, out of spite, could have wrecked his whole career but had refrained from doing so. Neither did the boy seek to profit from the predicament in which he found his father placed by asking anything of him. And yet Edward felt no love for the young man who stood before him. There were no ties or memories accumulated through the years.

Katya's training stood Peter in good stead. In greeting his father he showed both deference and respect, mixed with considerable dignity. He bowed low over his grandmother's hand as he so often had over Madame Mohkov's and the old countess'; he managed to make the same polite gesture when he was introduced to the woman who had taken his mother's place. But silently he passed harsh judgment on her faded beauty, exaggerated, it seemed to him, by her flowered hat, her smartly tailored suit. A poor second, he thought, to his own mother—tall and fair with a carriage no less distinguished than that of Madame Mohkov.

A fierce pang over her own childlessness shot through Agnes. She had not imagined how much this meeting was going to cost her, and yet she would have endured twice as much in order that Edward might realize his ambition. But no longer were the things for which he fought important to her. In the years of her half invalidism public issues had lost their meaning.

"How do you do?" was Jeremy's stiff salutation when Peter was presented to him. In the depths of his soul he hated this young man, the living proof of his son's folly in marrying a Russian adventuress. No doubt she had been behind this slanderous attack upon Edward. Jeremy had swallowed the most bitter pill of his life to save his son politically, and yet that son could not be counted on politically.

When Peter in his progress over the room came to Bettie, she gave him a good, comfortable kiss. "I remember your mother," she said to him. "I was just a little girl, but I was thrilled with her beauty. I want you to come and see your cousins—four of them." She smiled happily.

After the luncheon, as they were standing in the lobby, Edward mentioned college to Peter. If the boy had to be known as his son, he wanted him to be a credit. "I have other plans, but thank you for thinking of it." Peter spoke with respect, but Edward thought he caught a slight note of sarcasm in his voice.

The sense of well-being which had come to Agnes the night Edward had asked her to help him carried her through the day. When Edward helped her into the car for the ride back to Oakland with his parents, she was able to smile. But weariness claimed her before they had covered half the distance of their return and she fainted.

"All this damned business, displaying that upstart son!" Jeremy grumbled, as in response to his wife's frantic command he stopped the car at the first gas station and went to get water.

"Jeremy, hold the cup nearer, so I don't spoil her dress," Beatrice commanded, sponging her daughter-in-law's forehead.

"If Edward would get in with the right people, vulgar displays like today would be unnecessary. The people I stand for wouldn't let scandal touch their candidate. No wonder Agnes fainted, having to meet that young bastard."

"Oh, hush, somebody might hear you!" Beatrice dampened her handkerchief again, thinking, Agnes is no wife for Edward. No spunk, no getup. She was half angry at her daughter-in-law's failure, half triumphant because no one was able to take her own place in her son's life.

Opening her eyes, Agnes caught her mother-in-law's expression of condemnation. I can't blame her, she thought. I ought to be well and strong.

60

PETER had stipulated that both of his appearances in the company of his father should be at week ends so he wouldn't have to ask to be let off from work at Shasta Dam. After that, he thought, I can forget all about the Dodds. But what he had not counted on was the publicity connected with the luncheon in Sacramento. Brought up in obscurity, he had no conception how completely his connection with a prominent family would lift him out of that obscurity. Everyone at the dam looked at him in a new way. He wasn't one of them any more. Even his boss's attitude toward him had changed. "I see you were only getting a little practical training before going on to college. Of course I admire you for wanting to make your way on your own when you didn't really have to."

"I'm not going to college, not until I go on my own money," he told the man.

"Don't be a fool. Take what's coming to you."

"Anyway," Peter replied, "I want another year under you. Is that O.K.?"

"If that's the way you want it," his friend answered. "Your father put you here. It's not up to me to put you out."

During the following week Peter found that the strain which loyalty to his father put on him was harder to endure than he had expected. It was not easy to force himself to say, and say convincingly, that he and his mother had always refused the support which Edward Dodd offered them. Try as he would, he could not rid himself of the bitterness which robbed him of his former happiness and also of the ability to concentrate on his studies. If he could believe that, some day, men like Lesly would not be allowed to hog the land and that the big private electric companies would not be allowed to hog all the power resources of the state, then would not his support of his father lose its bitterness? He must look at his father as the representative of the people. But his grandfather was head of one of the power companies, fighting for monopoly. "I wonder if I get that one?" he asked himself.

So his mind trod the treadmill of his perplexities as, day after day, he set his teeth to meet his changed position. Saturday morning he went into the small building where relief maps and drawings of the dams and future canals had been set up to show the public how The Valley could be freed from the fear of drought. Peter was resentful of being detailed to such a task. It seemed to him, in his sensitive state, that he was appointed to do this easy work simply because it was now recognized that he was not dependent for his livelihood on learning to be a practical engineer.

A young girl leaning over the rail began asking him questions. She was obviously trying to attract his attention. "One of the curious," he said to himself. "She won't get much out of me." He gave her the briefest replies possible.

"You just don't wish to be nice, do you, Mr. Dodd?" Her voice was saccharine.

"Beg pardon?" he asked, swinging round to look at her.

She laughed, showing her pretty teeth. As she moved on, his eyes followed her. California's wealthy outdoor girl, he thought—long-legged, vigorous, well-built and perfectly sure of herself. She was wearing a dark skirt and pale-blue sweater. He looked after her, shaken a little out of his absorption in himself.

Once again during the morning he caught sight of her in the groups coming and going. Then he forgot her. He was starting for Fresno that afternoon for his second meeting with his father, this time in the southern part of The Valley. If the southern papers hadn't carried the story before, they probably would now. He winced, thinking of J. T.'s scorn. One thing about it, he didn't have to meet the Dodd family this time. The dinner was to be with a group of men and women interested in Edward's campaign. Public, of course.

It had been arranged for Peter to fly down in a private plane in order that he arrive in time for a late dinner. It was his first flight. As he looked down on the checkered perfection of The Valley, his old love for it stirred in him.

John Dodd met him at the airport. Seeing the familiar figure standing just within the rail, Peter felt a renewed sense of faith in him. In the last week one thing had become clear to him: John Dodd was his friend. Cemented into the very fabric of his boyhood was this man's genuine affection for him—his endless patience, yes, and his tenderness. He believes my father is going to carry the ball, Peter thought, as he shook his uncle's hand. Why don't I just accept his conclusions and stop all this milling around in my own mind?

When they reached the hotel, the party had already gone into the dining room. To give a casual, natural air to the son's arrival, thought Peter, all his cynicism stirring again. It's all so damned calculated. He followed John to the table, silently took his seat.

"Hello," a voice on the right said. "My name is Marion Talbert."

"Well, hello, Marion," he answered. She wasn't wearing the blue sweater, but she was the girl he had seen earlier in the day at the dam. "How'd you get here?" he asked.

"How did you?"

"By air," he said. No wonder I didn't like her this morning, he thought; she obviously belongs to my father's stratum of society. He took pleasure in emphasizing to himself that he did not fit among his father's people or friends. His manners were all right. His mother had taken care of that. Inside himself he might feel awkward, but this girl wasn't going to find that out.

He gave his attention to the general conversation which centered round the coming campaign. There were a great many references to persons whom Peter did not know even by name. The emphasis was on personalities. There was evidently a definite set close to his father who were his intimates, and these gathered at the table were among those intimates. It was obvious that Edward was flattered by what the woman at his right was saying to him.

Suddenly it flashed over Peter that his father was far removed from the problems of The Valley. Any sincere interest he may once have had in such problems was merely an attitude of mind with him now. His advocacy of water distribution was not a vital living issue with his father any longer. Studying him, Peter came to the conclusion, He is affable, but not kindly, unless I miss my guess.

"You're looking very morose for a young man whose father is about to go into the House of Representatives."

It was that girl again! Peter felt like being rude. According to his mother's training, he couldn't be rude to his elders, but when it came to girls of his own age, his training had been in the hard school of his own generation of American boys brought up in towns like Dodds-town. Nobody there ever gave quarter.

"If you want to know what I was thinking—" Peter looked her over with a none too flattering glance—"I was thinking that this table is full of people—including you—who, if I proposed they meet some of my friends, the dirt farmers they're supposed to be so interested in, would run a mile."

"You're awfully sure of yourself, aren't you? Just why do you set yourself up as the champion of the downtrodden?" Peter could see she was angry. That pleased him.

"Don't forget I'm the son of my father's divorced wife. I haven't lived his life. I've come up the hard way. Of course I chose it rather than any help from my father," he added, remembering again his promise to John not to let people think he'd been neglected.

"Poor little boy! Asking for sympathy, isn't he?"

The mock pity of her tone touched Peter's most sensitive side. "I'll take my girls from the canneries any day," he hit back and turned to the woman on his left.

As the son of Edward Dodd, Peter had interested Marion Talbert from the moment she had seen his picture in the paper, published after the meeting of the family in Sacramento. She had met Edward and Agnes socially, and this sudden emergence of Edward's heretofore unacknowledged son made her curious to see how much of a bond, if any, existed between father and son. For this reason she had maneuvered through her mother, who was doing some work in Edward Dodd's campaign, to secure an invitation to the dinner in Fresno. When Peter proved to be so different from the young men she knew, despite the anger he roused in her, she could not forget him.

Putting aside her anger, she decided to accept a long-standing invitation to visit friends in Redding. She knew they were acquainted with the head engineer at the dam and that he often came to dinner. It would be easy to suggest they ask Senator Dodd's son whom she had met in Fresno to come with him some evening.

Going out now for every diversion that came his way, Peter accepted the invitation. Marion did not quarrel with him this time.

He wasn't sure that she was as stuck up as he had thought her before. To test her he asked if she'd take a drive with him the next evening. "My car hardly holds together, but I think it would take you as far as Chico where those fancy friends you were talking of live."

"Of course," she answered.

During their drive Marion came to the conclusion that Peter's remarks which had so angered her the first night she had met him were not made as she had thought because he hated people better off than he, but from a deep and genuine hurt over his father's rejection of him. Now she felt real pity for him but she didn't intend he should know it. She distrusted any such soft emotion in herself. She had early learned it got her into trouble. She had pitied her father and he hadn't liked her.

By the end of the week Peter was making love to her with a vehemence that she feared might catch her off guard. Little by little, unwillingly, uneasily, she fell in love with him and her guards went down.

Then his went up. "I can't marry you, for I've only what I earn," he told her. "It's not that, though."

"You mean you're afraid of me?"

"No, of marriage. I don't know how a husband behaves. I've never seen one——" He stopped. He hadn't forgotten those words of hers at the dinner about the poor little boy seeking pity. He did not want to expose himself to her barbs again. In Marion's love for him he felt was a streak of hardness. "I don't want to be responsible for kids. Suppose we didn't get along very well."

"Oh, skip it! In the first place, we're talking about ourselves, not about people who aren't born. In the second place, let them take it. We had to."

"What do you mean, we had to?"

"I mean just what I say. My father and mother are separated. I'm getting along all right."

"That's another reason then for our not marrying. Neither of us knows what it's all about."

"You're a Caspar Milquetoast," she snapped. "I wouldn't want to marry a man with no more guts than you have. You have to take a chance in marriage as in everything else."

They quarreled, each hurling bitter denunciations at the other. And then, quite suddenly, they made up, Peter pulling the car to the side of the road and silencing Marion's angry words by pressing his lips against hers in a fierce, passionate kiss.

61

KATYA regretted Peter's sudden loss of a place in the community. She felt it would have been a balancing influence just now. In the past on Saturday evenings he had gone over to the café, danced with the local girls, played pool with the boys, "had himself a time," as he put it, come back lighthearted and content. She could understand why he did not go now. From the day the picture of the united Dodd family appeared in the paper, people came into the café just to stare at her. After a few days she had given up her work behind the counter. Something like this had evidently happened to Peter. They were again isolated; this time not because they were foreign but because of Edward's prominence, something from which neither she nor her son gained any advantage but from which they could not extricate themselves. If from the first they had borne Edward's name, there would have been no occasion for the present curiosity about the relationship.

Katya was worried about her son. His single-minded devotion to his work was gone. Certainly that was not good; neither was the violent, almost savage, love he and Marion seemed to have for each other. Was this emotion a release for Peter from the bitterness he bore his father? Katya had only such thoughts to keep her company these days. Peter was seldom home.

On this Saturday evening from across the way at the café Katya could hear the rhythm of dancing feet above the blare of the juke box. Peter had gone out early saying he didn't know when he'd be back. She supposed he was with Marion, who, after a few weeks' absence, was again visiting in Redding. She heard a car before her door, brakes grinding to a stop. Often someone bound for the café parked before her house. But she heard footsteps on her porch, and Peter came in. He was obviously excited. "Well, my good father has been elected—and I've bought myself a decent car," he said, flinging himself down in the chair opposite her.

"You've spent what you've been saving to go to college! Oh, Petya," she exclaimed, "why?"

"I'm not going, Mother. We'll be in the war against Germany in a few months. I'm going to enjoy myself before that happens."

"Petya, don't, don't do that!" she cried, a note of anguish in her voice.

Peter looked at her with somber, penetrating gaze. "I did what you wanted about declaring myself to be Edward Dodd's son. I've done a lot of thinking since then. I don't know where I stand on anything just at present. You've brought me up to believe I was a poor boy, that I must work for everything I had. Except for the land. That, you told me, was an inheritance. Still, even with that, we were little people taking a stand with little people. Our only hope against men like Lesly was to stick together. When we lost the land, I buried myself in engineering. I said to myself, 'From now on I'll be satisfied just to do a good job.'

"Then comes John Dodd, telling me men like Lesly were trying to smear my father in order to keep him from getting to Congress where he can act for the people. So then I do the noble act—and where does that get me? It gets me just this! I'm out with the men I work with. I'm out with folks like J. T. and Song. I'm the rich guy now, eating at the feed trough of the Dodds, the Dodds of Doddstown." Peter's lips curled in scorn.

"Petya," exclaimed Katya, "I won't let you talk so about your father's family."

Peter passed his hand through his hair which rose rebelliously from his forehead in a cowlick like his father's. "You've got to hear me out, Mother. You never have. 'Russian family feeling' you're always talking about makes it disloyal for me to see my father objectively. Well, we're not in Russia, and I'm not a Russian. To go on: As I'm now classed with the Dodds, why don't I benefit by their riches? According to Marion, all I have to do is to ask my father for things. He's only waiting with outstretched arms to have me suck up to him."

Katya rose, anger and dignity in her bearing. "I shall not sit here listening to such talk. You shall not speak such vulgar words about your relationship to your father."

As if he had not heard her, he continued: "Why I don't do it, I don't know. I figure I'm entitled to it. Somehow, there's something about the whole deal that makes me unwilling to take his money." He looked at his mother. "Can I believe in my father?" he challenged her. "I think I have the right to know why you separated."

"What has my divorce to do with you, Petya?" she demanded. "And what has it to do with his service to the people? You forget yourself. What is between your father and me is between your father and me."

"All right, Mother, if that's the way you want it." Again he passed his hand through his hair, got up, went toward the door. Then he turned. "How about taking a look at my car?" His tone was light, even airy. She could hardly believe this was the same person who had spoken so earnestly, so bitterly a moment before.

Angry as she had been with him, she had been in communication with him then. Now he had shut her out. She wanted to weep.

"The car's a dandy of her kind," he said. "Of course not the best make." She detected a wistful note in his voice. He loved machinery, and only perfection in a car would really satisfy him. And she knew, too, he wanted to go to college. And yet he wouldn't take anything from his father.

What is it? she thought, sitting alone after he had gone. Doesn't he trust Edward? Why did I keep from him what he wanted to know about his father and me? Surely that has nothing to do with Edward's public life. We were both so young. It was his parents really. Why had she not told Petya everything? Or was it because telling him would strengthen his supicion of his father? But why, why had she refused and lost her opportunity to draw close to her son? She owed nothing to Edward.

But what was it Petya had said about being in the war soon? Petya fighting side by side with the Russia which had exiled her! For a moment she wished she had never left the Russian community in San Francisco, that she had brought Peter up in the tradition of the old Russia, kept him out of the full swing of life in the country of his father.

62

PETER did not wait for war to be declared. Two months later he volunteered for ground work in the Air Corps, his love of machinery making him select it, his modesty not letting him ask to be trained as a pilot. However, he was tested to see what aptitude he had for flying. When sight and hearing, together with stability tests, indicated he was pilot material, he was sent to officers' training school, and at the end of the first year of the war he received his wings, a proud moment which he wanted to share with Marion.

That evening he went over to the near-by town to see her. He wanted to pin a replica of his wings on her. In the last months his love for her had changed. Now tenderness and the desire to protect her were a part of it. He wished she would allow him to be more protective, but she seldom let her guards down, his spitfire of a girl who had stayed near him no matter how uncomfortable her quarters were.

He hoped he could make her understand why he felt they should wait to marry, for tonight he must tell her he would be going overseas in a few days.

He pinned the wings on her dress, then told her his news.

"Then of course we'll be married!" she exclaimed.

"Darling, it can't be that way. Suppose I shouldn't return. I couldn't leave you to be a widow. And perhaps——"

"Why can't you if that's what I want? Peter, don't you see it would be better than nothing. Please, Peter!"

But Peter with the memory of his mother's struggles said, "I couldn't do it. It wouldn't be fair." He held her in his arms trying to quiet her. She was crying in heartbroken sobs more like a man than a woman, as if it humiliated her to cry. "Hush, my dear, it would be worse for you than it is now if we married. Don't you see I don't want to tie you down? I mustn't. It isn't fair." His own tears fell on her hair but she did not know they were there.

It was very late. He loosened her arms and stood up. "I've got to go, darling. It won't be long, I hope. Oh, darling, we'll be married the first minute I'm back."

"I guess you want it that way, don't you?"

"What way?"

310   THE CLEFT ROCK

"Oh, to be free."

"Darling, it's you I'm thinking about. You do believe me, don't you?"

"Oh, of course," she said, but she didn't. If he loved her as she loved him he'd be willing to take the risks. But for the moment she wouldn't think about it. She gave and accepted one last passionate embrace.

But when he was gone something out of her childhood told her she had been deserted. Oh, hell, that's what I get for caring, she thought. I'd better brace up. Life isn't as pretty as I've been thinking it was. Maybe if I hadn't gone soft he'd still like me.

That very night Peter left secretly for India. In another month he was flying over the Himalayas to China and back the same day. Altitude, danger, the long exacting hours in the air left him neither the strength nor the time to reflect on the changing character of his life. But leaping up out of the past, faces and voices came to him in a succession of pictures and sounds: the spasm of pain which had passed over his mother's face when he told her he had enlisted, the look of respect in the eyes of his engineer friend when he told him he was volunteering as a private, Song's blotted letter, J. T.'s final sarcastic remark about the noble warrior, Marion's broken sobbing the last night they were together.

As the months went by, one by one the happenings before his departure faded. Only the hours he had spent with Marion remained clear and vivid. Nights he dreamed of her. Then came the letter from her telling him she was to be married the next day. Never had he felt pain like this. Marion his girl! He had not married her in spite of her pleading, because he felt he must leave her free until his return—not burden her with possible widowhood, but it had never occurred to him that she would not wait for that return!

In those terrible first days after he received her letter, he made up his mind that he had been simply an episode in her life.

Well, he had left her world—let it go on without him, he told himself. After that for a time there was only the present from which no voices rose, no faces, no feeling of home, nor of loved ones. Waking or sleeping, he now saw only the jagged, unearthly, white peaks of the Himalayas he daily flew over; the broken, half-obliterated cities of China set in the lush, green countryside; the airfield in Chabua where at the end of the run, drugged with exhaustion, he stumbled over to the officers' quarters.

He was a soldier, taking orders, he and the two men, his copilot and engineer, who flew with him—three men alien in temperament and experience, a unit of effort once they took their places in the plane to make the flight over the Himalayan Hump, indifferent to their plane's cargo, the danger the same whether they carried supplies so urgently needed to keep China alive, or the luxuries so often smuggled in. They were soldiers doing what they were told to do.

Then, when his mind had reduced life to the routine of his daily flight, an urgent need to find a larger habitation for his spirit arose within him. One night he woke, wanting something, wanting it terribly, but not knowing what it was. In the white wilderness of the Himalayas a plane had been lost that day and with it some of the men he had known best. Until now he had believed he coveted death for himself, the best way out of a smashed world. But he had awakened with the realization that he wanted to live. To find what? Slowly his desire took shape. What he was searching for was The Valley, deep-folded between the mountains of California.

He lay on his back looking up at the ceiling, knowing now he wanted to live to go home to The Valley, where he had lived as a child, to till the soil; there to refute the destructiveness and greed which he had been cynically accepting as man's fate. More vivid to him than the hut with the sleeping men were memories of Mishka directing the flow of water between the rows of cotton, and the engineers at work on the concrete wall of the dam.

As the days went by, he began to think more and more of John Dodd. He became a kind of symbol to Peter of the deeply creative man. Often he would ask himself, How would John Dodd act in India? Thinking in terms of John Dodd, he seemed to see more clearly his way. He began to read. The overseas books, so handy in a man's pocket, he read avidly, searching out some knowledge of life John Dodd had which he wanted for himself.

The cocoon of his own unhappiness into which he had retreated seemed to be unwinding, while he emerged from it into the lives of the men around him. Endlessly they talked about home. He found they, too, had beautiful secret valleys of which they dreamed. There was a boy from the South who talked of the Tennessee Valley where there were completed dams and comfortable homes to replace former poverty. Peter talked about the valley project, how when it was completed, the waters held behind Shasta Dam would be distributed to the farmers, power lines crisscrossing The Valley, electricity in every farmhouse, and The Valley itself—its soft, pliable, sandy loam so quickly turning to desert—given the water to keep it fertile.

What many men seemed to want was to see living, growing things which would blot out the scenes of death around them.

In the burning heat of India's summer, with the thermometer standing at a hundred and twenty-five degrees, Peter found his mind drifting off in airy fancies. Like shreds of mist, fragments of Mishka's Biblical quotations drifted through his mind—"He watereth the hills . . ." "Take the rod . . . and speak ye unto the rock!" Centering his attention on Mishka's words for a time he could ignore the burning itching of his body covered with prickly heat, the sharp cramps of diarrhea. There returned to him something of the exaltation of his childhood when he had first seen The Valley drenched with rain.

His own country became less real, more a dream of perfection, as India pressed in upon his consciousness with its disturbing poverty, disease and fanaticism—children fly-covered and starving while the sacred cows roamed at will through the stalls in the open market eating the fruits and vegetables. He compared America with China, its hordes of half fed and its quasi democracy. Words from a book he had recently read kept coming to him: "Democracy, seeking to be born, tears the ancient womb of China out of which it must come." But his own country, America, was the proud possessor of democracy!

63

AT THE TIME, Edward had thought his acknowledgment of Peter as his son meant little or nothing to him—a mere political necessity. It was disconcerting in the days that followed to find he was arguing with himself over the validity of the relationship. I owe him nothing, his mind said, but his heart would not go along. John's accusation that he had neglected his duty as a father he could not easily refute, once he had seen the boy. There was enough likeness to the Dodds in Peter to give Edward the feeling of relationship. That the boy had had none of the opportunities lavished on Tom's sons he found difficult to justify.

Guilt, which had risen in him the night he left Katya, long reduced to mere uneasiness as success had come to him, now spoke with insistence, taking on a new form—neglect of his son. With an effort of will he pushed it from him, occupying his mind first with his campaign and then, after his election, with plans for his life in Washington.

Agnes had decided not to accompany him. She would have been equal to the extra exertion such a move would have entailed, only if Edward needed her, only if he had made again some such demand on her as he had the night he told her about Peter, but he had not.

"Probably your decision is wise," he said. "The responsibilities of a larger social position might be too much for you." In the days before he left he hovered over her, believing he hid his eagerness to be off to his new duties and life. The old necessity to live apart from her was more urgent than ever, now that she knew about Peter. Too, because of her long-continued illness he looked forward to leading a less hampered life without her near him.

When he reached Washington it seemed this eagerness was indeed justified. He was at liberty now to live in an objective world full of activities and decisions. Not since his first months in China had he felt so free to follow his own convictions. Here, he was not subjected to the pressure his father and mother had always introduced into his public life. Even Edward's sister Margot, who represented his father's attitudes, was in Washington for only a few days after his arrival, as her husband had not been re-elected to Congress.

Edward took over their apartment in one of the larger hotels. The first night he moved leisurely around the spacious rooms with their well-chosen furnishings, which he had bought from Margot, placing the few personal things he had brought with him—books and a half-dozen pictures. Then he went again from room to room, rejoicing in his independence. He was alone at last where he could be himself.

The Washington he came to know was made up of men and women whose temperaments and convictions fitted his. They were interested in the social conception of government, to which he had always been responsive. The city's avenues and circles awoke in him something of his old recognition of beauty, dulled during the last years by his struggle to fulfill his ambitions.

In the House he found himself voting courageously and intelligently on national and international matters. With war pressing hard on the heels of the United States, California's factional disputes over water were shelved for the time being, all the various factions united now in urging appropriations for the water project. California must be ready to take her part in providing food for the country if war came, and for this she must have sufficient water.

He was alone in his apartment on a Sunday in December, a little over a year after he had come to the capital, listening to a symphony concert on the radio. He had closed his eyes in order to lose himself in the music when, suddenly, it stopped and the voice of the announcer told him his country had been attacked. With a purity of purpose he had never before experienced, the new Edward Dodd, the Edward Dodd of Washington, pledged himself to his country.

A few days later as he entered the corridor which led to his office in the House Office Building, an old friend of his father, a man named Gillion, came toward him, holding out his hand. "Congratulations, Dodd! Great news about your son."

"What do you mean?" For a moment Edward did not grasp the fact that the man was speaking of Peter.

"So he just went off and did it! All the better. He's one of the first in our state to volunteer, according to an item in the California papers."

"He's independent. Inclined to do his own thinking," Edward answered, a door in his mind swinging open to admit Peter. He felt the stirrings of a father's pride, and then the door, swinging wider, seemed to lead back into the recesses of his memory, to corridors blocked off and forgotten.

Since Edward had come to Washington he had built for himself a real if fragile independence. He needed now to give it substance by admitting what John and his grandmother had long ago tried to get him to admit, that in leaving Katya he had allowed his judgment to be taken over by his father. So far as possible, he could then go about setting right his injury to Katya and to his son. In fact, all they asked of him now was to fulfill his promises to the people of The Valley. If he should do that, Peter would begin to trust him, and that might later lead to understanding between them. For one moment of vision he glimpsed the possibility of living at peace with himself. He would take Agnes back into his life, work for the things he believed in.

But it was tragically impossible for Edward to cleanse the dark corridors of his memory of deeds he had done in the name of his father. Quickly he raised his guards, shutting Peter out. Again he was afraid of himself, seeking approval from the outside world.

"Come in, Mr. Gillion. I hope you bring news of my father." He ushered the visitor into his private office.

Now Edward was unable to believe that Mr. Gillion's remark about Peter was made in kindness. Rather it seemed that it had been made in the name of his father and bore the sarcastic implication old Jeremy would have given it.

"We'll have to hold things for our boys until they get back," Mr. Gillion said as he bent his rheumatic knees, lowering himself into the chair Edward pulled up for him. "Hand over a good world to them. It's about that I've come to see you," he went on. "I'm here for some of the power interests of California. I know you've pretty consistently stood for government distribution of power from government-built dams. I admire you for sticking to what you believe, but I think just now, with a war on, we need to bury our differences. We must stand together."

"What's your plan?" Edward pulled a memorandum pad toward him, making marks on it. Had Gillion come to intimidate him? All his old fears were coming out of hiding.

"Well, just this!" Mr. Gillion drew his chair closer. "The government will be in no position to put in power lines when Shasta Dam is finished. Let us help out in the emergency—government supply the dynamos and we the power lines. Then, after the war, we can take up the matter as to whether some lines would be better owned by the government." He paused, observing the effect of his words. There seemed to be none. "Give us the chance now to be a real public servant," he urged.

"Why did you come to me?" Edward asked.

"I'll tell you frankly," said Mr. Gillion, studying Edward's profile, all he could see of Dodd's face as he bent over his desk. "We feel because of your support of the Bureau's position you would have influence with the Secretary. We don't want the Secretary of the Interior to get the impression that we are trying for a monopoly at a time when the country's up against it."

"You have the idea the Secretary would listen to me?" Edward asked, not thinking freely as he had of late, but in terms again of his father. It would aid Jeremy Dodd right now to have his son take such a stand. He knew his father was in the midst of the delicate business of merging his company with the one Gillion represented.

"And you believe your plan is in the interest of the people of California?" Edward put down his pencil and looked at his visitor.

"You'll have to judge for yourself," said Mr. Gillion, rising. "All I can say is I have two grandsons who have volunteered. Does that answer your question?"

"Give me the details in a memorandum," Edward told him, "and I'll see what I can do." There was no reason, really, why he shouldn't present these ideas. During the war such arrangements would economize materials. The Secretary of the Interior would be the first to see this. But Edward knew that, if he presented it, he would be doing it to curry favor with the power people and his father. Now suddenly, however, he felt it necessary to be in their favor.

As the country's tempo was stepped up by the demands of war, so also was the tempo of Edward's life. He welcomed the importance of the work that kept him in Washington attending Congress, which was sitting continuously, but during the second summer of the war he made a hurried trip to the coast in answer to a letter from Agnes. When he entered her room he was startled to see how frail she looked. He sat down on the bed beside her, took her hand in his. Gently he stroked her hair.

"Why did you send for me, dear? I was worried for fear you were less well than usual, so I dropped everything and caught the first plane."

"I wanted to see you once more," Agnes said.

"You will see me a great deal when the war is over," he answered, ignoring the implication in her words.

"Yes," she said, "when the war is over, you will go on to greater accomplishments."

On Edward's last day at home his father had a long talk with him. "Now that the merger has gone through, I am retiring in the fall, Ed," Jeremy said. "Tom, you know, is well placed with the new company. It's for you and Tom to carry on."

"Don't think, Father, that just because I advocated you power people be allowed to put in the lines leading from Shasta Dam, it means I intend to advocate a monopoly after the war," Edward answered. Is there no limit, he thought, to what Father wants of me?

"I've spent a good deal of my life helping to establish a great power company in northern California," Jeremy replied, "half the time trying to keep you from destroying it. I hoped at last I had your support. But I guess I can't expect to get it. Perhaps because money has come to you so easily, you enjoy destroying the sources that have made it for you."

"That's a pretty hard accusation," Edward answered. "You give me no credit for having convictions."

Jeremy Dodd had risen and was standing where the light from a near-by window fell directly on him. Why, he's terribly old, thought Edward with a shock, noticing how heavy were the pouches under his father's eyes and that his lids under his thinning eyebrows were so dark they looked bruised. The impression he now gained of his father was of a man who was spent. Edward wished he had not opposed the aging head of the family in this, their last talk before he went back to Washington.

"I've something to show you before you go!" Jeremy went over to his desk, took a clipping from under a paperweight and handed it to Edward. "This was sent me from one of California's gossip sheets! Read it out loud," he commanded.

"John Dodd's marriage to Katya Suvorov was announced yesterday," Edward read. "It will be recalled that once before she bore the name of Dodd. The divorce was mysteriously covered up by the Dodd family and the statements given out years later left many people unsatisfied. Our representative at large is in town." He felt his throat constricting, but he went on reading. "Edward Dodd might explain, but perhaps he has reasons to withhold full information. Perhaps he will be a greater figure in the state if he doesn't say anything more about his treatment of his former wife and his son. One wishes the lady better luck this time."

"I've just one thing more to say, Ed." Jeremy reached out his hand for the clipping. "As I've tried to explain to you before, this sort of publicity wouldn't need to happen to you, or to me, if you'd play your hand right."

The door opened and Beatrice Dodd, now a wispy old lady, came in, saving Edward from the necessity of answering. He had only to say good-by to his father, who had seated himself again in his chair by the window.

"I'll go with you to the door." His mother slipped her arm through her son's. Once out of hearing of Jeremy she said, "Your father is angry with you. But, my dear, he's wrong when he blames you. It's John who has married that woman. Do be discreet, Edward, in all you do in Washington. Your father is getting old. He needs your support." She kissed him and he was free to go.

The next day as Edward crossed The Valley in the train he drew the blind to shut out the light and heat, but he could not shut out the smarting memory of the editorial's slur of him as husband and father. It must have been John, he kept thinking, who had given the press information for the article. John urged on by the woman he had married. As the day wore on the conviction grew in Edward that John all through the years had tried to wreck his career. John had been the evil genius injecting into his childhood and innumerable times since ideas about camps and Doddstown and responsibilities to The Valley which had distorted Edward's relationship to his father. Remembering him as he had looked yesterday Edward sensed he had not much time to redeem himself with his father.

The last two years of the war brought a definite change in Edward.

He seemed much older and much more suave in manner. He was less the constant worker, more the frequenter of social gatherings in the national capital. Listening to many conversations, he kept in touch with the shifting pattern of political thought. The group he had first come to know in Washington he saw little of these days. They no longer seemed important people to him.

He returned to California only once in that time, hastily summoned at the death of his wife. In the hours on the plane he took himself to task for leaving her alone so much these past years. And yet it had been inevitable, in the midst of war, that he should be chained to Washington. Even now his vote was needed on certain important questions coming up. Agnes' death brought him no deep grief; only the larger grief that one feels when one confronts death. He had thought his marriage was as definitely over as if he and Agnes had been divorced.

He stayed on after the funeral, held there by the demands his parents made on him. His mother had taken over the task of determining what to do with the things in his San Francisco apartment. Didn't he want some of them sent to Washington? Why didn't he buy a house there? Sometime she might need such a home. "Father——" She always broke down at this point. "I can't bear to let you go, Edward. Couldn't you stay with us until——" Again she broke down.

"Bettie will come any time you need her," Edward assured her, "and you have Tom and Margot."

"I always forget you're so important. Of course I'll be all right with Bettie. It's nice to think you've become such a great man." His mother smiled up at him through her tears.

Her words helped to confirm Edward's own feeling that probably this would be the last time he would see his father. Jeremy was eighty, and an old eighty, his body thin and gaunt. His hands, even when they rested on his chair arm, trembled, his gaze was uncertain. Only his voice was unchanged. It boomed from his frail old body like a great gong, shaking the structure that housed it. But his mind planned and schemed as it always had.

"There'll be a great deal to be done once the war is over," he kept telling his son, hammering home his points as if he still could not believe he had Edward's support. "We've got to get back to where we were before. Business has lost ground. War has done for us. Things like the T.V.A. I don't like. We don't want anything like that started in our valleys. Here's a thing I'd like to see you work for—I'd like to have as much as possible of the Central Valley program taken away from the Reclamation Bureau and put in the hands of the Army.

The Army'll need work after the war is ended, and they have no crazy
social programs to put over, such as the Federal Government has hung
around the neck of the Reclamation Bureau. The hundred-and-sixty-
acre limitation on water is an infringement of a man's rights. Where's
our free enterprise? And the power companies should distribute the
power generated at the government dams and get the returns."

In these days given them to be together Edward sought to pile
evidence upon evidence of his fidelity—assurances his father might
take with him that would leave Edward forever afterward conscious
that he had erased from Jeremy's mind the years of his apostasy.

"Father," he said one afternoon toward the end of his visit, "you've
never expressed yourself on what happened to the power line down
the west side of The Valley the Bureau wanted to put in. You know
the President asked the House Appropriations Committee to include
money for it in next year's budget."

Jeremy nodded. "And you helped to block it."

"Then you did know I had a part in it! That I strongly opposed it
when I testified before the committee!" exclaimed Edward.

"Of course," said his father, adding after a pause, "You're beginning
to justify my original faith in you."

Beginning! thought Edward. If I could ever satisfy Father. He
must know I worked damned hard to block that.

His former supporters seemed to want proof too. Some of his old
friends who had worked for his election came to see him. Like his
father, but with very different implication, they said, "There will be
a lot of things to work for after the war—the water question will be
up again." Their dissatisfaction with his accomplishments—if they
had any—they did not voice openly, except Mrs. Talbert, Marion's
mother.

"You aren't by any chance letting us down, are you?" she asked
Edward.

"Why do you say that?" he demanded. "Haven't I built up the
prestige of California in the House? And in times of war you have to
give up some things you'd like to see done."

"I'll tell you what," she said. "I'll consider the matter closed if
you'll dispense a little patronage in my direction."

"Are you looking for a job?" he asked.

"For my daughter." She was very much in earnest now, he saw;
all the banter had gone out of her voice. "She married at the beginning of the war. I didn't think too much of the idea. The boy was
killed a month after he went overseas. There was a baby, and he died,
too. Marion is in Washington. She needs to be busy. You remember

Marion. She was at that dinner in Fresno. You know, the one where we stopped that bad little story going round." She laughed lightly, taking a mildly malicious enjoyment in bringing up the old affair.

Edward's first reaction was to refuse, but did it matter that the girl had been present at that political dinner? He did not want to lose the support of women like Mrs. Talbert. She was one of his most efficient campaign workers. "Send your daughter around. It just happens I'm in need of a secretary. Mine is getting married," he said.

It was the following winter that Edward saw an opportunity to play a major part in legislation that would be in line with the program his father had mapped out to him as essential if the big owners in The Valley were to be given the freedom they felt was their legal right.

The Rivers and Harbors Bill was out of committee ready to be reported on the floor of the House. Edward sought out one of the members of the committee. "Can't you add an amendment to the bill to get the one-hundred-and-sixty-acre limitation out of the Central Valley Project?"

"Pretty hard to do it now since the bill is out of committee."

"Why not introduce an amendment on the floor during floor debate?" asked Edward.

The afternoon the bill came to the floor it was moved that debate be limited. The House approved. After a couple of hours of discussion debate lagged.

The committee member rose to his feet: "Mr. Speaker, I offer a committee amendment eliminating the one-hundred-and-sixty-acre limitation from the Central Valley Project."

Those supporting the project as it stood were taken unawares. A few rose to speak but there was no concerted opposition. The amendment passed. The bill was read a third time. It passed with a large majority.

Edward was too busy at the time to call his father, but all the rest of the day he savored the pleasure it was going to be to tell him of the action in the House—a kind of culmination of his political career—and to hear his father's voice over the telephone saying, "Well done, good and faithful son."

It was six in the evening when he reached his hotel. "There's a long-distance person-to-person call awaiting you."

Could his father have learned his news? He said he had ways. It was Tom's voice that came over the wires. "Ed, Father had a stroke a few hours ago and died almost immediately."

So, after all, he would never be able fully to redeem himself with his father. If only his father could have lived long enough to see this major step forward in control of The Valley and know that Edward had been its originator!

But then when the Senate failed to pass the bill as it came from the House, Edward was thankful he did not have to confess to his father that he had spoken hastily. Jeremy Dodd would have seen in his premature report of the bill's passage into law an impulsiveness which did not inspire confidence. But Edward had been so sure the Senate would not jeopardize or delay the whole bill by contesting the amendment.

He did not know that his brother John, hearing that the House had passed the Rivers and Harbors Bill with the amendment exempting California from the one-hundred-and-sixty-acre limitation, had come to Washington to see the senator who had long supported the Homestead Act in the East and would understand that land limitation in the East was water limitation in the West.

When John explained to him what the amendment meant to the people of California, the senator, indignant that such an attempt should be made to undermine an old-established American principle, was ready to fight. He said: "If the bill is brought up as it now stands, I'll talk it to death."

The senator, faithful to his promise, watched as the bill took its intricate way through the conference committee until he saw the bill finally defeated.

64

THE war was over. Peter was on his way home. The crowded ship slowly rounded the tip of Asia, made its way up the coast of China, across the Yellow Sea, up the coast of Japan, steamed out into the Pacific. Peter's longing to see his own country became so great it partook of pain but before him at last was the Golden Gate and San Francisco, the city of his birth. There were only minutes left to count.

He had sent no word to his mother. He wanted to see her, not on the dock, but in The Valley to which he felt she belonged.

When his mother had written him of her marriage, he had felt very lonely. He was not of first importance to anyone in the world. And then the loneliness had given place to a sense of completeness he had never before experienced. Both his mother and he were completed in John Dodd. Husband and father—the vacancies in his mother's life and in his life filled.

According to her letters the place which John Dodd had bought after his retirement was on the edge of a small town on the east side of The Valley. There he intended to start his own school for boys. Watching through the train window, beholding again The Valley, Peter was caught up into the ecstasy of return. The crops in the valleys and plains of the Central Valley were so abundant, the roads were so smooth and so far-reaching. In the cities and towns men, women and especially children were so safe and so free. Safety and freedom a rock which could not be blasted from the American soil.

It was evening when he walked across the veranda of John Dodd's house and, finding the screen door unlocked, entered unannounced. He tiptoed along the hall toward the room from which the sound of voices came, stopped in the shadowed space outside. John was leaning over lighting his cigarette at the match Peter's mother was holding for him. He was just as Peter had remembered him, a quiet, thoughtful man, no longer young. How fine and disciplined his face! And his mother—Peter had not known that love would change a person so. Of course she was younger by many years than John Dodd, but she seemed younger to Peter than she ever had before. And radiant. That was the word for it. For a moment he felt an intruder. Maybe there was no place for him here.

Then his mother lifted her eyes and saw him. "Petya!" she cried, and stretched out her arms to him. The radiance in her face held, but mingled with it was something especially for him. When she released him, he shook John's hand, unable to voice the gratitude he felt toward the man who had—yes, who had opened the prison house in which his mother had lived ever since he could remember.

Suddenly he felt unutterably lonely. Marion's betrayal, something he had determined to forget, rose to haunt him in this hour of his return. Sternly he took himself in hand. He would not let her mar his home-coming.

Until late in the night the three talked. When John told him Shasta Dam had been finished and other parts of the water system were being built, it brought Peter to the question of whether or not he wanted to go about getting a degree in engineering. The time for it had passed, he reflected. After all, were all those dreams of The Valley he had had overseas just homesick longings? Wasn't what he wanted to do to till the soil? He remembered his quiet room in his mother's house on the ranch—the stillness when he woke in the morning. He had money in his pocket. He could go out and buy good land.

Peter didn't tell them what he had in mind. He had an idea his mother would be against the plan, her own bitter experience making her fearful. He didn't want the caution age would hold out to him. To branch out on one's own was each generation's right.

A week after his return he left them, saying he wanted to look up some friends in Fresno. On reaching the city, he went straight to a real-estate agent. Before entering the office he read a placard in the window:

FORTY ACRES FOR SALE
GOOD ORCHARDS
$25,000

Peter drew in a long breath, let it out in a low whistle. I suppose some sucker will fall for it, he said to himself. Can't possibly make a go of it. You'd need a hundred acres at $25,000 to succeed.

"What I want," he told the real-estate man as a few moments later he sat down opposite him, "is, say, fifty acres if it's in fruit trees or a hundred if in potatoes and cotton, or, say, eighty under cultivation and forty I can bring under cultivation when I can get water from the Central Valley Project. That's the quantity of land the Fresno Chamber of Commerce recommends for a good living, and my knowledge of farming tells me it's about right."

The man facing him smiled. "I wouldn't advise you to wait for the Reclamation Bureau to provide you with water. Not if you want to get a start before you're an old man. I doubt if the plan as it now stands will ever be fully carried out. How many years now have they been working on the idea? Mark my word, it'll be another fifty. Maybe not then. Either a lot of the canals and smaller dams won't be built by the government or the law will be changed doing away with limitation on acreage a man can get water for. I'd advise you to buy a tract already under cultivation, water rights well established. That's your surest bet. Suppose we take a look at what I have to offer."

At the end of the week Peter had seen nothing that he could afford to buy. The few good farms for sale were at a price that only a rich man going into farming as a hobby could afford. Those priced within his reach were either poor land or land without sufficient water. He decided to start out on his own and see what he could find. He'd buy one of the jeeps being put on sale by the War Assets Administration and ride over The Valley until he found what he wanted. Fearing there would not be enough cars for all who sought to buy, he decided he'd sit up all night to make certain he'd be among the first when the buying began. When at eight o'clock the evening before the sale he arrived at the place designated, he saw he wasn't the only veteran who had that bright idea. His place in the line was disturbingly far from the office, but as the night was cold, he counted on a few dropping out.

The men at the front rolled up in blankets and went to sleep, but farther down the line Peter and the other men squatted on the ground, trying their best to keep awake, so as to be ready to move up the moment somebody dropped out. The young chap just ahead of him, Peter noticed, was lame. It made him think of J. T. He must hunt him up as soon as he found his farm. Listening to the talk around him, Peter was surprised to find how many of the veterans wanted to go into farming—a lot of them men from other states. "My folks are farmers back east," the boy behind him was saying. "But I fell for this valley when I was here during the war. I thought about coming back all the time I was in Iwo Jima."

"A hell of a daydream!" a man who was wandering from group to group cut in. "Better go back where you came from, buddy. Buy good farm land in Central Valley! Where you going to get it?"

"Shut up, wise guy," the boy retorted. "I seen miles of land without a house on it going through on the train. Course there's good land for sale."

"The rich guys are ahead of you. A man bought fifty-five thousand acres awhile back. This valley is going in for industrialized farming," the man answered. "You know what I'm here for?"

"That's easy—to buy a jeep," Peter threw in.

"Yeh, but not to go hunting a farm."

"Look, you fellows." The man's voice dropped. "What's going to happen here is this. Bigger and bigger farms, bigger and bigger labor camps, laborers madder and madder about the shacks they get to live in. Nothin' to look forward to. The sooner it gets bad the sooner it'll get better."

"What do you mean?" Peter challenged.

"I mean what I say, it's the big guys that are going to make revolution easy. When you have a lot of small farmers, nothing doing. They're too contented, but men in dirty camps haven't anything to lose."

Peter was fighting mad. "Look," he said, "you take your talk of revolution away from here. This is America, not Russia."

With a laugh the man moved on.

It was noon the next day before Peter rode away in his jeep, heading straight for the west side of The Valley. The real-estate agent had convinced him there was no use attempting to buy on the more settled east side. With the money he had at his disposal the banks would not lend him the extra he would need. Land was too expensive there for a veteran with only a few thousand to invest, even if he could get a GI loan.

From early in the morning until dark day after day he sent his jeep bouncing over the roads, up and down and across The Valley, in towns and out, talking to everybody he could—seeing, thinking.

As the days went by, he began asking himself, What's happening to my country, or wasn't it ever the kind of a country the boys over in India talked about? Did we idealize it? For long distances the land stretched away into the distance—no comfortable farmhouses dotting it, only an occasional group of miserable one-room shacks for laborers and important-looking administration buildings on the large holdings. An occasional rural school, unpainted and in disrepair, stood out bleakly against the flat fields. Then again the impersonal stretch of acre upon acre, the marks of the plow ending only at the horizon.

Whenever he found any small acreage for sale, either it was poor land or with insufficient water. There were disturbing stories of greater and greater consolidation of land. An Eastern liquor company had bought up many small vineyards. A wealthy cotton man from the East had bought up fifty-five thousand acres, consolidating three holdings. Evidently, as the real-estate man had said, no one was expecting the acreage limitation to be put into effect. Shrewd businessmen wouldn't be buying land in such quantities if they thought they could get the benefit of government water for only three hundred-odd acres at the most. It looked as if the veteran wouldn't get much of a chance in The Valley. Still Peter wasn't willing to give up. There was a part of the east side he hadn't seen. He'd try there.

As he struck across to the east side, he began to feel reassured. This was more the America the boys overseas had talked about. The towns were made up of neat houses with green grass plots in front of them. The schools, low and spacious, were set in green shrubbery. Even if he couldn't find a farm to buy here, there were many moderate-sized ones where evidently men were making a comfortable living. And then even here on the east side of The Valley the houses began to grow scarce, but the great stretches of vineyards and orchards were more human-looking some way, he thought, than vast grain and cotton plantings. Probably because vines and trees were associated in men's minds with homes.

On he drove, along a road bordered on both sides by vineyards, seeing no tiniest weed, not one wild morning-glory vine, the pest of farmers, marring the smooth beauty of the sandy loam out of which the three-foot-high grapevines, sturdy as trees, rose, topped by green leaves and hanging bunches of grapes. At last rising out of the green expanse was a group of administration buildings shining in a new white paint. And beyond to the east against the far-off hills he saw the concrete walls and aluminum still towers of a winery. Then again the stretched-out low green canopy of waving grape leaves. One man owns this, thought Peter, almost with envy.

And then he came upon a town. At its entrance was a secondhand shop, spilling out on the ground in front of it broken-down beds, rusty oil stoves, cracked mirrors, the flotsam of the poor. Peter drove down the main street. Men coming in from the fields were entering the saloons. Children swarmed the dusty, empty places, and behind the buildings he could see shacks sprawled in grotesque fashion up to the very edge of the meticulously cared-for vineyards. Peter could think of nothing but a festering cancerous growth on the fertile earth.

I'll try the west side just once more, he thought. There must be something I can buy. And there, indeed, he found just what he wanted, a lovely spot in the San Joaquin Valley close up against the foothills of the coastal range. There was a FOR SALE sign at the end of an avenue of palms that led up to a tiled-roof ranch house flanked on one side by a vineyard. On the three other sides cotton with its opening bolls made the field look as if covered with a fall of snow.

Peter had a sense of getting home such as he had not experienced since his return. As he drove between the palms, he had the fleeting thought, This is the kind of place Marion would like. Why do I keep thinking of her? She never meant a word of what she said. She was using me to furnish her a little excitement. He brought his car to a halt at the end of the drive.

In response to his knock a woman came to the door. "I saw your sign. I wanted to inquire the acreage and the price," he said.

"It's a hundred acres," she replied, "and we're not asking as much as it's worth because we want to get away. I mean," she went on, "it's because of my family back east needing us makes us in a hurry to sell."

The price she quoted was indeed reasonable. Peter could hardly believe his ears. His luck was holding—first the jeep, now the farm.

"Suppose I come around tomorrow morning, as you say your husband won't be back until late this evening."

"If you'd like to stay the night, I could put you up. Then you could get things settled tonight or first thing in the morning."

Her eagerness roused in Peter a suspicion that something was wrong. "I'm afraid I can't, but I'll be here early," he said.

Driving slowly along the main highway, he saw ahead of him an unpaved road leading to the back part of the ranch. He turned into it. The cotton fields, healthy and full-bearing, hugged the way on either side. It was evidently well watered to produce such a stand. What's the catch? he kept thinking. Could it be the woman's urgency was merely the need to join her family? Sickness maybe. He wanted to believe it.

Then there ahead of him he saw what he told himself he had suspected all along—the high derrick used in drilling deep wells. He got out, walked along a path of heavy-bearing cotton on one side of him, uncultivated land on the other. A quarter of a mile from the derrick he came upon a stake. He walked on. Yes, just a quarter of a mile and another stake. In the distance another and yet another. So that was why the woman wanted to keep him for the night, sell to him before he found out how worthless the land would soon be.

In his wanderings up and down The Valley he had heard a rumor of a vast tract of new land being brought under cultivation by a company and that they were bordering their tremendous acreage with high-powered wells, squeezing out a lot of neighboring small fellows by syphoning off the underground water. Well, he guessed this was it.

Angry and disgusted as he was with the woman for trying to play such a trick on him, he felt pity for her, too. He remembered the night of his graduation and Mishka standing in the kitchen saying in a broken voice, "The water is gone." His chest felt tight.

65

PETER turned his jeep toward Doddstown, J. T. drawing him like a magnet. Perhaps he'd still take him into his business. Easy money he had said that time at the dam. I guess I know now why I haven't hunted him up before. Thought I knew more than he did. Guess I felt too darn superior. Smart guy I was, able to beat the game. A hero to myself. The great patriotic, chest-thumping American veteran returned from the soul-searing experiences of war. So Peter railed at himself, stabbing at the high enthusiasm with which he had started out to make for himself a place in The Valley.

If J. T. had had his way, he'd have pounded the sentimental good boy out of me long ago. That's what bothered him when we were kids.

Well, he'd tell him now he'd had a bellyfull. They'd get along.

It was late afternoon the next day when he reached Doddstown. It looked bleaker than ever. He drew up at the drugstore. They'd know where J. T. lived.

In response to his question the man at the fountain laughed, half derisively, half admiringly. "Look for the biggest house in town. Don't know where he gets his money, but he gets it." He went to the door, pointing out to Peter a pretentious-looking affair a block away.

Peter knocked at the door, excitement growing in him. A key turned in the lock, and the door opened. It was not J. T. standing in the doorway, but a slight, dark-haired girl.

"Song!" Peter exclaimed. He could say no more. Song married to J. T.! No, not that! He stepped inside, shutting the door behind him.

Song spoke hurriedly, nervously. "I must explain before J. T. comes in. He came to see me after father died. He was kind to me and he talked about you . . . the way I never thought he could—as if you were his hero. I guess after a while I got him mixed up with you. He said we needed each other." Her voice died away.

"And don't you?"

"He's doing something to me!" she cried. "He's changing me. I don't know." She raised her hand, brushing her hair back in a confused gesture.

"You're comfortable and you're not hungry," said Peter, seeing she was close to breaking down.

"Peter, he's evil . . . the slot machines—it's cover-up for something else. He's the political boss. People don't dare not do what he says . . . and . . . and . . . he's cruel to me." A flush spread slowly over her face and down her throat. "And . . . and . . . he's making me bad."

Something drawn out of his own past made Peter believe what she said. His fists clenched as he looked at the haggard girl who once had been so buoyant and gay. The irresponsible mood in which he had come was gone, the hold J. T. had on him was broken. Song needed him. Memories of their childhood claimed him and that moment in his early adolescence when looking at her he had felt himself brushed by something mysterious and disturbingly beautiful.

"Song, we've not much time," he said. "Listen to what I tell you before J. T. comes. You must let me get you away. Meet me down the road tomorrow or the next day, whenever you can plan it. I'll hang around and wait until you get your chance to slip off. Mother will take you in. When you get your divorce, we'll be married!"

Song struggled for control. "No, Peter, I can't go. He'd hunt us out and kill you. I know now what he's been after all the time. He felt he was destroying you through me."

"Me!"

"Look, Peter: you must go away from here and never come back."

"I won't unless you'll come with me."

"I'll never go with you. It's final, Peter. Hush, I hear him coming." She flung open the door, crying, "A lovely surprise, J. T."

A look of triumph passed over J. T.'s face as he looked at Peter. "I thought you'd turn up some day," he said, in greeting. "Come on in and we'll have a talk."

"I'll hurry with supper while you two visit," cried Song in a voice that sounded almost gay. "He says he has an engagement later in the evening, so he hasn't much time."

"Where?" asked J. T.

"He says he has to see someone in Sacramento tonight."

"Is Pete unable to speak for himself?" asked J. T.

Peter drove to Sacramento, arguing Song must have decided in that last minute that she would leave J. T. and that was her way of letting him know where to find her.

Each morning he went over to the square facing the hotel, thinking it would be the best place for her to find him. He walked up and down the aisles between the trees, glancing at every young woman who came toward him—his hope rising at some slight resemblance to Song in the quick walk of a small girl down at the far end of the aisle, his hope dying as she came nearer and the likeness to Song disappeared.

Two, three days went by. As the hours ticked slowly away his conviction grew that she would not come. But every time he reached that conclusion he rebelled against what would happen to her if left in J. T.'s possession. He'd have to think of another plan. He could not endure the thought of what she might become left to J. T.—the slow destruction of everything gay and good in her, until she was at last created in J. T.'s likeness.

He was tormented with the vision, and he was tormented with the unmistakable relief he felt in not having to marry her. He believed they could have made it work. It would have been a good marriage, but not a whole marriage, too much on her side, too little on his. In a sudden flash of understanding he realized that Song knew that when she refused to come with him. And he saw now why she had sent him to Sacramento—get him away, give him time to think. He believed she had guessed why he'd come back to Doddstown. She was fighting to free him from J. T. as she had as a child.

For the first time in his life Peter subjected himself to thorough self-examination. I've been like a pendulum, he thought. Hunting up J. T. was my habitual reaction, my defense against disappointment. If I'm ever going to make anything of myself, I must get my teeth into something. I've got to fight for what I wish to become, fight like hell. I don't know that I've got it in me.

For a little his discouragement was profound. Perhaps, as he had once said to John Dodd, he was no good. Doddstown was in his blood. Nobody from Doddstown ever amounted to anything. But something in him refused to accept defeat. What could he do? And to what purpose?

Why had he wanted a farm? he asked himself, turning the fierce light of self-examination on his most cherished wish. Hadn't he perhaps intended in the end not to be a small farmer but a big one? Just to prove to men like Lesly who once had been able to look down on him that he was their equal. Of course he had told himself he would be kind to the people under him. He blushed to think of the hypocrisy of his position. Kindliness wasn't the answer. The answer was a valley where men had an equal chance.

How did he fit into that? I guess, he said at last, if I were willing to serve The Valley, I could find a place. Yes, I guess that's what I need to do—become a public servant. He grimaced. Sounds kind of sappy—yet . . . I guess that's about it.

He crossed over to the hotel, lay down on the bed in his room without undressing. Exhausted, he fell asleep. In the morning he surveyed his intention soberly. Easy to say he was going to do something worth while, but just what? Still, the idea held. John Dodd, he believed, was the only person he knew who would understand what he was groping for. He would go home and talk to his stepfather.

Again he was in his jeep headed south. A strong north wind was blowing down The Valley. Wherever a man was plowing, clouds of earth particles enveloped him and his machine. The wind hurled the topsoil from the fields, tossing it wildly from great field to great field. Ahead of him, far off on the smooth plowed floor of The Valley the land seemed to lie under water—great lakes in which men in the distant fields appeared to wade. Peter knew this phenomenon of The Valley—the mirage of still pools of water in an arid land.

It was night when he reached his home, and he was more tired, he thought, than when he'd been flying the Hump, but he must talk to his stepfather before he could rest. To his mother's plea that he wait until morning, he answered, "Please let me talk to you now."

Looking first at one, then the other, Peter told his story of the weeks he had been away, holding nothing back, stumbling a little in his tale when it came to Song. A cry escaped his mother when he mentioned the girl's marriage. But she was silent when he spoke of how he had tried to take Song away from J. T.

"There is some reason why you are telling us this," John said. "Does it have to do with your own plans?"

"I want to get a government job," Peter answered, "in order to serve my country. Maybe it's that I'm working for a soft berth, and I don't want to strike out for myself now I have seen the hazards involved."

John had been sitting with his head resting in his hand. At Peter's last words, he dropped the hand which shaded his eyes, looked up with a strangely arresting smile. "Why not call it patriotism, Peter? During the war nobody apologized for wanting to serve his country. Why do you now? Let's take for granted that it's a very normal desire on your part. Just to be practical, why don't you try to get into the Bureau of Reclamation? Take part in the fight to enforce the one-hundred-and-sixty-acre limitation on water. As you have found out, only so will the average man get a chance at the land and water of the state. There's plenty of work there."

"Do you suppose I could?" asked Peter.

John studied Peter, trying to estimate how strong he was, how much injured by doubt and bitterness. When he was discouraged as he often would be in such work, could he be reached by powerful selfish interests? "You need to get a few things straight in your own mind, I'd say, before you decide," he said finally. "You need to realize you won't change people's thinking in a year or five or ten. The fight over water has been going on ever since California was first settled. It's a lifetime job, and then you may feel you've wasted your life. You will have to guard yourself against disappointment and discouragement. You may have to accept abuse. The forces you oppose may try to discredit you."

Peter knew of some of the prison reforms John Dodd had worked for, how few he had ever succeeded in bringing about. Would he, Peter asked himself, be able to stand up against repeated disappointments? He hadn't been in the past. Maybe this fire which had burned within him the last few days, fanned into life by his distress over Song, would die out as quickly as it had arisen. Could he stand firm if attacked? "Well, perhaps I've not the guts for it," he answered, once more unsure of himself.

"Yes, I think you have," said John. "But you need to have an understanding with yourself before you start out, or somewhere along the way you'll be sidetracked. The only person qualified to be a public servant is a man who does the job for the job's sake and for the satisfaction he will get out of it, and who never curries favor. That means the desire for wealth or power goes out the window. It's especially true in this fight over water."

There was a long silence. Finally Peter said, "Yes, that's what I want to do."

The wind drifting in through the open window lifted the light scarf lying around his mother's shoulders, drawing Peter's attention to her. He saw first a look of incredulity pass across her face and then an expression almost of exaltation.

She rose, came to him, kissed him on each cheek.

66

PETER found that his testing was to come sooner than he had anticipated. The processes of government were slow. After the filing of his application there was a delay of several months before the half-yearly civil service examination was again given. After he learned that he had passed, there was a delay of several more months before his appointment was made. It all wore on his eager, impatient spirit. But the day came at last when he was installed in an office of the Reclamation Bureau.

During those months the struggle over who should control government-built dams and canals had sharpened, for the issues of The Valley had become greater than The Valley. What was decided for California's Central Valley would set a precedent for the reclamation projects of the Missouri Valley (the vast central plain of the United States) and other regions such as Colorado and Oregon.

An attempt was being made to influence Congress to set a new pattern for the nation's public domain—land, water and power. The new pattern would release the eighty million acres of public grazing lands

and forest preserves to private interests; Army engineers whose building program did not demand equal-water distribution would replace
the Bureau of Reclamation whose program did. Private power interests were seeking to control all the power generated at the country's
dams.

Many of the men who for years had been engaged in this fight
against public ownership were gone, among them Jeremy Dodd, but
his sons had stepped into his place even as Jeremy had planned that
they should when they were boys. The two facets of himself—businessman and politician—were re-created in Tom and Edward. But
the schism in the family was still there—Peter, the son, pitted against
Edward, the father.

The Senate bill to do away with acreage limitation on the use of
water would be introduced in the House by Edward Dodd, it was
rumored. Peter's appointment on the Bureau had been made with
the idea that he would be a good liaison person between the Bureau
and the people, a new position created to combat unfavorable publicity of the Bureau. His early life on a valley farm where the need
for water was such a constant problem gave him the experience needed
to present to the farmer the value of government controls on water
and power.

As Edward Dodd was more and more often quoted in opposition to
what the Bureau was doing, Peter lost all confidence in his father.
Bitterly he told himself that he, Peter Suvorov, had been played for a
sucker. Giving out to the public that Edward had always been a
loving father! Had Peter refused to do so, the great Edward Dodd
might not now be opposing what he had promised to stand for during
his election campaign. Bricket, back from duty with the Army in
Japan, was disappointed in Edward too, but his disappointment was
nothing compared with Peter's disillusionment.

Peter took some comfort in the fact that now he didn't have the
embarrassment of acknowledging that the man who had failed to keep
his promises to the people of the state was his father. Since his
return from India no one he had met had connected his name with his
father's. In the crowded happenings of war and postwar, he hoped
interest in the personal relationships of the Dodd family, prominent
as they were in politics, had been lost sight of. Gratefully Peter accepted his privacy with the opportunity to be like the men around
him. But there was one drawback to his obscurity. How small it made
his influence as set against his father's! Then he realized his very obscurity had its own particular power. He remembered the time in his
childhood when, with all the odds against them, the people had voted

down the big interests. He, as in his childhood, was again identified with the people.

Peter's first assignment was to visit the irrigation districts in the southern part of The Valley and talk over with them the contracts for water the Bureau could offer them. One winter morning when the sun shone forth from a sky as uninterrupted of rain clouds as if it were summer, he started out.

As the Weather Bureau said The Valley was entering a dry cycle, it ought to be a strategic time for him to counteract the adverse publicity going round, Peter thought, as he headed toward the office of the irrigation district first on his list, one of the oldest in that part of The Valley. It had its own dam up in the mountains, which in most years banked up a sufficient water supply for every farmer in the setup. An hour's ride brought him to the town where the office was located. He parked his car in front of a big window on which was lettered: HIGH SIERRA IRRIGATION DISTRICT, and down in one corner in smaller letters: ENGINEER, P. S. LEWIS.

It was a busy office that Peter entered. A man standing at the telephone covered the mouthpiece long enough to ask his business.

"Is Mr. Lewis in?"

"No, he isn't."

"Will he be in soon?"

"Can't tell," said the man. "The lining of one of our ditches has broken down. He's out seeing what has to be done. Anything I can do for you?"

"I'm one of the Reclamation Bureau men," said Peter. "I just dropped in to acquaint your office with what we're doing."

"I'm afraid I can't help you out on that—guess you'll have to see Lewis. He's the one to talk to."

"Suppose I come around this afternoon," Peter suggested.

"Make it tomorrow morning. Pretty certain to catch him if you get here around nine."

It was a ride of a couple of hours to the headquarters of the next district. He could make it before lunch time, Peter decided. He thought of telephoning, but decided not to. His idea had been to make no set appointments—drop in casually, try to establish a friendly basis for discussion. As he was determined to carry out that plan, he'd have to take a chance on catching the engineer in. He had gone only half the distance when with a grinding sound his jeep came to an abrupt stop. Rear end is out, he said to himself, climbing out. Hope they have a tow car in the next town which can pick up the jeep.

It was a comparatively unfrequented road and no car was in sight.

He'd have to foot it until someone came along to give him a ride. A car sped past him. Perhaps he'd have better luck with the next one. He'd walked about two miles, he thought, when a queer-looking contrivance stopped beside him, a kind of penthouse set on a jeep chassis. A boyish-looking man leaned out. "Give you a lift?" he asked. "Take it that's your jeep back there a bit. Live around here?"

"Well, no, I'd not call it near," Peter replied, climbing in. "Think I can get a tow in the next town?"

"Best place to go is Bakersfield. Little out of your way, but you're sure to get help there. That's where I'm headed for."

"Guess what I planned is pretty well shot for today," said Peter, "so I may as well go along."

"A farmer?" asked his companion.

"No, Bureau of Reclamation."

"Didn't I see you in the line the night we got our jeeps? I'm the fellow who was so sure he'd find a place to buy. Remember?"

"Well, did you?" asked Peter.

"Not so you'd notice it."

"Neither did I," said Peter. "What you doing now?"

"Rattling round, kind of on the loose. Money used up. Guess I'll go back east. Tell you what I'll do," the boy went on: "I'll take you where you want to go, after you get your tow in Bakersfield. It don't matter much where I go."

It was around three when they arrived at the door of the irrigation district office. "Thanks a lot," said Peter. "You've changed my luck for me." The other grinned and drove off.

The engineer was in, but he pleaded urgent business. "I can't give you much time today," he said, "and I may as well tell you right now we're not for these government controls. We know we've got water even if in a dry year we run a little short. If we sign up with you fellows, you're just as like as not to take even that from us."

"We don't want to take it away from you," said Peter.

"With your setup we couldn't keep the state decree we now have for the water behind the dam which we put in ourselves up in the mountains. Isn't that about right?" the man demanded.

"We'd like to put in a series of small dams high up in the mountains so there'd be next to no runoff. These dams would put extra water behind your dam. Wouldn't you feel," asked Peter, "that it would be worth giving up your decree to take in its place a contract assuring you a steady supply of water from a government-owned water conservation?"

"Give you the right to rule us," the man answered. "Frankly, no."

In an hour's talk, all the time the engineer said he could spare, Peter found no way to break down his suspicions.

It was late when he got back to Bakersfield and found the repair work on his jeep couldn't be finished before ten the next morning. He'd have to spend the night there. He went from hotel to hotel trying to find a room. Finally several miles out of town in a rather dilapidated motel he was able to get a small room without bath. The restaurants, too, were crowded.

Things were booming in Bakersfield despite the threat of drought. The big farmers in the neighborhood had deep wells. They were even bringing new land in. That the underground-water level was dropping didn't seem to bother them. Conservation was just a word here. The pumps they put in each year reached deeper as the underground-water level receded. A large operator had drilled two thousand feet to get the water he wanted. Cash crops were making him a millionaire. The near-by oil wells put the finishing touch to the town's boom.

The next morning about ten Peter started out again in his jeep to see Lewis, the engineer who had been out the day before. This interview, too, proved discouraging. I couldn't get to first base with him, Peter reflected as he left the office. Lewis had called the Bureau a "gigantic hoax," its officials "designing demagogues." Imported phrases was Peter's decision as he set out for the office of a public accountant who handled the business of a number of irrigation districts.

But this time there was no hostility. He had come by chance to the man Appleton, whom Bricket had consulted six-odd years before about the scandal going around concerning Edward Dodd. Appleton had always been a stanch supporter of the Bureau. When Peter told him his business, he said, "Glad to meet you, Mr. Suvorov. Like to come into my office?" Suvorov . . . Suvorov, Appleton was thinking, as he led the way to the room at the back. That was the name. How does Dodd's son fit into Edward Dodd's present performances—or doesn't he?

"I dropped in to get your slant on what the Bureau is trying to do," Peter began.

"Let me ask you a question," Appleton countered. "What do you think about what our representative at large is doing to oppose the Bureau?"

"I think he's selling us down the river" was Peter's prompt reply.

"All right, I'll tell you something," Appleton said, motioning Peter to one of his two high stools. He climbed up on the other, hunching his heavy shoulders, bringing his head down between them like a wise old frog. "A disembodied voice has been singing sweet bedtime ditties to those who are in charge of irrigation districts. Every town's got somebody singing the ditties, trying to make 'em believe they'll bring them water, bring them electricity—just let them get the government out! Never be any shortage of electricity then, they say. The Reclamation Bureau, they tell them, wants to rob God-fearing farmers of water."

"Yes, I've been meeting that kind of talk—but is it universal?" asked Peter.

"Universal! You can taste it in your coffee. What's more, things look bad for the Bureau's chief. I read in a Redding paper a few months back how men in Washington bragged they were going to get him. Guess they will, too, if they keep on. Hearings in California, hearings in Washington, needling him about how he runs the district office. A man can't take that kind of punishment forever."

"What can we do about it?" Peter asked.

"I dunno." Appleton shifted around on his high stool. "Even what you're doing is liable to be misinterpreted. They could say that you're spending government money to put the Reclamation Bureau's plan over, couldn't they?"

"I'm a government official, appointed to inform the farmers," Peter answered. "How are the farmers to know about the Bureau's work if we don't tell them? If that's so, anything I do could be misconstrued."

"Exactly," said Appleton.

Peter had been in Appleton's office longer than he realized, for when he went through the front room the girls had gone. Outside he was surprised to see that the sun had set. It was the time when as a boy he used to sit on the steps of his mother's house, tired after the work of the day, looking out over their fields. Then he remembered it was at this hour he and his mother had left the ranch for the last time. If Appleton were right, again he faced defeat. He and all the men of the Bureau. And he, through his father, had helped to bring it to pass!

In the second town he went through he stopped for dinner. There was a good hotel here. He paused in front of the coffee shop. He and Marion Talbert en route to the Yosemite had lunched here. How long ago it seemed!

All at once he remembered he was still a young man, wanting more than anything else to bring back that spring day before he had gone to war. He could see Marion as she had looked then, sitting opposite him at a small table by the window, her hands clasped under her chin, her black hat framing her pert young face. The memory of her was too vivid, too painful.

He went in, sat down at the counter. After he had ordered, he set himself to read a newspaper he had bought earlier in the day. In large type heading the right-hand column were the words: BATTLE OVER CENTRAL VALLEY WATER. The article was an account of a statement made before the State Assembly at Sacramento by a spokesman of one of the largest land corporations. He was reported as saying, "We want water for a tract of land forty miles long. We would like this water by legislation. If we can't get it here, we'll probably have to go to Washington and ask Congress to do away with the appropriation for the reclamation project." Peter pushed the paper away, went out and got into his car, drove north to the town where he had a room in a rooming house.

67

Two years and Peter had become somewhat accustomed to the uphill struggle of the Bureau. He knew now by bitter experience what John had meant when he warned him that a public servant has to do the job for the job's sake, and that he must not expect people to understand why he was doing work that brought him small personal gain. Sometimes it seemed they trusted him the less for it. He was still, as he thought of it, just about where he was when he started, when it came to changing the thinking in The Valley. As John had said, the water question had been with them for a hundred years and it looked as if it might be with them for another hundred—or worse still, the hundred-and-sixty-acre limitation might be done away with once and for all.

Although his father had gone against his campaign promises to support the water project, unaccountably he had been re-elected the year before to the Congress of the United States. He was now sitting as representative at large on the House Committee which was holding hearings on the amount of water any one man could have—relative to a bill before the House to do away with the limitation on acreage set up in the original act. Already Congress had cut the appropriations for the building of dams and canals in The Valley. Early that winter the construction work had stopped, the appropriations having been expended. The heads of the Bureau of Reclamation and men in

the California regional office were under investigation for proceed-
ing so rapidly with construction work that they had not made the
money last out the fiscal year. While the investigation had taken its
course, back in California the steam shovels, the cement mixers stood
idle, the reclamation project at a standstill.

The Valley was facing the worst drought in its history! There was
not enough water in the reservoirs to irrigate the drought-plagued
valleys and furnish power for the factories and homes of the cities and
towns of the state.

Peter was making this caustic estimate of valley conditions en route
to see his mother and stepfather before leaving for Washington, where
he, too, as a member of the Bureau was to be interrogated.

The ride took longer than he had planned. He had to make a long
detour as the road he generally used was closed, dust clouds making
it unsafe for travel. The Valley seemed about to be given back to
the desert. Barley and winter wheat had not sprouted although it
was March, and the fields as far as he could see were brown and desolate. The farmers he talked to were discouraged, some even desperate.
If he had been able to buy land when he returned from India as he
had so much wanted to do, he would be in the same plight, Peter
reflected—and yet he felt he would be willing to face almost any
difficulties to be working the land. Whether because the blood of
Russian landowners flowed in his veins, or because of what Mishka
had taught him, he felt a compelling need to minister to the earth.
The dry fields seemed as alive to him as a human being facing want.

A sudden wind sprang up and he was enveloped in clouds of dust.
He could see the road ahead for only a few yards. He switched on his
lights. Cars coming toward him had their lights on, too, but they
were faint almost like the yellow glow from a badly cleaned oil lamp.
He was forced to drive more and more slowly. In a small town he
stopped for gas. The attendant asked, "What do you think—another
Dust Bowl? That's why I left Oklahoma. What's this country coming
to?" He spat out the dust he'd drawn in while he was talking.

As Peter drove on the wind dropped and the air slowly cleared. He
was in orchard country now. Here farmers were harder hit than the
others, for if their trees died from lack of water it would take years to
replace them, whereas the grain farmers would lose only a year's crop.
In some orchards Peter saw a thin trickle of water in the irrigation
ditches, in others none.

Stopping in a town for lunch he fell into conversation with a man
he had met before, who was sitting next him at the lunch counter.
Peter knew this man had bought an orange ranch a year before and

put into it all the money he and his wife had. The trees were young and more vulnerable to lack of water than older trees with deeper rootage. He had good pumps, Peter knew, but the underground-water level was low. "How are you getting on?" Peter asked.

"Not too good, not enough power. I'm managing to get some water by hitching my tractor up to the pump," the man replied.

Later in the day Peter stopped in at the office of a county agent. There was a government agriculture expert talking with the agent. "I was just telling Bill here that the valley farmer is going to have to stop depending on God Almighty and the electric company."

"Still not willing to talk water conservation?" said Peter.

"No, he prefers to set his chin and hope for rain. Anyway, suppose crops are short, the limited supply hikes the price. If God has not seen fit to send down rain, he seems to have provided the city consumer with a bank roll."

"Well, I suppose we keep trying," said Peter. "Now I've got to be off."

When he turned into the drive leading to his stepfather's house he saw John and a couple of boys harnessing a tractor to their pump. John called out, "I'll be with you in a minute. We're short on electricity, but we can manage with the tractor." Peter joined them and helped to slide the belt into place.

As they walked back to the house Peter said, "You seem to have a good crop of boys, the first crop of any kind I've seen."

"Yes," answered John, "I've taken on as many young vagrants as I could, in fact more than I should. With the drought itinerant laborers are up against it. When there isn't enough food, the older children get thrown out to shift for themselves. I've a couple of boys, too, from families on strike at the large grape ranch. But let's find your mother."

"I'm leaving for Washington tonight," said Peter as they walked toward the house.

"Under investigation?" asked John.

"Well, up for testimony. I guess it amounts to investigation," Peter answered.

"Which committee?"

"The House committee."

Neither of them mentioned the fact that Peter would stand before the tribunal of his father. Or was it the other way, thought John— Peter the real tribunal, his father in the dock?

"Have you been on the west side lately?" asked John.

"No. Why?"

"Well, it's something to see," John replied. "I had to go over to what I supposed was undeveloped land, the back door really of the west side, to hunt up the family of one of my boys. I could hardly believe it when he said there was a camp over there. Enormous new acreage was being brought under cultivation."

"That's the kind of land the Bureau planned to open up for veterans when they had money enough to put in canals for irrigation," said Peter.

"Well, whoever owns it," his stepfather replied, "has money to put in very deep wells and Diesel engines, for they're getting ready to plant rice."

"No!" exclaimed Peter.

Katya heard her son's voice and met them at the door. "How nice, Petya, to surprise us!" she cried as she came forward to kiss him.

"I'll be with you as soon as I wash up," said John, leaving them.

"You look tired." Katya studied Peter for a moment. "What has happened?"

"Nothing much. The country kind of gets you when you drive through it. I'm leaving for Washington tomorrow," he added, thinking he was changing the subject.

"For pleasure?" she asked and smiled.

"For business," he answered.

"Come, we'll have some tea." She took his hand and together they went into the dining room where the old samovar was already bubbling and gurgling. This was the one Russian custom Katya had never given up. "Tea isn't tea without a samovar," she always insisted. "Then you tell people your thoughts."

Gratefully Peter sipped the hot tea but he was unusually silent and Katya did not press him to tell her what troubled him. It was a time, she saw, to keep hands off. How near I came when he went overseas, she was thinking, to try to bind him to me! She had gone again to live with the Mohkovs in order to hold herself stiff to receive the news that might come of his injury or death. For this reason she had again refused to marry John, saying to herself, It was here in this room that Petya was born. It was his haven. She must keep it ready against his return. Only later had she seen that she had wanted to make Peter little again and in need of her. Only when she had finally married John had she let her son go free.

Peter was thinking how restful it was to be with his mother. She was a kind of haven—a quiet place where he could work out his problems, or try to. He found his apprehension over his appearance before the committee in Washington leaving him. When John joined them Peter thought, How do two people get to understand each other so perfectly that the room seems full of harmony?

As often before, the three of them talked late into the night. Finally Peter rose saying, "I've got to go. Any good book you can lend me, John, to read on the train?"

"How about *Democracy on the March?*" John picked up a small book lying on the table in front of the couch. Peter opened it, saw John had marked various passages. "Yes, I'd like to read this," he said, remembering the boy in India who had talked so much about the Tennessee Valley. He slipped the book into his pocket.

As he drove through the darkened towns where the lights were out to save power, his thoughts went back to the one time he had seen his grandfather Jeremy Dodd. A strong, ruthless man, had been Peter's estimate of him; a fighter. He'd talked a good deal about his business. "If the family would stick together," he had said, "we needn't have the government's long nose poked into our affairs." He had looked straight at Edward when he had said it. Well, if the old man were alive, he'd be satisfied with his son now, for Edward, Peter understood, was on the side of the power companies who in a time of emergency were attempting to get the use of all the power generated at Shasta Dam at the price they had distributed government power during the war. Anyway, John and I are still left to fight, Peter reflected.

The next afternoon, from the train window Peter beheld The Valley baking under a brilliant sun. By and by the foothills appeared but not clothed in their winter green; neither were they golden with ripened barley as in the summer. They were dun-colored and lifeless-looking. A few thin cattle were pastured here and there. Then the low hills gave place to the Sierra range. Peter thought of the first time he had seen the mountains and of his wonder when John had driven him into their sharp-canyoned depths. As the train moved upward, slowly circling the mountains, he looked to see snow, the hope for next year's water supply, but only when they topped the range was there any and then merely a layer, thin as frosting, coating the ground, no heavy snow pack filling the canyons and covering the mountains' flanks.

And then, as the train slid quickly down the other side of the mountain, snow began to appear in abundance and it lay thick on the plains. All the next day he looked on lands buried in snow. Peter had never before seen the great plains of America, the Mississippi and Missouri valleys. Only now when he saw them in their vastness, did he fully realize the greatness of his country.

In this mood he read the book John had given him.

When the train reached Washington and he walked through the station and saw the dome of the Capitol building rising up out of the city through the mist of falling snow, My country, man's hope, he thought, remembering India and China.

That night Peter woke suddenly, unable for the moment to realize he was in a hotel room in the city of Washington so strong was the feeling that he was in Doddstown. He must have been dreaming of the fight in the vacant lot behind Ike's saloon for there was the same brackish taste in his mouth he had had the night he tried to kill Pedro.

He rose, went and sat by the window looking out at the snow-enveloped city. As he lighted a cigarette he saw that his hand was shaking. Was the gray wash of Doddstown seeping over him at the very hour of his meeting with his father? He dressed and went out determined to walk off the mood of defeat threatening him.

68

EDWARD stopped at his office to pick up some memoranda his secretary was preparing for him from reports sent by friends of his in California. Drought conditions, they said, made it necessary that the private companies should be given all the power generated at Shasta Dam. If such an arrangement were made it might help to end the dispute with the Reclamation Bureau which claimed right to put in lines of their own.

"Is there any word from the hearings out west on the ending of Forest and Grazing Services control over the ranges, Marion?" he asked as he took the memoranda she had prepared for him.

"You mean you're going to support that too?" asked Marion.

Edward was annoyed. "The representative from the West who is promoting the measure hardly deserves such a remark, does he?" he countered. "You can see by the present drought that we need more grazing ground."

"I read somewhere he was firmly tucked in the stockmen's saddle-bag." Marion had been the dutiful secretary as long as she could. This latest addition to Edward Dodd's program she felt she could not take. "If that's your line I suggest you find a new secretary," she said, making no effort to keep the distaste she felt out of her voice. "I don't think I like you very well, Mr. Dodd," she added for good measure.

Ignoring her caustic rejoinder Edward contented himself with reminding her not to be late to the hearings this morning. "I want careful notes." He turned and went out, impervious to her scorn but annoyed that he would have to bother to break in a new secretary.

When he reached the Capitol, he walked up the long flight of steps outside instead of going in at the lower entrance. Yesterday's snowstorm on top of a long winter of snow and ice made him crave a few minutes more of today's sudden burst of sunlight, before entering the Capitol's dark corridors, but he did not linger long, feeling the pressure of a morning in committee. He was working carefully this time to see that nothing prevented the one-hundred-and-sixty-acre limitation being cut once and for all out of the Reclamation Project.

The room where the hearings were being held was slowly filling up with witnesses, reporters and spectators. At the front on a platform some two feet high stood a narrow kidney-shaped mahogany table with comfortable leather chairs for the members of the committee set in its circular inner side. Pitchers of water and glasses were placed at regular intervals. Below was a long oblong golden-oak table where the men and women of the press were already seated and just behind them were Marion and the other representatives' secretaries. Through a door at the front one committee member after another entered, took his seat, talked to his neighbor, sampled the water in the pitchers.

Those who were to testify were seated informally among the spectators. Peter was sitting in the back row next to a young man who said he was a student come to see American procedure firsthand. "You here yesterday?" he asked Peter. "No? Well you should have been. Boy, did they pin it on the small farmers! Made them squirm all right. You'd think they were doing something subversive."

Peter felt a sudden tightening in his throat. The door at the front had opened and he saw his father enter, stop to speak to one of his colleagues, then take the chair at the farther end of the table. He looked older than when Peter had last seen him. His hair had turned gray around the temples, his face was fuller than Peter had remembered it. He had the air of a man who had arrived and knew it.

Unfolding a paper he had previously laid on the table the chairman announced, "I'll call the witnesses in the order listed. Will Mr. Lesly please come forward. I believe you represent the big farmers. What have you to say on the limitation of water to one hundred and sixty acres?"

"Men like me," said Mr. Lesly, "are tired of being pictured as the big, bad land barons. The west-side farmer has to be able to finance a well going down eighteen hundred or two thousand feet. And he has to work six thousand acres or more to be efficient. Small acreage isn't efficient. It means less grain and cotton for the world."

"I have been informed," said the chairman, "that for this reason limiting the amount of water any one owner could buy would ruin the Central Valley financially. Is that your opinion?"

"It certainly is," Mr. Lesly answered.

"Thanks for your clear testimony," said the chairman.

"Lesly is getting off easy. The chairman wasn't so kind yesterday to the small farmers," whispered the student to Peter.

"Next on our list is another valley farmer. Will Mr. Drechler please come forward."

A tall, lean man with red hair rose from his chair behind the reporters and took his place below the dais where the committee sat looking down on him. Mr. Drechler looked up and, not waiting to be asked what he had to say, burst forth: "I've been fighting for the big farmer for years. The time has come when the California farmer has got to be let alone. First it's how much water we can have, then it's how we run our camps for itinerant labor. Now I said when the war was on, if these camps were good enough before the war, can anybody tell me why these mildewed brain-trusters, these so-called social reformers can't throw their pet hobbies aside and get down to winning the war? They're always talking about housing conditions and baths and showers—they tell us we have got to have bathtubs!

"Our boys in the jungles of Malay, in the deserts of Egypt are sacrificing their lives, I said, so that we might live. They did not ask for housing conditions. Isn't it your duty," Drechler demanded, looking from one to the other of the committee, "now we are trying to win the peace, to see we're let alone?"

Scarcely pausing for breath he went on: "I am telling you, the people talking about camps and water limitation are twisted minds. I don't care if they are giants in literature, I don't care if they are professors of economics; the time has come when these crackpots have got to leave California farmers alone. It is the duty of the Congress to carry this mandate to the proper places so that an end can be placed to these destructive statements of the so-called social reformers. They are not social reformers, they are peddlers of bunk, and I hope they will hear me and understand."

Turning to Edward, the chairman asked, "As California's representative at large have you any questions to ask the witness?"

What will he say? thought Peter. Surely he can't go along with an insult like that to the people who elected him.

"I'd like to ask the witness this." Edward looked down at a paper on which he had been making notes. "If your land was broken up into small farms, Mr. Drechler, land would have to be taken out of production to build homes, wouldn't it?"

"Yes and——"

"Just a minute." Edward raised his hand as if to stop the volume of words that he feared might come from Drechler. "Wouldn't it throw a good many laborers out of employment to break up the farms into small units and bring in a lot of small owners who'd do a good deal of their own work?"

"That's it," said Drechler.

"Thank you," said Edward. "I wanted to clear up this point for the record."

Why, the double-crosser! thought Peter, his anger rising. He's trying to play it both ways.

"The next to testify——" the chairman studied his paper—"is an official of the Department of the Interior." He paused a moment, then read out the name. "I understand you are opposing the representative's bill, before the House, for doing away with the acre limitation. Will you explain to the committee why?"

A man seated just behind the press rose and in a clear voice made his statement. "I support the historic reclamation policy because when I was appointed to my present position, I took an oath to defend the laws of the United States, and this is one of them."

"Are you not," asked his interrogator, "advocating, however subtly, a division of land more after the ideals of Russia than America?"

"The Homestead Act, as I understand it, was signed by Abraham Lincoln," the man answered. "And the National Reclamation Act was passed in 1902 with the unanimous support of every western delegation in Congress. It bears the signature of Theodore Roosevelt."

"You are sure you are not using those events to build up a dangerous philosophy."

"Mr. Chairman, may I interrupt?" asked a member of the committee. At a nod from the chairman, he asked, "Are we not confusing the two Roosevelts in this matter of acreage limitations? As our witness has pointed out, it was Theodore Roosevelt who set up the reclamation laws. Let me emphasize, it was Theodore not Franklin. I should like to hear what the witness has to say about the urgency for the reclamation work in California."

Laughter and clapping broke out among the roomful of onlookers. The chairman rapped for order. Peter felt a kind of fear settling over him. All he had learned from John Dodd, all he had dreamed of and thought he was fighting for when he was in India, was being discredited in this room. He remembered his chief as he had looked when he had passed him this morning in the corridor going in for another hearing before the Senate Finance Committee. His face was gray and tired-looking.

Peter scarcely heard the official's concise, clear statement of the need to conserve every drop of water in the arid Western states by the use of proper dams and other conservation measures. But he heard him say, "A former witness mentioned that only big landowners could afford to put down wells two thousand feet. I want to say that no one should put down wells that deep. We're drawing on our water bank account when we go that deep."

As the official sat down, the chairman, again looking at his paper, said: "Will Mr. Suvorov, representative from the California Office of the Bureau of Reclamation, please come forward."

At the reading of Peter's name Marion started. Peter in this room! As he came forward and passed close to her, sitting well to the front of the room, she felt rising within her unbidden, undesired, the old tumultuous emotion Peter used to awaken in her, something she thought ended in the soberer love she had felt for the man she had married and for whom she still grieved. Then came the old anger against Peter and the humiliation she had felt when he had refused to marry her in those last days they had been together.

"Your name, I see, is Russian," the chairman began.

Peter had an uncanny feeling that his life was repeating itself. A little boy standing on the school steps had been so designated.

"Was your citizenship lately attained?"

"I am a native American," Peter answered.

"But of Russian ancestry."

Peter hesitated, looked to the end of the table where his father sat. Edward Dodd had shifted his position slightly when Peter's name was called. His face did not betray his consternation—he was caught in the meshes of a web of his own weaving. He could not repudiate the son he once had publicly acknowledged. That would be a political blunder of the first water. But something deep within him refused to accept Peter as his son. He found himself suspended in inaction.

Watching the scene Marion felt her anger against Peter changed to anger against Edward. How could he refuse to acknowledge the son he had once asked to defend him! Then all other emotions were swallowed up in pity for Peter, standing waiting, she thought, for the recognition he would not be given.

"Evidently Mr. Suvorov does not wish to answer the question regarding his name," the chairman said, turning to the committee.

"Yes, I am ready to answer," said Peter. "I paused a moment thinking it was proper that I should let my father speak first, but perhaps he had the same thought about me. Mr. Chairman, my name has been incompletely given. It is Peter Suvorov Dodd. I am the son of Representative Dodd. As such I have inherited his name."

The room grew very still.

"We are an old California family," Peter went on. "My great-grandfather, I believe, was one of its pioneers. He helped to develop the land. As such he was valuable to California and true to the American tradition."

Suddenly swinging round so that he faced Edward, Peter said in a cold hard voice, "What the large owners have said today, and you, sir, through implication have stamped with your approval, is a corruption of the American way of life. The monument which you and your father have raised to remember the family is Doddstown. It stands in the middle of those great farms that you fear might lose a few precious acres if men built homes and worked their own farms. So instead we have shanties, eight by twelve, into which a family is squeezed."

Peter's voice was like a whipcord lashing out at the men who he felt had betrayed him and The Valley. He was a man with all old Jeremy's will power and force, fighting as old Jeremy would have fought but for another purpose. He turned to the committee. "Gentlemen, you should go and see Doddstown before you make your report. The people in the shanties named it after our family. It stands for vice and poverty and delinquent children. Mr. Lesly, who bought the Dodd acres, is carrying on this corruption."

The chairman looked from Peter to Edward. Then as Representative Dodd made no sign or protest, he turned again to Peter. "You are testifying, I believe, for the Bureau of Reclamation."

Quickly Peter now started to outline the bold imaginative plan men of vision had had for The Valley. "A sacred trust they have given us to support the homestead ideal which has made this a nation of homes——"

"Just a moment," said Edward.

Peter's anger had not moved him from his inaction. Anger was a two-edged weapon that cut both ways. But it was dangerous to have so much hope and daring adventure let loose in this room, dangerous to Edward also, reviewing his young self. The only way to destroy the vision Peter was setting forth, which he too had once had, was to drive harder against his old convictions. He must go through now to the bitter end with the role he had selected. He could wait no longer to speak. But he must choose his words carefully lest he make some political blunder.

"I'm certain my colleagues will bear with me," he said, turning away from Peter and toward the members of the committee, "if for a moment I seem to allow the high office I hold to degenerate into the purely personal. It is with sorrow and shame I have listened to a man who calls himself a Dodd blacken the family's name. Because of this and because the personal bears on a situation I have been trying to emphasize here, I must speak. The Bureau, it has been claimed, has men ill prepared for their work, and my son—it is hard for me to say this—is one of the least fitted to be a member of it. I would like to remind him of his own statement to me, made several years ago, that he did not wish my help in educating him. He preferred to do other things than go to a university. He has no technical training for his work. His testimony on water and its uses in California would, I think, not be safe to accept."

Now, indeed, did old Jeremy come to life in Peter! "My father's reasons aren't good enough. My qualifications aren't to be looked down upon in America," said Peter, turning to the chairman of the committee. "I am a valley child. I was a valley farmer until Mr. Lesly managed to get hold of my mother's farm. I learned engineering in the school of——"

Before he could go on, the chairman called the next witness.

And then the committeeman who had protested before again entered a protest. "We have brought this man here to testify because he is a Bureau official," he said. "As long as he holds that position I think he should be heard."

"Thank you," said Peter. "Gentlemen, you have been told that limiting a man to water for one hundred and sixty acres holds him to peasantry. This is not so. I would like to present the reports I have prepared refuting this." He walked around the reporters' table and, standing just below the dais, handed to each committeeman a small bundle. "These you can study at your leisure. You'll find among them a folder from the Fresno Chamber of Commerce telling how much land a man needs to support a family. A hundred and sixty acres for cotton is the largest acreage given. There's a detailed account of a man who owned sixty acres of cotton and has sent three boys through college.

"And now," he said, "in case my father still feels I should be disqualified . . ." He paused a moment looking straight at Edward. A shorter man standing as he did below the dais would have had to look up, but Peter's eyes were on a level with his father's. "I speak for the veterans. My qualifications, sir, one hundred flights over the Hump from India into China."

Clapping broke out among the spectators. It spread to the reporters grouped around the table below the dais where the committee sat in silence.

"The hearings are adjourned until afternoon," said the chairman in a loud voice.

Peter stood watching as they left the room, his scornful gaze on his father who was chatting affably with the chairman. The door closed behind them. Peter walked quickly to the side door, making his way between the reporters and the curious.

Marion hurried after him. She lost sight of him as he turned quickly into a side corridor. He's trying to throw any reporters off his track, she thought. Then she caught a glimpse of him striding toward the elevators. "Peter, Peter!" she called. "Please wait."

He turned. "Well," he said. "And you, too."

"Don't let's begin hurting each other as we used to do," pleaded Marion. "We're both different now. The man I married—he was killed more than two years ago. Perhaps we need each other. Your father this morning——"

"Let's pass that up," Peter answered.

She wasn't going to let Peter put her off. He needed her help. She could see how spent he was. Indeed, he had been through an ordeal and although he had come off victorious she doubted if he realized it, feeling still the sting of his father's words.

"Come," she said with something of her old briskness. "What we both need is some coffee."

Through luncheon Peter held the conversation above the personal, but afterward, when they were sitting in the hotel lobby, gradually his reserve left him and he began telling her of his effort to find a farm and of his work with the Bureau. When Marion found he was unmarried the world seemed brighter than it had for a long time. Maybe what she had thought about his leaving her wasn't true after all. After that they seemed to draw closer together although they were still walled off from their old intimacy. When she told him she had been Edward's secretary she sensed his withdrawal. But when he learned why she had resigned things were better between them once more.

Peter's train left for California in another hour. Peter rose to go, still holding at a distance the girl he had once loved but only liked now, so he told himself.

"I'll see you off," said Marion. "Nobody should start a journey without someone to see him off."

It was cold outside and getting dark when they started for the station. Marion pulled the hood of her coat over her hair. Peter studied her for a moment then looked away. "I'd better call a taxi," he said.

She couldn't let him go like that. "Couldn't you manage to forgive me?" she asked.

"I've nothing to forgive. You married the man you wanted. That's all there is to it, isn't it?" In spite of himself Peter's voice was tight with feeling.

"No, not all there is to it."

"Well, what else is there?"

"Oh, skip it," she said. Immediately she wished she hadn't spoken that way. She sounded hard. It was difficult to give up the outward manifestation of what she once had been. Then for a moment another man seemed to be standing opposite her, the husband who by the spell of his gentleness had broken through her hardness, reached down to the self hidden away since childhood.

"Peter, I've got to make it plain to you that when you went away I thought it was because you wanted to be free, that I was just—you know—just an episode in your life. That you didn't really love me—" and in a lower tone—"as I loved you."

"That's what I thought about you!" he exclaimed. But then he remembered the pain of those weeks and months when he had tried to erase her from his mind. He meant to make no mistake this time. He wasn't ready yet to let his heart go.

"Look, Marion: I've nothing much to offer you, perhaps never will have. I make no apologies for that fact. I've made myself bitter enemies today, saying what I did, but I'm glad I said them. They're true. I may lose my job. There's an effort to get the men who think as I do out of the Bureau. Maybe it will succeed. Then it will be hard going. Could you take it? Tell me, Marion, could you?"

"I'd hate it," she answered, "but I'd love to do it."